MICROSCOPIC ANATOMY OF THE DOG
A Photographic Atlas

MICROSCOPIC ANATOMY OF THE DOG
A Photographic Atlas

By

WILLIAM S. ADAM, A.B., M.S., Ph.D.
Formerly Instructor
Department of Small Animal Surgery and Medicine
College of Veterinary Medicine
Michigan State University
East Lansing, Michigan

M. LOIS CALHOUN, B.S., M.S., D.V.M., Ph.D.
Professor, Department of Anatomy
College of Veterinary Medicine
Michigan State University
East Lansing, Michigan

ESTHER M. SMITH, B.S., M.S., Ph.D.
Professor, Department of Anatomy
College of Veterinary Medicine
Michigan State University
East Lansing, Michigan
and

AL W. STINSON, B.S., D.V.M., M.S.
Associate Professor, Department of Anatomy
College of Veterinary Medicine
Michigan State University
East Lansing, Michigan

CHARLES C THOMAS • PUBLISHER
Springfield • Illinois • U.S.A.

Published and Distributed Throughout the World by
CHARLES C THOMAS • PUBLISHER
Bannerstone House
301-327 East Lawrence Avenue, Springfield, Illinois, U.S.A.
Natchez Plantation House
735 North Atlantic Boulevard, Fort Lauderdale, Florida, U.S.A.

© 1970, by CHARLES C THOMAS • PUBLISHER
Library of Congress Catalog Card Number: 75-91844

With THOMAS BOOKS *careful attention is given to all details of
manufacturing and design. It is the Publisher's desire to present books
that are satisfactory as to their physical qualities and artistic possibilities
and appropriate for their particular use.* THOMAS BOOKS *will be true
to those laws of quality that assure a good name and good will.*

Printed in the United States of America
EE-16

Preface

The widespread use of the beagle dog as an experimental animal has created a need for a reference which focuses directly on the histologic characteristics of the dog as well as those which this species shares with other animals and man. Therefore, this atlas is intended to be a reference for the experimental investigator, students in human and veterinary medicine, and those in other health-related fields.

Twenty, six-month-old, purebred beagle dogs from known ancestry were used in this study. While most of the dogs were physically mature at this age, it must be emphasized that there were some differences in the maturation level among the animals studied. Nonetheless, the photomicrographs in this atlas reflect fairly uniform morphologic characteristics of young animals.

Several methods of tissue procurement and fixation were employed in an effort to obtain optimum sections. Some of the dogs were anesthetized prior to the insertion of venous and arterial cannulae. The animals were exsanguinated and then perfused via the cannulae at a constant pressure of 80 mm of Hg with either 10% buffered formalin or a mercury-formol-saline solution. While the perfusion method of fixation allows harvest of a maximum amount of tissues from one animal without postmortem change, it does prevent the collapse of the vascular channels, and many sections exhibit very striking vascular architectural patterns. For this reason, several animals were euthanatized with sodium pentathol and the fresh tissues were dissected out and placed in any one of several fixatives. The majority of the sections were stained with hematoxylin and eosin; however, other stains were used in order to emphasize certain structural details.

The introductory remarks preceding each chapter are designed to point out characteristic features of the dog as well as introduce pertinent comparative histology. It is hoped these comments will make the reader of this text more aware of the differences as well as the similarities in the microscopic anatomy of various species of animals. Perhaps this information, even though meager, may stimulate investigators to search for other dissimilarities and document the comparisons.

In selecting the slides for photography, an effort was made to include the most important areas of each system and to emphasize those structures and organs which are peculiar to the dog. Low-power photomicrographs are used throughout the atlas to help orient the reader to the whole section. These are followed by increasingly higher magnifications in order to demonstrate structural and cellular detail.

Diagrammatic line drawings are included in each chapter and provide

NOTE: This study is supported in part by Contract No. PH 43-65-100 within the Special Virus-Leukemia Program of the National Cancer Institute, NIH, USPHS.

the reader with the location and plane of section from which the photo-micrographs were made. The level number found at the end of each figure title corresponds to that same number on the accompanying drawing.

The usefulness of this atlas is further enhanced by including a rather extensive bibliography. The references have been selected carefully to avoid duplicating those included in the *Bibliography of the Dog,* by Marcus Mason (The Iowa State Press, 1959).

The culmination of an effort such as this involves the contribution of many individuals. It is therefore with sincere gratitude that the authors acknowledge the assistance and cooperation of several persons in particular: Mr. Tom Alguire, Miss Linda Bertal, Dr. Gabel Conner, Mrs. Rosemarie Daniels, Mr. Robert Ewing, Mrs. Barbara Hamlin, Mr. Ken Holmes, Mr. Andrew Poole, Dr. Esther Roege, Mr. Roger Sanders, Mr. Payne Thomas, and Mrs. Margaret Thorp, librarian.

Contents

MICROSCOPIC ANATOMY OF THE DOG
A Photographic Atlas

Chapter 1

Integumentary System

In general, the microscopic structure of the skin of the dog resembles that of other domestic animals and man. The comparative thickness of the skin of various body areas is illustrated in Plate 2 (Figs. 1-12). It is thickest on the dorsum of the head and neck and decreases in thickness caudally, laterally, and ventrally. Integumentary papillae first reported in dogs by Lovell and Getty (1959) were observed in the beagle dog.

Because of the protective hair coat the epidermis is thin except over the hairless areas. The stratum lucidum is most prominent in the digital pad but insignificant or absent elsewhere. Epidermal pegs are present only in the foot pads, planum nasale and lip. The stratum corneum is thick on the foot pads and thin on the nose.

Hair follicles generally occur in groups of three, the main or guard hair being larger than the smaller associated hairs. The roots are separate but just below the sebaceous glands, the hairs enter a common follicle and emerge in a cluster.

The tactile or sinus hair is typically the carnivore type, which differs from that of other domestic animals by having a proximal trabeculae-free portion in the annular blood sinus located between the inner and outer layers of the dermal sheath. A sinus pad projects into this space.

In the dog as in other domestic animals, but in contrast to the human species, the tubular skin glands of the body are apocrine in type and open into the hair follicle. Merocrine glands opening directly onto the surface are found in the foot pads. A special glandular structure, the anal sac, found in carnivores, contains only apocrine glands in the dog. Sebaceous circumanal glands are related to both the anal mucosa and anal skin. The so-called caudal or tail gland, located on the dorsum of the tail a short distance from the sacrum, is not as prominent in the dog as in the cat. According to Lovell and Getty, 1968, the hair follicles in this area contain only one hair and both the sebaceous caudal glands and apocrine glands are large. Apparently these glands are not very well developed in the six-month-old beagle dog. Other prominent sebaceous glands are located in such mucocutaneous junctions as the lip, prepuce and labium vulva.

A characteristic pattern of plaque-like elevations and grooves on the hairless planum nasale corresponds to the finger prints of man and is used in dog identifications. In contrast to the smooth foot pad of the cat, the surface of the canine foot pad has heavily keratinized conical papillae. Previous reports to the contrary, a few nasolabial glands were observed in two animals.

We were most fortunate to get such an excellent saggital section of the claw. Its relationship to the phalanges, tendons and foot pad are well illustrated.

INTEGUMENTARY SYSTEM

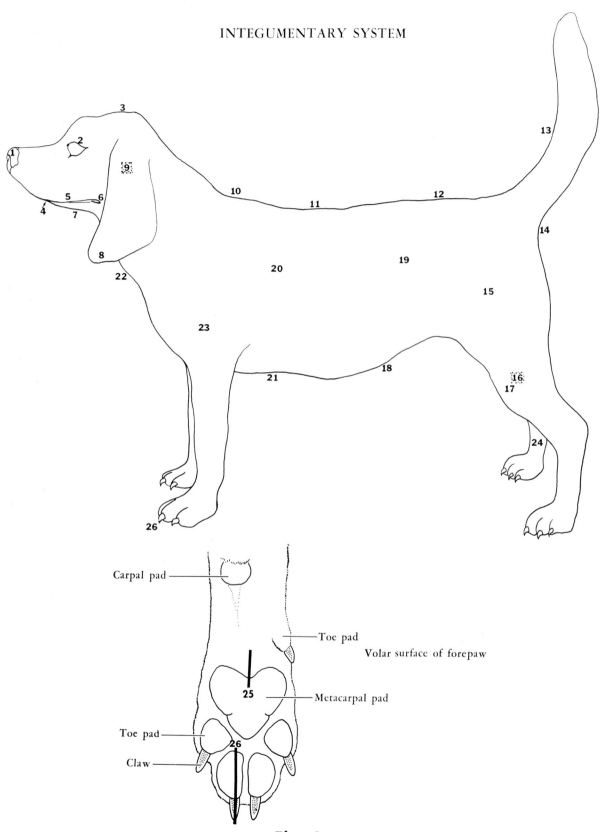

Carpal pad

Toe pad

Volar surface of forepaw

Metacarpal pad

Toe pad

Claw

Plate 1

Plate 2

Comparison of General Body Skin Areas
The figures in this plate are arranged along the horizontal axis to illustrate areas from the cranial to the caudal region of the body. Likewise, they are arranged along the vertical axis to illustrate areas from the dorsal to the ventral region of the body. The sections are all longitudinal. (H&E X29)

Figure Number	Level
1. Head (dorsal)	3
2. Neck (dorsal)	10
3. Thoraco-lumbar reigon (dorsal)	11
4. Sacral region (dorsal)	12
5. Neck (ventral)	22
6. Thorax (lateral)	20
7. Abdomen (lateral)	19
8. Thigh (lateral)	15
9. Forelimb (lateral)	23
10. Thorax (ventral)	21
11. Abdomen (ventral)	18
12. Hindlimb (lateral)	17

Plate 2

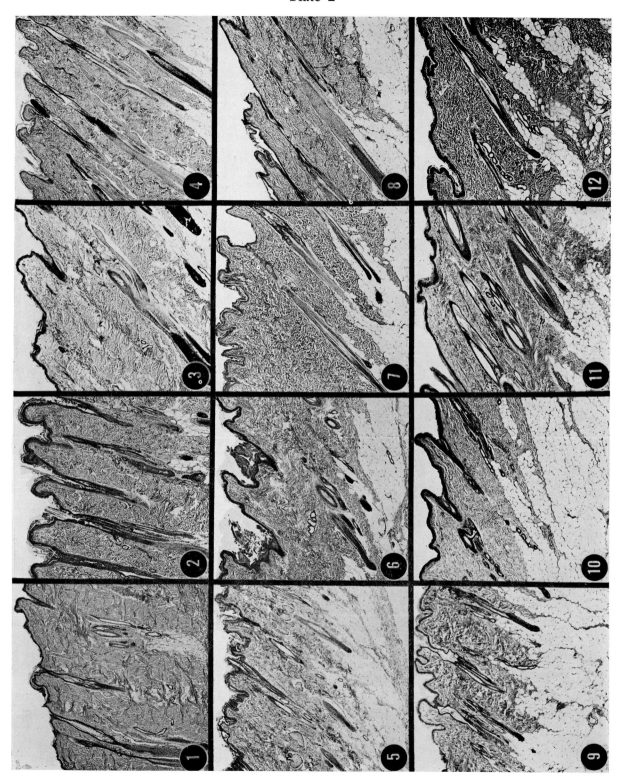

Plate 3

FIGURE 1. Typical hairy skin area. Longitudinal section, Level 11. (H&E X28)
  a. Opening of a hair follicle
  b. Epidermis
  c. Papillary layer of the dermis
  d. Reticular layer of the dermis
  e. Arrector pili muscles
  f. Sebaceous glands
  g. Sweat glands
  h. Sweat duct
  i. Roots of hair follicles
  j. Adipose tissue in subcutis

FIGURE 2. Typical hairy skin area. Cross section, Level 11. (H&E X45)
  Cross sections of the hair groups appear at various levels. Notice that one or more large hairs are joined by several smaller hairs and emerge from a single opening at the surface.
  a. Hair groups just above the epidermis
  b. Hair follicles just below the epidermis
  c. Typical cluster of three large hairs with adjacent lanugo hairs. Also refer to Plate 12, Figure 4.
  d. Sebaceous glands
  e. Arrector pili muscles
  f. Sweat gland ducts
  g. Adipose tissue

FIGURE 3. Integumentary papilla. Level 21. (H&E X160)
  a. Papilla
  b. Hair follicle
  c. Cluster of small hair follicles, sweat ducts and sebaceous glands

FIGURE 4. Epidermal pad of a tylotrich follicle, Level 24. (H&E X390)
  a. Stratum corneum
  b. Stratum lucidum
  c. Stratum granulosum
  d. Stratum germinativum
  e. Tactile cells of Merkel (Mann, 1968)

Plate 3

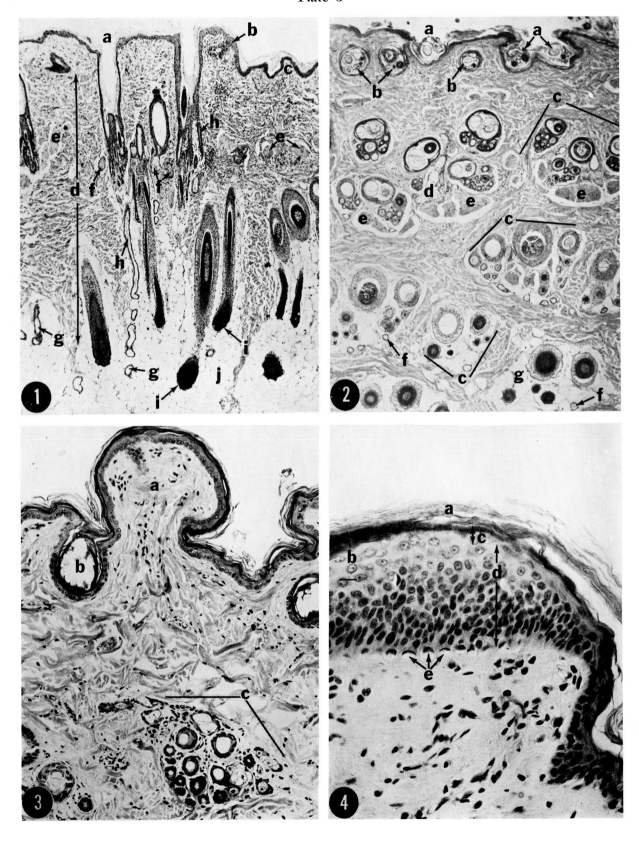

Plate 4

FIGURE 1. Thick section of skin revealing the coiling of the sweat glands. Longitudinal section, Level 25. (H&E X29)
 a. Coiled sweat glands
 b. Sweat duct
 c. Hair follicles

FIGURE 2. Dermis of the prepuce. (H&E X49)
 a. Sebaceous glands
 b. Hair follicle
 c. Coiled sweat glands
 d. Adipose tissue

FIGURE 3. Coiled active sweat glands of the prepuce. (H&E X145)
 a. Sweat glands
 b. Myoepithelial cells
 c. Adipose tissue

FIGURE 4. Sweat duct and related structures. Level 11. (H&E X340)
 a. Sebaceous gland
 b. Arrector pili muscle
 c. Sweat duct
 d. External root sheath of a hair follicle

Plate 4

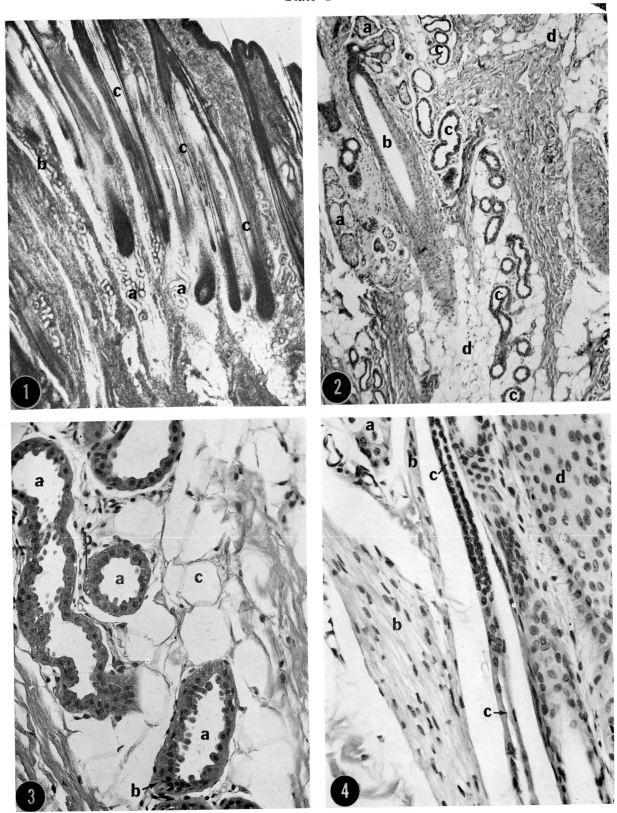

Plate 5

FIGURE 1. Typical sebaceous glands. Cross section, Level 5. (H&E X240)
   a. Lumen of the hair follicle
   b. Opening of a sebaceous gland duct into a hair follicle
   c. Disintegrating alveolar cells (holocrine secretion)
   d. Large cells filled with fat droplets
   e. Small peripheral cells with fat droplets
   f. Blood and lymphatic vessels

FIGURE 2. Labial glands. Vertical section, Level 4. (H&E X105)
   a. Hair follicle
   b. Labial gland lobules (sebaceous)
   c. Sweat glands
   d. Dermis

FIGURE 3. Preputial sebaceous gland with branching lobules (a). Oblique section. (H&E X120)

FIGURE 4. Caudal gland. Longitudinal section, Level 13. (H&E X120)
   a. Hair follicle
   b. Sweat duct opening into the hair follicle
   c. Sebaceous gland duct
   d. Lobules of the sebaceous caudal gland
   e. Arrector pili muscle
   f. Dermis
   g. Sweat gland
   h. Adipose tissue

Plate 5

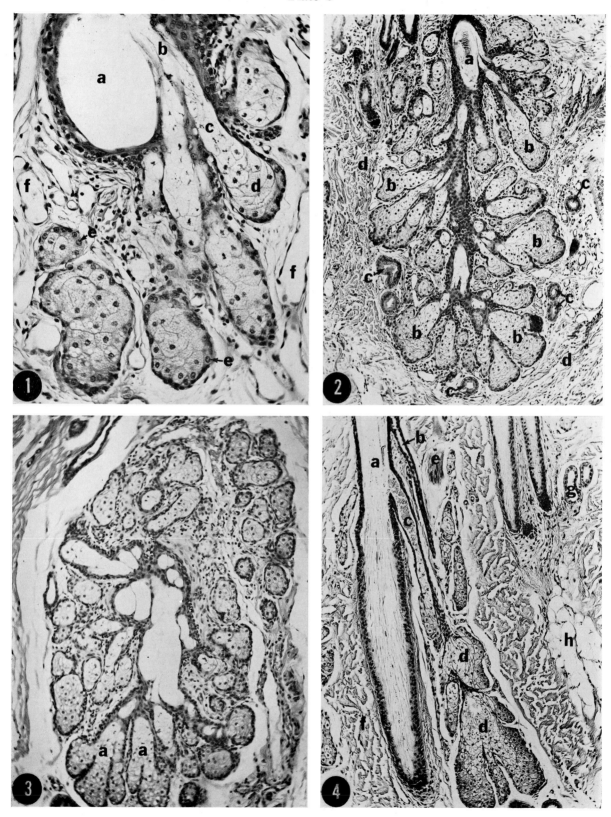

Plate 6

FIGURE 1. Anal sac. Longitudinal section, Level 14. (H&E X5)
    a. Anal sac lumen
    b. Anal sac duct
    c. Anal sac glands
    d. Lymphatic tissue
    e. Circumanal glands

FIGURE 2. Anal sac duct. Longitudinal section, Level 14. (H&E X29)
    a. Skeletal muscle
    b. Sebaceous glands
    c. Stratified squamous epithelium
    d. Cellular debris in the duct lumen

FIGURE 3. Wall of the anal sac. Level 14: (H&E X110)
    a. Stratum corneum
    b. Vein
    c. Duct of the anal sac gland in the stratified squamous epithelium
    d. Anal sac glands

FIGURE 4. Circumanal gland. Longitudinal section, Level 14. (H&E X670)
    a. Proliferative polyhedral basal cells
    b. Nonsebaceous gland cells (Parks, 1950)
    c. Intercellular canaliculi

Plate 6

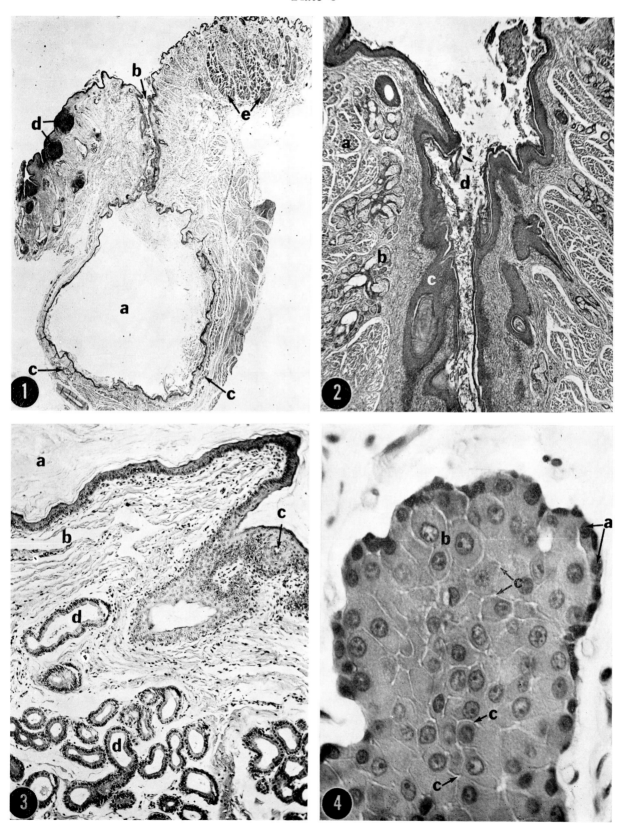

Plate 7

FIGURE 1. Hair follicle. Cross section. (H&E X610)
   a. Medulla
   b. Cortex
   c. Cuticle of the hair
   d. Cuticle of the internal root sheath
   e. Huxley's layer of the internal root sheath
   f. Henle's layer of the internal root sheath
   g. External root sheath
   h. Vitreous membrane
   i. Connective tissue sheath

FIGURE 2. Hair follicle. Longitudinal section. (H&E X610)
   a. Medulla
   b. Cortex
   c. Cuticle of the hair
   d. Cuticle of the internal root sheath
   e. Henle's layer of the internal root sheath
   f. External root sheath
   g. Vitreous membrane
   h. Connective tissue sheath

FIGURE 3. Bulb of a hair follicle. Longitudinal section. (H&E X340)
   a. Dermal papilla
   b. Pigmented cortex
   c. Cuticle of the hair
   d. Huxley's layer of the internal root sheath
   e. Henle's layer of the internal root sheath
   f. Beginning of the external root sheath
   g. Connective tissue sheath
   h. Capillary
   i. Subcutaneous fat

FIGURE 4. Hair follicle with follicular folds. Longitudinal section. (H&E X850)
   a. Hair
   b. Follicular folds (foldings of the inner root sheath)
   c. Duct of a sebaceous gland

Plate 7

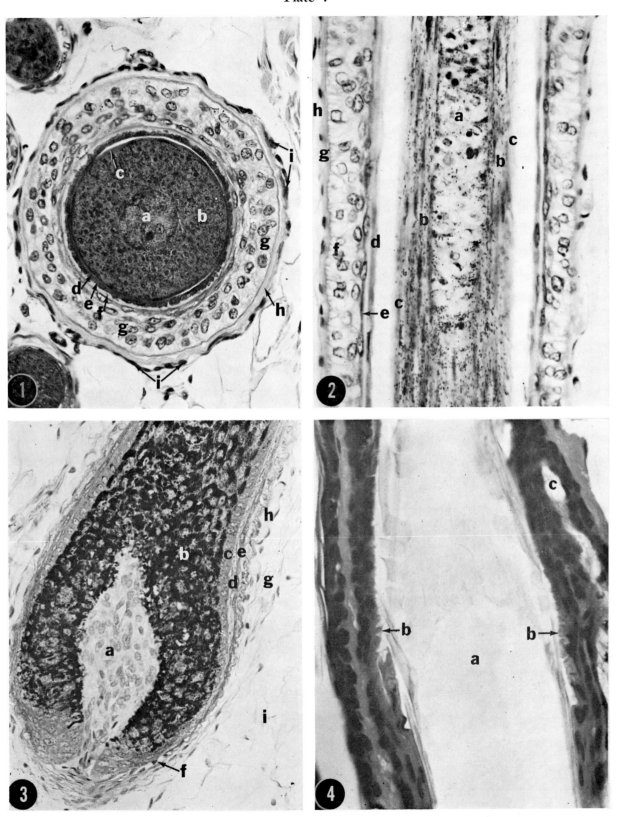

Plate 8

FIGURE 1. Tactile hair. Longitudinal section, Level 7. (H&E X40)
    Notice: Lines at 2, 3, and 4 refer to the approximate plane of cross
    sections of a similar hair shown in Figures 2, 3, and 4.
    a. Outer layer of the dermal sheath (white fibrous connective tissue)
    b. Cavernous blood sinus with trabeculae
    c. Inner layer of the dermal sheath
    d. Glassy membrane
    e. External root sheath (similar to that of the ordinary hair)
    f. Hair
    g. Sinus pad—an enlargement of the inner dermal sheath
    h. Annular sinus filled wtih blood (nontrabecular)
    i. Sebaceous gland
    j. Opening of sebaceous glands
    k. Skeletal muscle (attaches to the outer layer of the dermal sheath)
    l. Nerve bundles
    m. Papilla of the hair
    n. Ordinary hair follicles of adjacent area (notice the comparatively
       smaller size)
FIGURES 2, 3 and 4. Tactile hair. Cross sections at levels in Figure 1 indi-
    cated by lines 2, 3 and 4. (H&E X40)
    See letter designations for Figure 1.

Plate 8

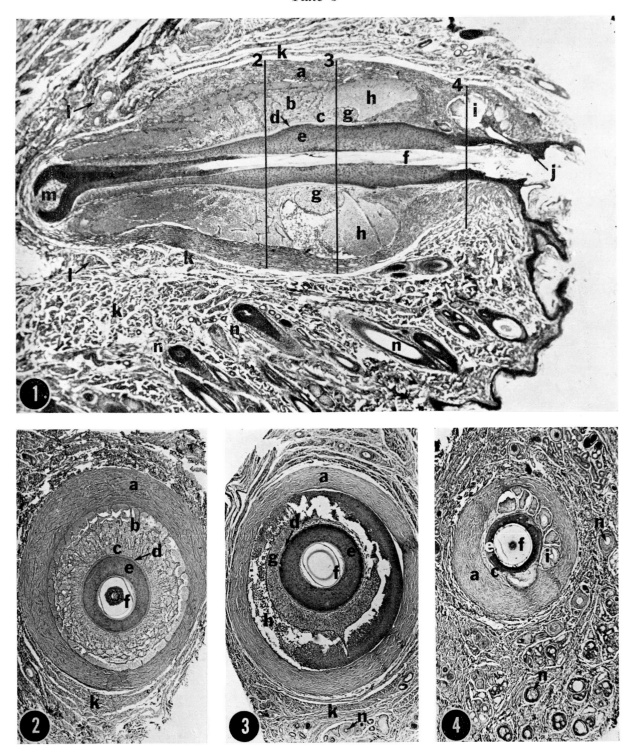

Plate 9

FIGURE 1. Eyelid (upper). Longitudinal section, Level 2. (H&E X14)
    a. Skeletal muscle
    b. Lymph nodule
    c. The point at which the stratified squamous epithelium changes to the pseudostratified ciliated columnar epithelium of the palpebral conjunctiva
    d. Tarsal plate (collagenous fibers surrounding the tarsal gland)
    e. Duct of the tarsal gland (sebaceous)
    f. Eyelash
    g. Glands of Moll (modified sweat glands)
    h. Zeis gland (sebaceous)
    i. Skin

FIGURE 2. Planum nasale. Cross section, Level 1. (H&E X40)
    a. Characteristic epidermal plaques (a) and grooves (arrows) which form the pattern of canine "nose prints" used for identification
    b. Stratum papillare
    c. Blood vessels
    d. Stratum reticulare

FIGURE 3. Nasolabial glands. Cross section, Level 1. (H&E X180)
    a. Gland acini
    b. Ducts

FIGURE 4. Scrotum. Cross section. (H&E X49)
    a. Integumentary folds
    b. Hair follicles
    c. Sebaceous glands (sweat glands are present but not in this field)
    d. Smooth muscle bundles from the dartos muscle

FIGURE 5. Labium vulvae. Oblique section. (H&E X27)
    a. Stratified squamous epithelium
    b. Hair follicles
    c. Sebaceous glands
    d. Sweat glands (notice large numbers)
    e. Adipose connective tissue

Plate 9

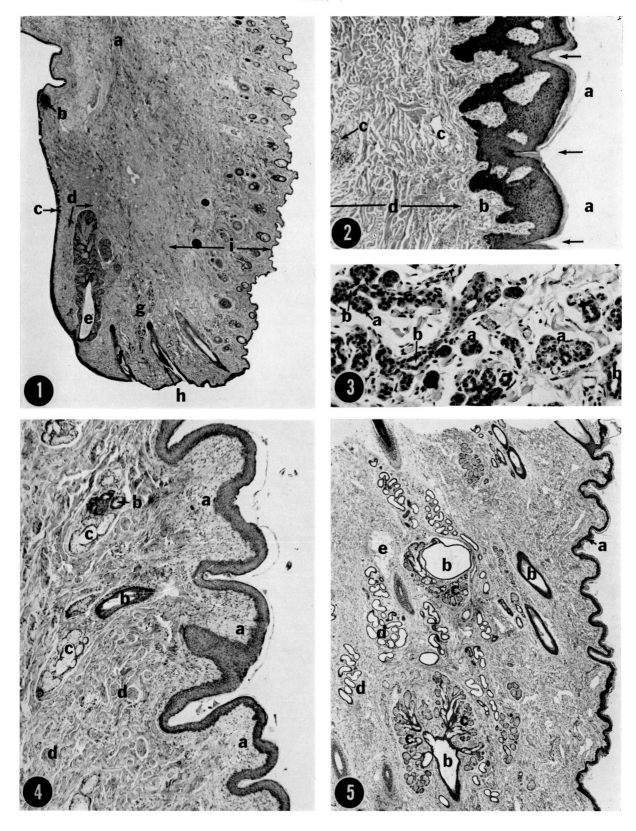

Plate 10

FIGURE 1. Claw and foot pad. Sagittal section, Level 26. (H&E X6)
- a. Proximal phalanx
- b. Middle phalanx
- c. Distal phalanx
- d. Ungual crest
- e. Joint cavities
- f. Skin
- g. Claw fold
- h. Noncornified epidermal layers of the claw
- i. Dorsal ridge
- j. Stratum corneum of the epidermis of the claw
- k. Dermis or corium
- l. Area of the sole
- m. Limiting furrow between the sole and digital pad
- n. Epidermis of the digital pad
- o. Dermis of the digital pad with clusters of coiled merocrine sweat glands and fat
- p. Articular cartilage
- q. Tendons
- r. Cluster of five Pacinian corpuscles

FIGURE 2. Foot pad at the junction with hairy skin. Sagittal section, Level 25. (H&E X150)
- a. Epidermis with horny surface
- b. Dermis
- c. Merocrine sweat glands and fat
- d. Hair-sebaceous gland complex
- e. Coiled sweat glands
- f. Skeletal muscle

FIGURE 3. Merocrine sweat glands of the foot pad. Cross section, Level 25. (H&E X490)
- a. Coiled sweat glands
- b. Gland duct
- c. Capillaries

Plate 10

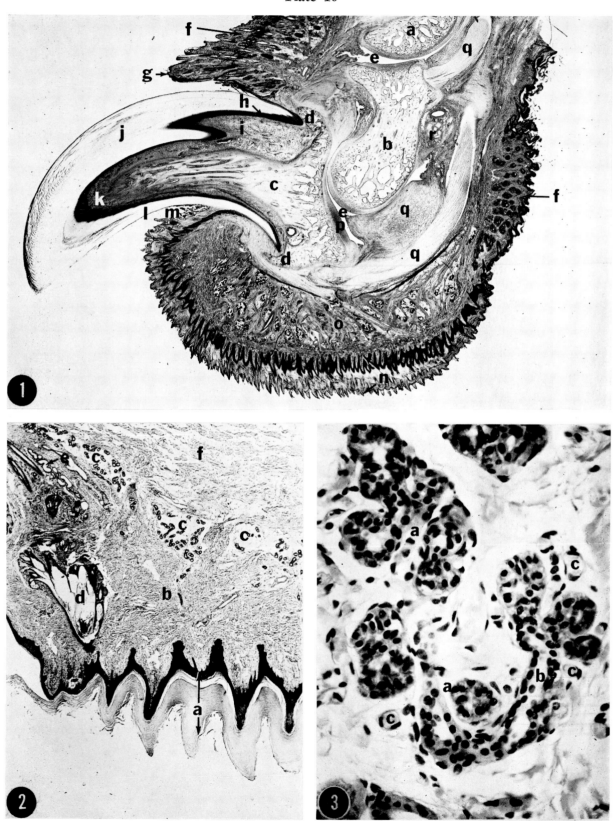

Plate 11

FIGURE 1. Pinna of the ear. Longitudinal section, Level 8. (H&E X47)
  a. Skin of the dorsal or outer surface of the ear. Notice that the hair follicles are more numerous than in the ventral side.
  b. Skin of the ventral or inner side of the ear. Notice that it is thinner than that on the dorsum.
  c. Auricular cartilage (elastic)
  d. Blood vessels traversing one of the many foramina in the cartilaginous plate

FIGURE 2. External ear canal. Cross section, Level 9. (H&E X110)
  a. Desquamating stratum corneum
  b. Thin stratum germinativum
  c. Hair follicles
  d. Sebaceous gland
  e. Dermis
  f. Ceruminous glands
  g. Blood vessels
  h. Elastic cartilage
  i. Perichondrium

FIGURE 3. Ceruminous glands. Cross section, Level 9. (H&E X650)
  a. Glands lined with cuboidal epithelium
  b. Edge of an adjacent gland with the cuboidal epithelial cells cut in cross section
  c. Myoepithelial cells

Plate 11

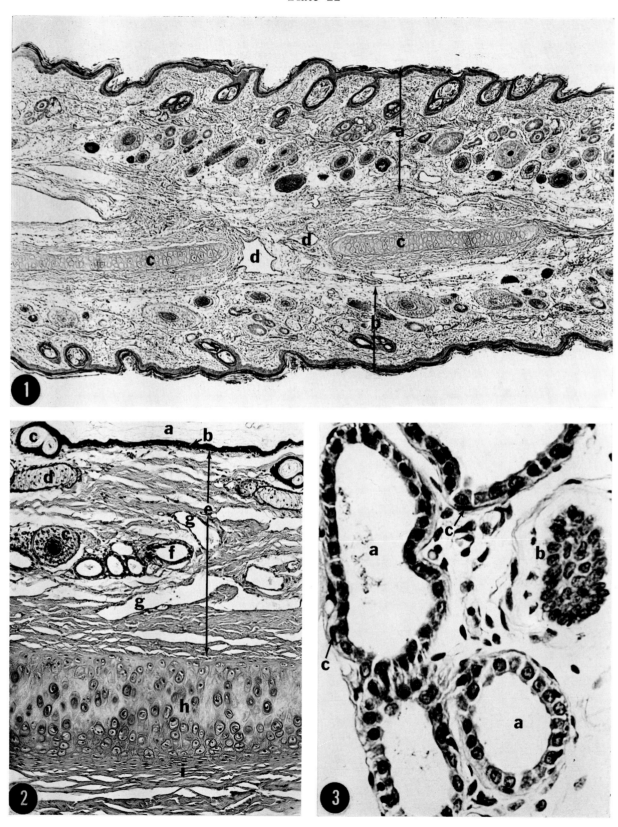

Plate 12

FIGURE 1. Teat. Longitudinal section. (H&E X23)
  a. Hair follicles
  b. Rudimentary teat canals (six in this plane)
  c. Rudimentary glandular tissue consisting of elementary ducts and epithelial buds
FIGURE 2. Rudimentary mammary gland containing duct-like strands of epithelial tissue with some evidence of budding at arrows. Longitudinal section. (H&E X140)
FIGURE 3. Arrector pili muscles and associated structures. Longitudinal section, Level 13. (H&E X100)
  a. Arrector pili muscle attaching to the hair follicle
  b. Hair follicles
  c. Sweat glands
  d. Sebaceous gland
  e. Adipose tissue
FIGURE 4. Hair follicle group in external ear. Cross section, Level 8. (H&E X175)
  a. Fibrous connective tissue enclosing the cluster of hair follicles
  b. Primary hair follicle
  c. Loose connective tissue surrounding at least 20 secondary hair follicles cut at various levels
  d. Arteriole

Plate 12

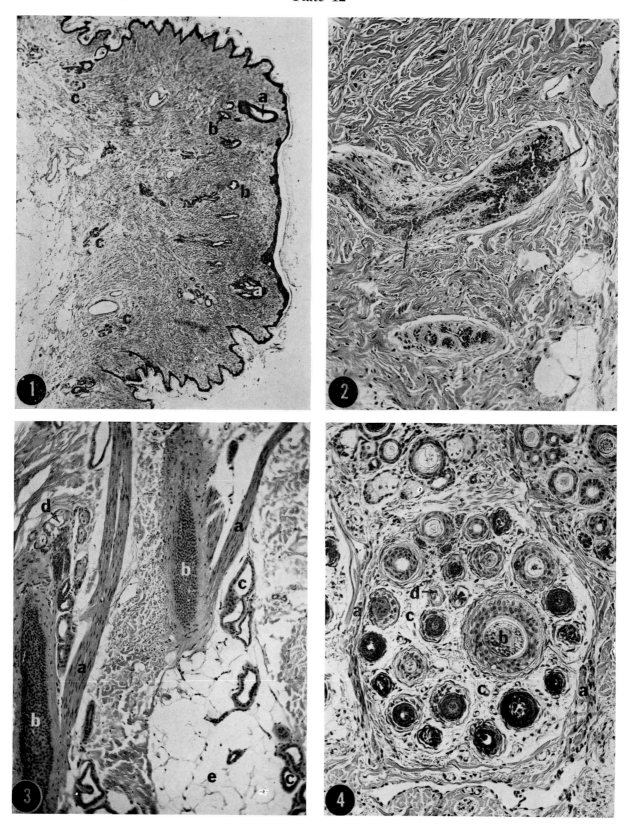

Plate 13

FIGURE 1. Elastic connective tissue in the dermis. Notice the elastic fibers (arrows). Their relation to the guard hair (a) is well illustrated at the right. Longitudinal section, Level 21. (Weigert-van Gieson X150)

FIGURE 2. Elastic connective tissue fibers attaching to the basement membrane (arrow) of the external root sheath just above the annular sinus of a tactile hair. Longitudinal section, Level 7. (Weigert-van Gieson X780)

FIGURE 3. Arrector pili muscle attaching to a hair follicle by elastic fibers. Oblique section, Level 10. (Weigert-van Gieson X280)
  a. Arrector pili muscle
  b. Small muscle bundles separating and inserting on the hair follicle by elastic fibers
  c. Notice three elastic fiber bundles connecting the muscle to the hair follicle.
  d. Hair follicles cut obliquely

FIGURE 4. Arrector pili muscle terminating in a bundle of elastic connective tissue just under the epidermis. Longitudinal section, Level 10. (Weigert-van Gieson X690)
  a. Arrector pili muscle
  b. Elastic connective tissue fibers
  c. Collagenous connective tissue bundles

Plate 13

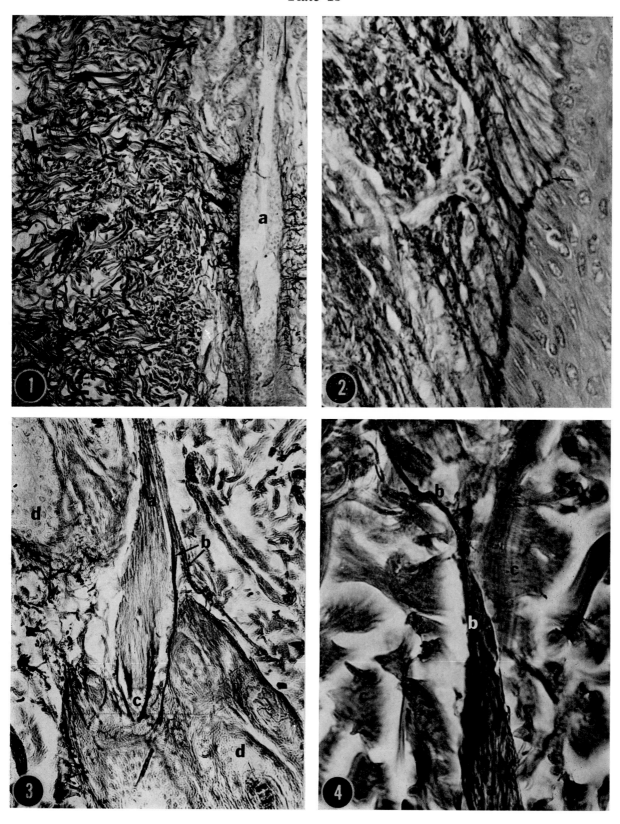

Chapter 2

Cardiovascular System

Generally, the structures of the heart are very similar in most of the domestic animals and man. There are three features peculiar to the dog which seem pertinent to mention here. The Purkinje fibers in the canine heart are not as abundant as they are in man; however, their morphology is similar. James (1962) reported that the intercalated discs are slightly more prominent than in the human heart. The canine cardiac skeleton contains patches of fibrocartilage, while in man this is made up of heavy collagenous fibers. In the ox and horse bone may be found in this area.

Neither the microscopic anatomy of the various levels of individual blood vessels nor comparisons of the blood vessels of different species and breeds have been studied to any extent. Such studies remain to be done. We have illustrated only the major vessels.

CARDIOVASCULAR SYSTEM

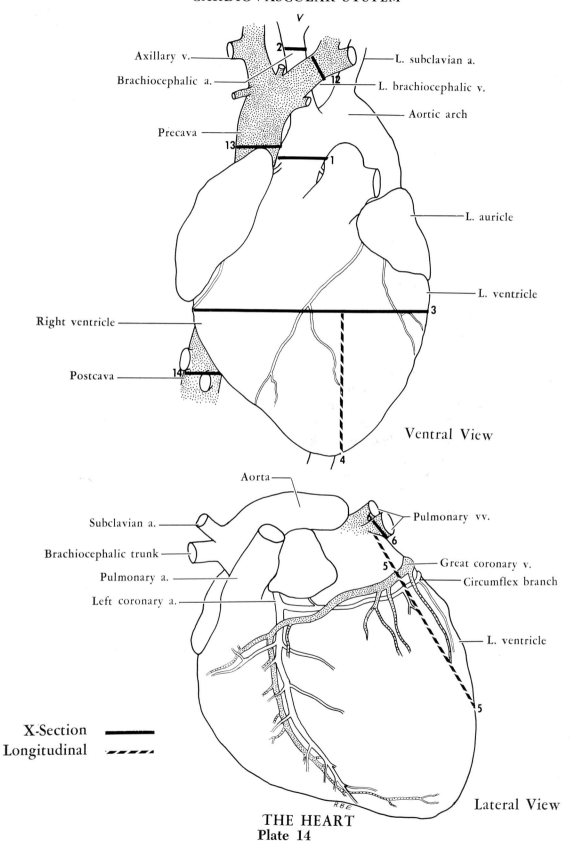

Axillary v.

Brachiocephalic a.

Precava

Right ventricle

Postcava

L. subclavian a.

L. brachiocephalic v.

Aortic arch

L. auricle

L. ventricle

Ventral View

Aorta

Subclavian a.

Brachiocephalic trunk

Pulmonary a.

Left coronary a.

Pulmonary vv.

Great coronary v.

Circumflex branch

L. ventricle

X-Section

Longitudinal

Lateral View

THE HEART
Plate 14

Plate 15

FIGURE 1. Atrioventricular junction (right side). Longitudinal section, Level 5. (H&E X8)
- a. Atrial wall
- b. Ventricular wall
- c. Coronary groove containing fat, right coronary vein and a branch of the circumflex coronary artery.
- d. Root of the atrioventricular valve

FIGURE 2. Valve. Longitudinal section, Level 5. (H&E X120)
- a. Endothelium covering the valve
- b. Collagenous fibers extending into the valve
- c. Myocardium

FIGURE 3. Cardiac skeleton. Longitudinal section, Level 5. (H&E X110)
- a. Cardiac muscle
- b. Fibrocartilage

Plate 15

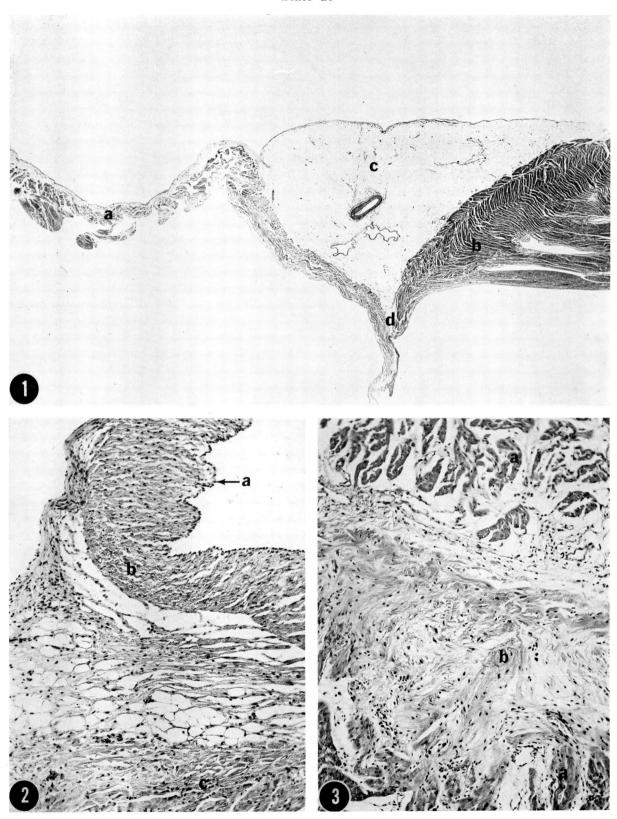

Plate 16

FIGURE 1. Ventricular endocardium. Cross section, Level 3. (H&E X480)
   a. Endothelium
   b. Subendocardium containing Purkinje fibers at arrows
   c. Myocardium
FIGURE 2. Ventricular epicardium. Cross section, Level 3. (H&E X830)
   a. Mesothelium
   b. Subepicardial layer of connective tissue
   c. Myocardium
FIGURE 3. Ventricular myocardium. Longitudinal section, Level 4. (H&E X380)
   a. Myocardial fiber (notice cross striations)
   b. Intercalated disk
FIGURE 4. Ventricular myocardium. Cross section, Level 3. (H&E X380)
   a. Fibers with myofibrillae
   b. Centrally located nuclei
   c. Capillaries

Plate 16

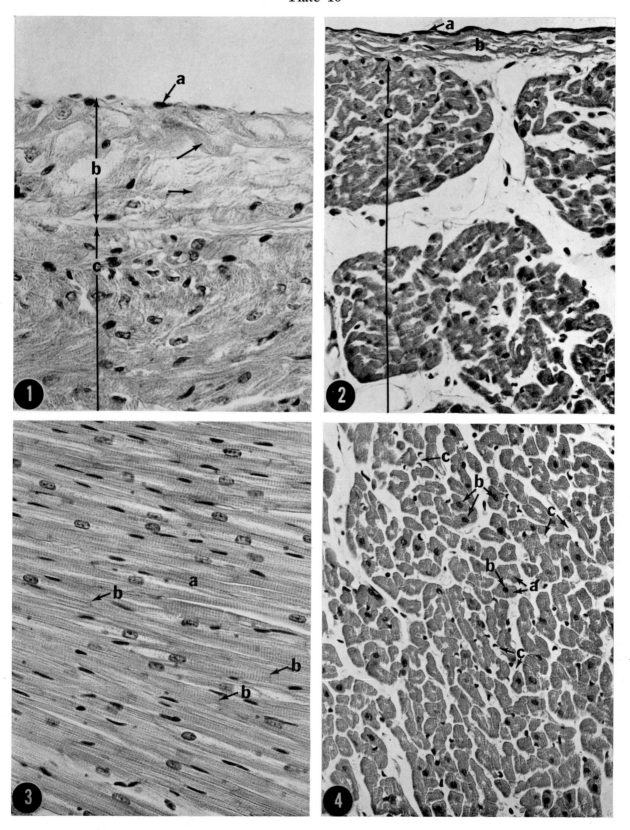

Plate 17

FIGURE 1. Coronary artery. Cross section, Level 5. (H&E X300)
  a. Endothelium of the tunica intima
  b. Internal elastic membrane
  c. Tunica media made up primarily of smooth muscle
  d. Isolated elastic fibers in the tunica media
  e. Tunica adventitia
  f. Adipose tissue of the coronary groove

FIGURE 2. Coronary vein. Cross section, Level 5. (H&E X300)
  a. Endothelium of the tunica intima
  b. Tunica media
  c. Tunica adventitia
  d. Adipose tissue of the coronary groove

FIGURE 3. Pulmonary vein. Cross section, Level 6. (H&E X12)
  a. Tunica media
  b. Tunica adventitia containing cardiac muscle
  c. Tunica adventitia without cardiac muscle
  d. Mesothelium
  e. Area seen in Figure 4

FIGURE 4. Pulmonary vein. Cross section, Level 6. (H&E X160)
  a. Tunica intima
  b. Tunica media
  c. Cardiac muscle terminating in the fibrous tissue
  d. Tunica adventitia
  e. Mesothelium
  f. Vasa vasorum

Plate 17

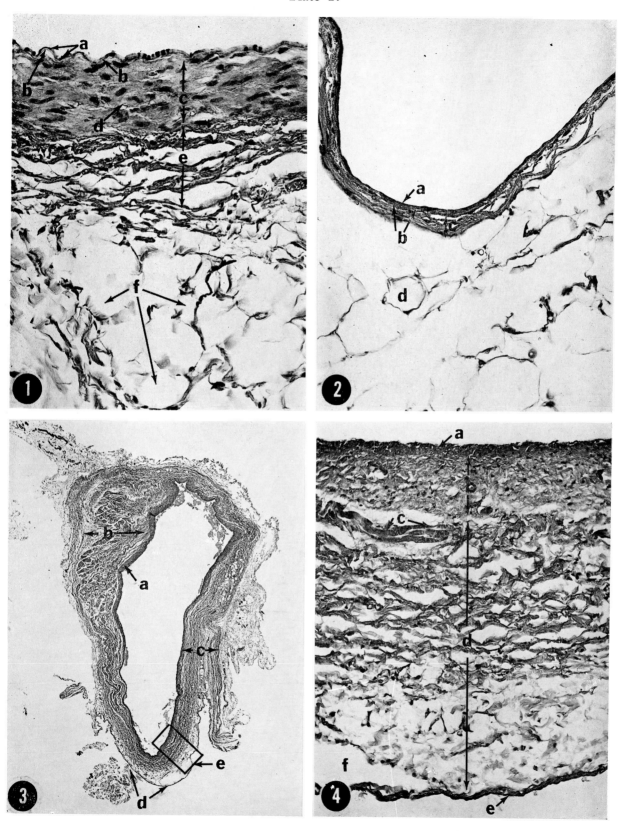

CARDIOVASCULAR SYSTEM

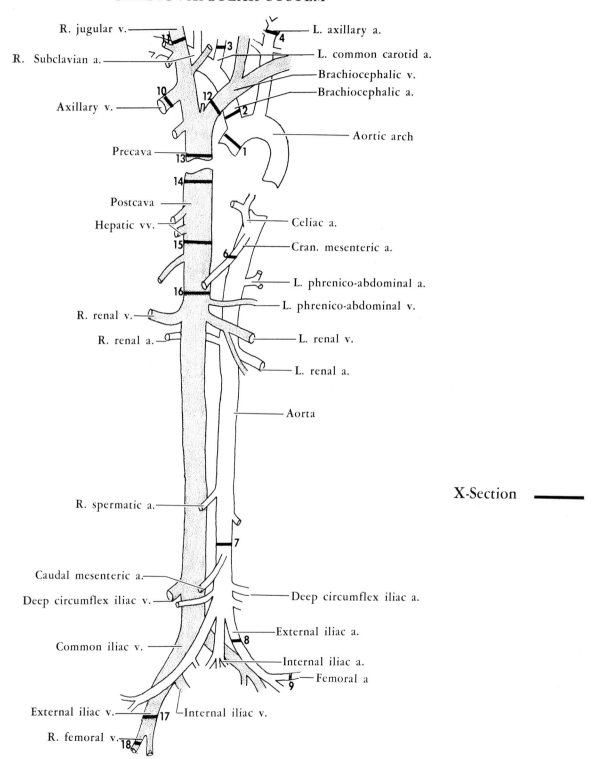

R. jugular v.

R. Subclavian a.

Axillary v.

Precava

Postcava

Hepatic vv.

R. renal v.

R. renal a.

R. spermatic a.

Caudal mesenteric a.

Deep circumflex iliac v.

Common iliac v.

External iliac v.

R. femoral v.

L. axillary a.

L. common carotid a.

Brachiocephalic v.

Brachiocephalic a.

Aortic arch

Celiac a.

Cran. mesenteric a.

L. phrenico-abdominal a.

L. phrenico-abdominal v.

L. renal v.

L. renal a.

Aorta

Deep circumflex iliac a.

External iliac a.

Internal iliac a.

Femoral a

Internal iliac v.

X-Section

Blood Vessels

Plate 18

Plate 19

FIGURE 1. Ascending aorta. Cross section, Level 1. (H&E X100)
  a. Endothelium of the tunica intima
  b. Tunica media composed of smooth muscle and elastic laminae (arrows)
FIGURE 2. Ascending aorta. Cross section, Level 1. (H&E X700)
  a. Elastic laminae
  b. Smooth muscle fibers cut somewhat tangentially
FIGURE 3. Abdominal aorta. Cross section, Level 7. (H&E X140)
  a. Endothelium
  b. Internal elastic membrane
  c. Tunica media composed primarily of smooth muscle with elastic laminae
  d. Portion of the tunica adventitia composed of collagenous fibers
  e. Interrupted external elastic membrane
FIGURE 4. Abdominal aorta. Cross section, Level 7. (H&E X700)
  a. Endothelium
  b. Tunica intima
  c. Internal elastic membrane
  d. Elastic laminae of the tunica media
  e. Smooth muscle fibers of the tunica media

Plate 19

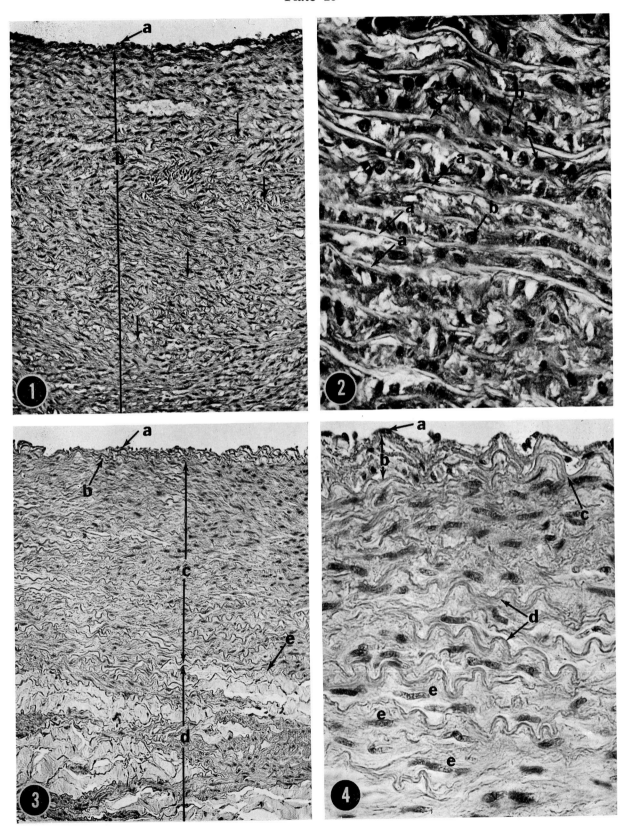

Plate 20

FIGURE 1. Precava through a region near the heart. Notice the cardiac muscle. Cross section, Level 13. (H&E X140)
  a. Endothelium of the tunica intima
  b. Thin tunica media
  c. Tunica adventitia composed of three layers
      (1) Inner (connective tissue)
      (2) Middle (cardiac muscle)
      (3) Outer (connective tissue)
  d. Vasa vasorum

FIGURE 2. Precava through a region where the cardiac muscle terminates. Cross section, Level 13. (H&E X140)
  a. Endothelium of the tunica intima
  b. Thin tunica media
  c. Tunica adventitia
  d. Isolated bundles of cardiac muscle

FIGURE 3. Postcava near the heart in a region containing cardiac muscle. Cross section, Level 14. (H&E X130)
  a. Endothelium of the tunica intima
  b. Tunica media
  c. Tunica adventitia composed of three layers
      (1) Inner (connective tissue)
      (2) Middle (cardiac muscle)
      (3) Outer (connective tissue)
  d. Mesothelium

FIGURE 4. Postcava through a region near the heart where the cardiac muscle terminates. Cross section, Level 14. (H&E X150)
  a. Endothelium of the tunica intima
  b. Tunica media
  c. Tunica adventitia
  d. Cardiac muscle terminating in collagenous fibers

Plate 20

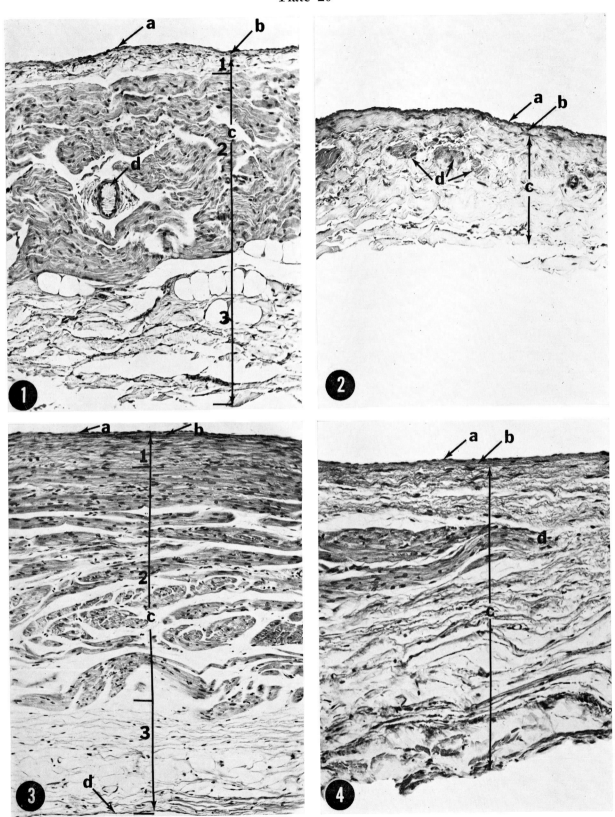

Plate 21

FIGURE 1. Postcava in a region where the cardiac muscle terminates. Cross section, Level 14. (H&E X420)
- a. Cardiac muscle fibers
- b. Collagenous fibers

FIGURE 2. Postcava. Level 15. (H&E X140)
- a. Endothelium of the tunica intima
- b. Tunica media composed of one or two layers of circular smooth muscle
- c. Tunica adventitia in three layers
  - (1) Inner (connective tissue)
  - (2) Middle (longitudinal bundles of smooth muscle)
  - (3) Mesothelium

FIGURE 3. Postcava. Ventral wall. Cross section, Level 16. (H&E X140)
- a. Endothelium of the tunica intima
- b. Tunica media composed of one to two layers of circular smooth muscle
- c. Tunica adventitia in three layers
  - (1) Inner (connective tissue)
  - (2) Middle (longitudinal bundles of smooth muscle)
  - (3) Outer (connective tissue)
- d. Mesothelium

FIGURE 4. Postcava. Dorsal side. Cross section, Level 16. (H&E X140)
- a. Endothelium of the tunica intima
- b. Tunica media composed of three to four layers of circular smooth muscle fibers
- c. Tunica adventitia containing only scattered bundles of smooth muscle (see arrows) in the middle layer. Notice absence of mesothelium on this side of the vessel.
  - (1) Inner (connective tissue)
  - (2) Middle (collagenous connective tissue with scattered bundles of smooth muscle)
  - (3) Outer (connective tissue)

Plate 21

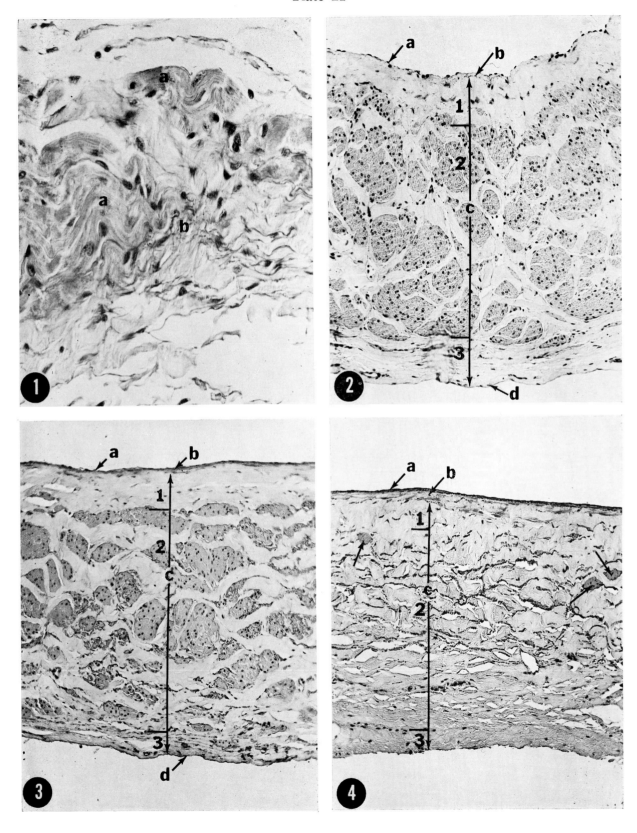

Plate 22

FIGURE 1. Brachiocephalic artery. Cross section, Level 2. (H&E X250)
    a. Endothelium
    b. Tunica media composed of smooth muscle and elastic fibers
    c. External elastic membrane
    d. Tunica adventitia
FIGURE 2. Brachiocephalic vein. Cross section, Level 12. (H&E X240)
    a. Endothelium
    b. Tunica media
    c. Tunica adventitia
FIGURE 3. Axillary artery. Cross section, Level 4. (H&E X300)
    a. Endothelium
    b. Tunica intima
    c. Internal elastic membrane
    d. Tunica media (notice mixture of elastic and smooth muscle fibers)
    e. External elastic membrane
    f. Tunica adventitia
FIGURE 4. Axillary vein. Cross section, Level 10. (H&E X300)
    a. Endothelium
    b. Tunica media made up of one to two layers of smooth muscle
    c. Tunica adventitia
    d. Adipose tissue

Plate 22

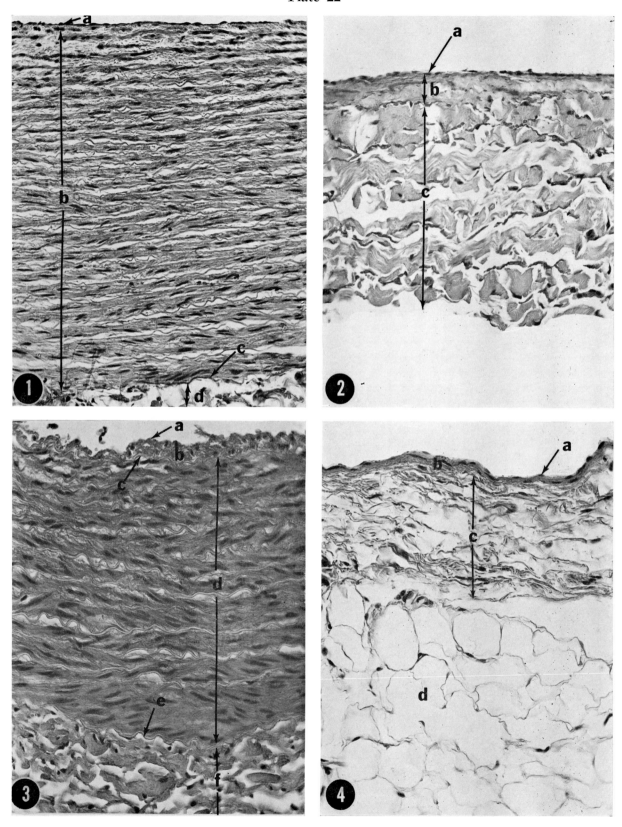

Plate 23

FIGURE 1. Carotid artery. Cross section, Level 3. (H&E X300)
   a. Endothelium of the tunica intima
   b. Internal elastic membrane
   c. Tunica media containing muscle and elastic fibers
   d. Tunica adventitia
   e. External elastic membrane

FIGURE 2. Carotid artery. Cross section, Level 3. (H&E X650)
   a. Endothelium of the tunica intima
   b. Internal elastic membrane
   c. Smooth muscle of the tunica media
   d. Elastic connective tissue fibers

FIGURE 3. Jugular vein. Cross section, Level 11. (H&E X300)
   a. Endothelium of the tunica intima
   b. Tunica media
   c. Tunica adventitia

FIGURE 4. Jugular vein. Cross section, Level 11. (H&E X650)
   a. Endothelium of the tunica intima
   b. Smooth muscle of the tunica media
   c. Adventitia containing a few smooth muscle fibers (arrows)

Plate 23

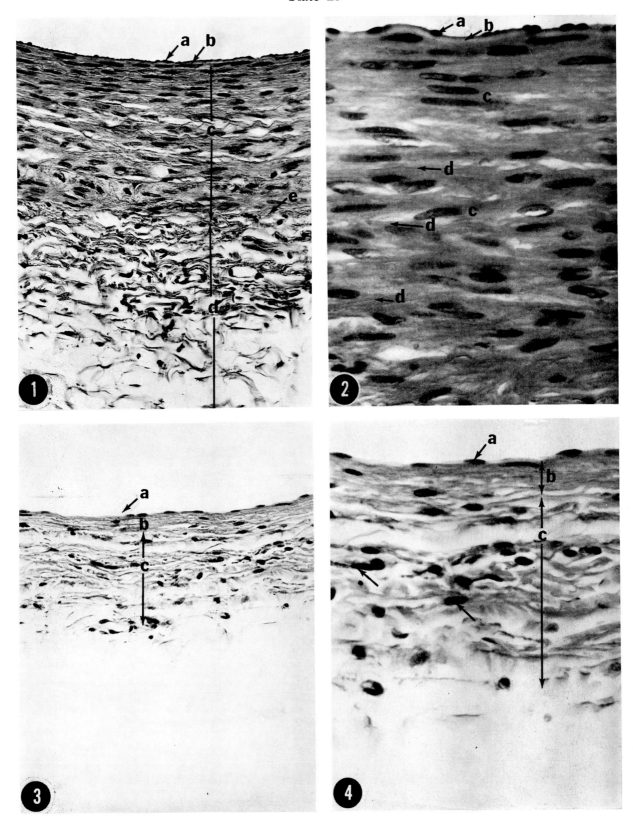

Plate 24

FIGURE 1. The carotid body seen near a branch of the internal carotid artery. Cross section. (H&E X180)
   a. Muscular artery
   b. Carotid body
   c. Loose connective tissue
   d. Vein

FIGURE 2. Carotid body. Cross section. (H&E X290)
   a. Epithelioid cells of the carotid body
   b. Arteriole
   c. Venules filled with blood

FIGURE 3. Carotid body. Cross section. (H&E X310)
   a. Epithelioid cells of the carotid body
   b. Sinusoids
   c. Arterioles
   d. Capillaries

Plate 24

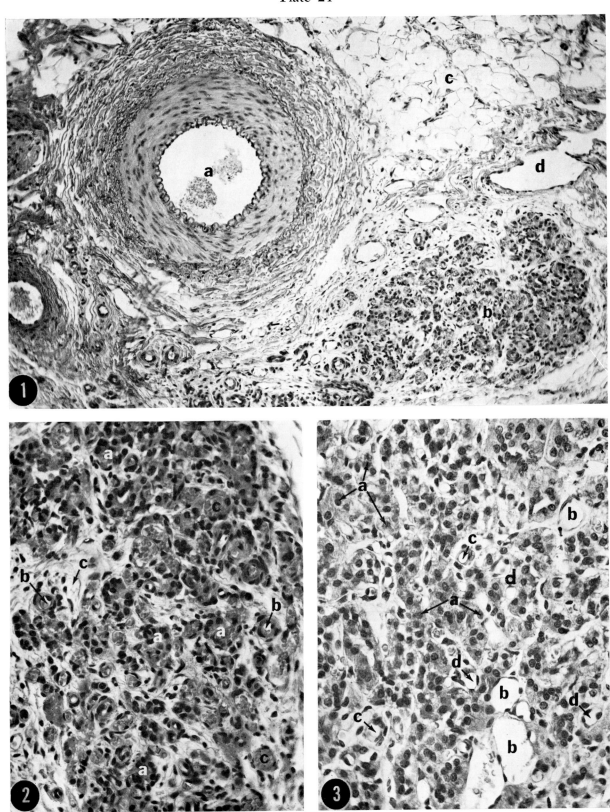

Plate 25

FIGURE 1. External iliac artery. Cross section, Level 8. (H&E X300)
    a. Endothelium
    b. Internal elastic membrane
    c. Tunica media composed of smooth muscle
    d. Isolated elastic fibers in the tunica media
    e. External elastic membrane
    f. Tunica adventitia

FIGURE 2. External iliac vein. Cross section, Level 17. (H&E X300)
    a. Endothelium
    b. Tunica media composed of smooth muscle fibers
    c. Tunica adventitia

FIGURE 3. Femoral artery. Cross section, Level 9. (H&E X300)
    a. Endothelium
    b. Internal elastic membrane
    c. Tunica media composed of smooth muscle
    d. Elastic fibers in the tunica media
    e. External elastic membrane
    f. Tunica adventitia

FIGURE 4. Femoral vein. Cross section, Level 18. (H&E X300)
    a. Endothelium
    b. Tunica media
    c. Tunica adventitia

Plate 25

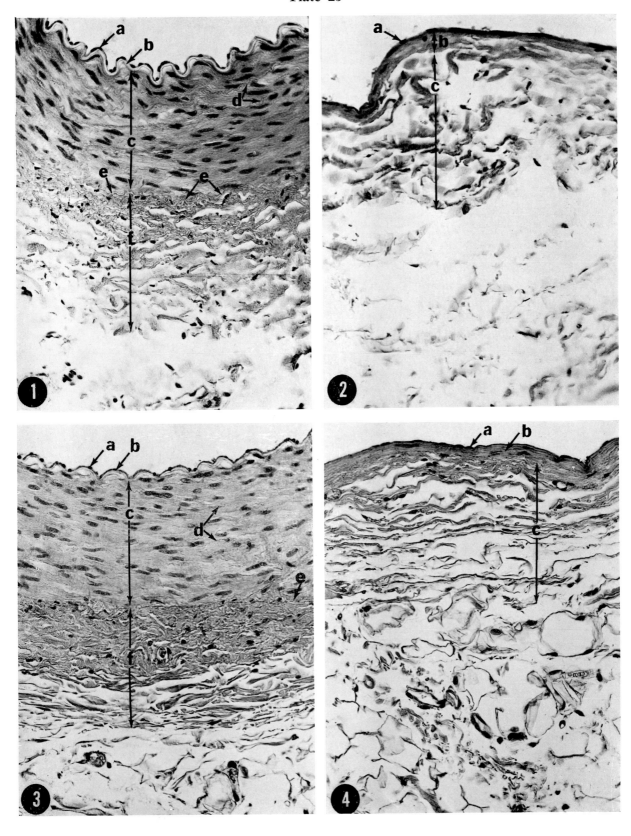

Plate 26

FIGURE 1. Portal vein. Cross section. (H&E X32)
   a. Tunica intima
   b. Tunica media
   c. Tunica adventitia
   d. Mesothelium
   e. Nerve bundles in the mesentery
   f. Adipose tissue in the mesentery
FIGURE 2. Portal vein. (H&E X430)
   a. Endothelium of the tunica intima
   b. Tunica media composed of two to three layers of smooth muscle
      fibers
   c. Tunica adventitia composed of three layers
      (1) Inner (connective tissue)
      (2) Middle (layer of smooth muscle)
      (3) Outer (connective tissue)
FIGURE 3. Cranial mesenteric artery. Cross section, Level 6. (H&E X435)
   a. Tunica intima
   b. Tunica media with the muscle fibers cut somewhat tangentially
   c. Tunica adventitia
FIGURE 4. Arteriovenous anastomosis in the lamina propria of the tongue.
   (H&E X340)
   a. Irregularly disposed epithelioid cells
   b. Modified smooth muscle cells in the vessel wall

Plate 26

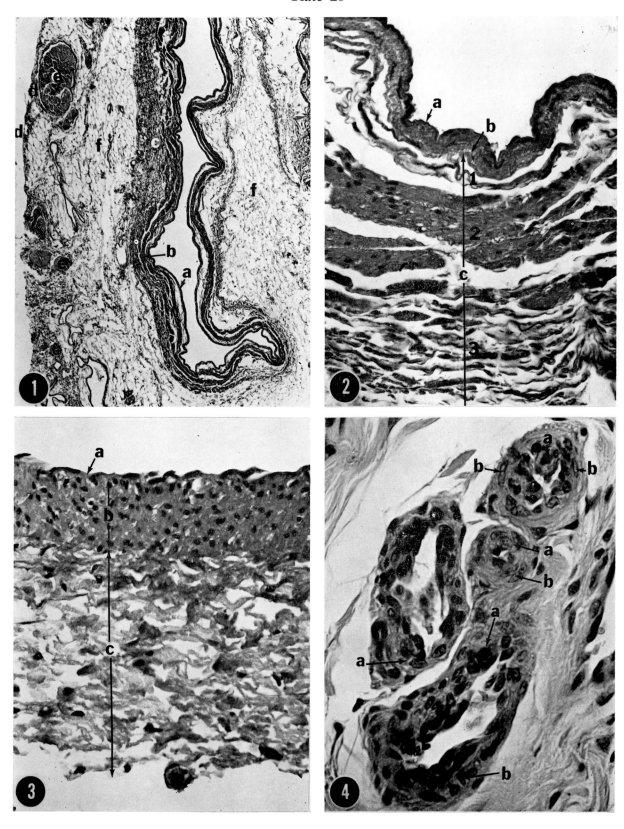

Plate 27

FIGURE 1. Thoracic duct. Cross section. (H&E X42)
    a. Tunica intima
    b. Tunica media
    c. Tunica adventitia

FIGURE 2. Thoracic duct. Cross section. (H&E X300)
    a. Endothelium
    b. Smooth muscle of the tunica media
    c. Collagenous fibers of the tunica adventitia

FIGURE 3. Lymphatic vessel. Longitudinal section. (H&E X350)
    a. Thin wall of a lymphatic vessel lined with endothelium
    b. Valve
    c. Arteriole in the surrounding connective tissue
    d. Venule in the surrounding connective tissue.

Plate 27

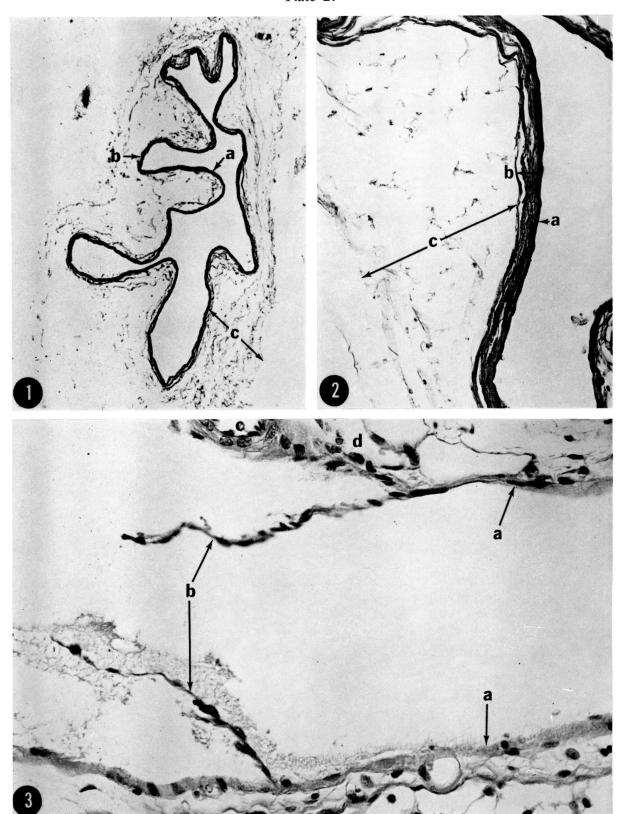

Chapter 3

Lymphatic Organs

Solitary and small aggregated follicles are particularly abundant in the rectum, anal canal, prepuce and third eyelid. While the dog does not possess a vermiform appendix, the cecum is characterized by numerous lymph follicles.

The canine lymph node is very similar in function and morphology to that seen in man and most domestic animals except the pig in which the germinal centers typical of the cortex are more centrally located and the tissues characteristic of the medulla are at the periphery. The lymph node of the dog possesses a well-defined capsule containing elastic and smooth muscle fibers which continues as a framework of septa and trabeculae. Most of the nodules are situated in the cortex where they are surrounded at least in part by the lymph sinus. In the medulla, the lymphoid tissue occurs as anastomosing cords of lymphocytes. Hemal nodes are not found in the dog.

The spleen of the dog is rich in trabeculae and muscle fibers but poor in white pulp. The well-defined capsule is composed of a superficial fibro-elastic layer and a deeper layer of smooth muscle. In the dog, the muscle fibers are interwoven in a plexus, whereas in the horse and cow the muscle fibers are arranged in layers. Fibromuscular trabeculae containing blood vessels project into the pulp where the abundant red pulp of the spleen of the dog, horse and cat acts as a "storage" organ for blood cells which can be expelled by the contractile elements of the framework. In contrast, the "defense" spleen of the rabbit and man has fewer trabeculae and muscle fibers but abundant lymphatic tissue.

The white pulp forms a lymphatic sheath which accompanies the arteries and at intervals expands to form the splenic nodules.

In the spleen of carnivora, granulocytes develop postnatally from myelocytes. Megakaryocytes are characteristically seen in the red pulp of carnivores and swine. The sinusoidal circulation of the spleen is a subject of continuing speculation. According to Zappala (1962) the dog has a segmental arterial distribution very similar to that of man, but the tributaries of the vein of the dog are between the segments instead of within the segments as in man.

The thymus is a distinctly lobulated organ located almost entirely in the precardial mediastinal septum and surrounded by a delicate but distinct capsule. The medullary substance is not clearly separated from the cortex and is often continuous through several lobules. Hassall's corpuscles are characteristically prominent in this age group. Remnants of the thymus are present in the dog through old age.

The palatine tonsil of carnivores differs from that of man, horse, ruminants and swine in the absence of well-defined epithelial crypts. A bulging outward or an infolding is responsible for the increase of mucosal surface. The tonsillar glands in the carnivora are mixed rather than mucous as in man. Their ducts open on the tonsillar surface and not into the crypts.

LYMPHATIC ORGANS

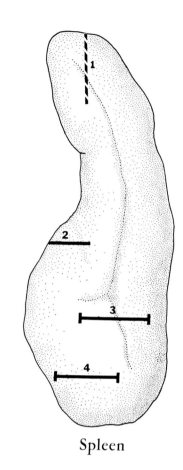

Spleen

| X-Section | ——— |
| Longitudinal | ✂✂✂ |

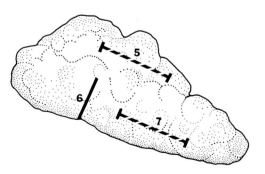

Thymus

Plate 28

Plate 29

FIGURE 1. Spleen. Longitudinal section, Level 1. (H&E X15)
  a. Capsule
  b. Trabeculae
  c. Trabecular vein
  d. Splenic nodules (white pulp)
  e. Germinal center
  f. Red pulp

FIGURE 2. Spleen. Compare with Figure 1. Longitudinal section, Level 1. (Reticular stain X11)
  a. Capsule
  b. Splenic nodule
  c. Red pulp
  d. Trabecular vein

FIGURE 3. Splenic capsule and red pulp. Longitudinal section, Level 1. (H&E X310)
  a. Mesothelium
  b. Capsule
  c. Red pulp
  d. Trabecular vein

FIGURE 4. Spleen capsule and underlying red pulp. Longitudinal section, Level 1. (Reticular stain X400)
  a. Reticular fibers of capsule
  b. Red pulp
  c. Venous sinus

Plate 29

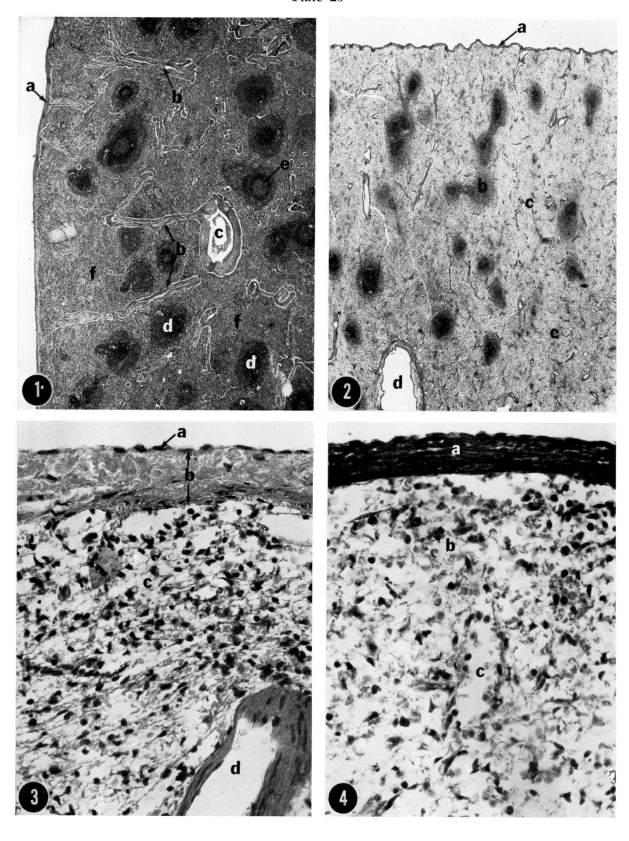

Plate 30

FIGURE 1. Spleen. Cross section, Level 2. (H&E X170)
  a. Capsule
  b. Red pulp
  c. Splenic nodule (white pulp)
  d. Trabecula
  e. Megakaryocyte
  f. Central artery

FIGURE 2. Red pulp of the spleen. Cross section, Level 3. (H&E X310)
  a. Trabecular artery
  b. Red pulp
  c. Venous sinus filled with blood

FIGURE 3. Splenic nodule and red pulp. Cross section, Level 3. (H&E X170)
  a. Red pulp
  b. Splenic nodule
  c. Central artery
  d. Megakaryocytes

FIGURE 4. Central artery of the spleen and artery of the pulp. Cross section, Level 3. (H&E X380)
  a. Splenic nodule (white pulp)
  b. Central artery
  c. Pulp artery
  d. Red pulp

Plate 30

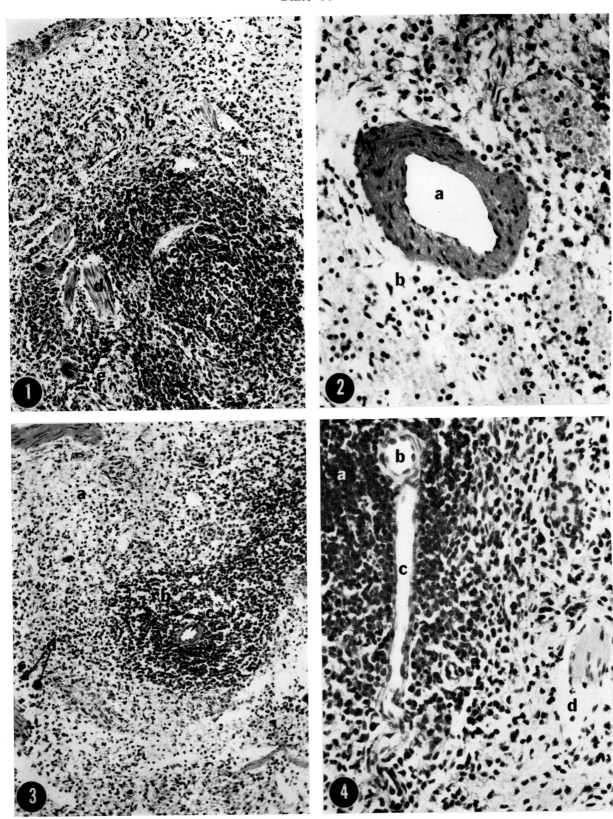

Plate 31

FIGURE 1. Red pulp of the spleen. Cross section, Level 4. (H&E X450)
    a. Artery of the pulp
    b. Splenic sinuses
    c. Pulp cord (cords of Billroth)
FIGURE 2. Red pulp of the spleen. Cross section, Level 4. (H&E X450)
    a. Sheathed artery
    b. Sheath (of Schweigger-Seidel)
    c. Splenic sinus
FIGURE 3. Red pulp of the spleen. Cross section, Level 4. (H&E X160)
    a. Trabecular vein
    b. Pulp vein
    c. Splenic sinus
FIGURE 4. Megakaryocyte. Cross section, Level 4. (H&E X2100)

Plate 31

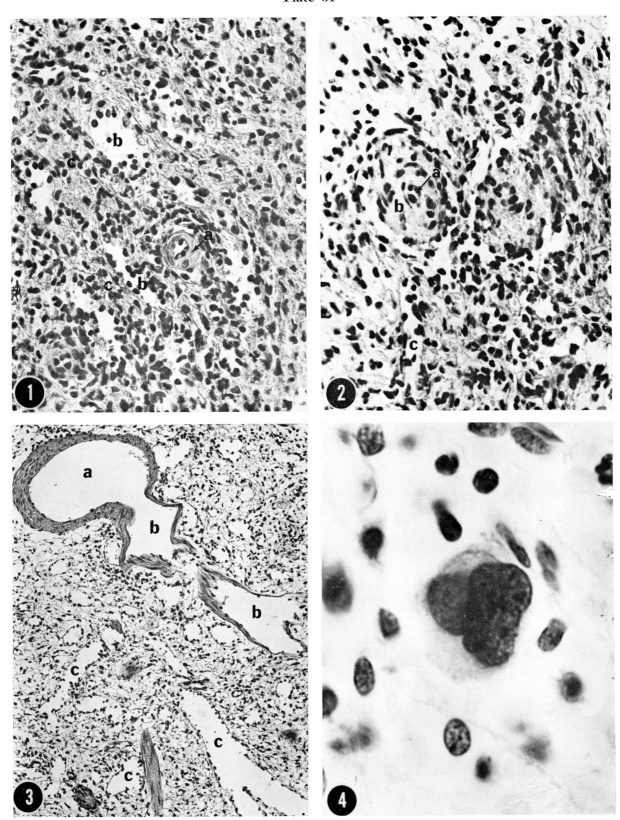

Plate 32

FIGURE 1. Lymph node. (H&E X24)
   a. Capsule
   b. Subcapsular sinus
   c. Cortex
   d. Medulla with prominent medullary sinuses at the arrows
   e. Medullary cord
   f. Cortical nodules with germinal centers

FIGURE 2. Lymph node. (H&E X30)
   a. Afferent lymphatic vessel
   b. Efferent lymphatic vessel at the hilus
   c. Cortical nodule
   d. Subcapsular sinus
   e. Area seen in Figure 3

FIGURE 3. Lymph node capsule and efferent lymphatic vessel shown in
   Figure 2. (H&E X380)
   a. Subcapsular sinus
   b. Capsule
   c. Smooth muscle of the lymphatic vessel
   d. Efferent lymphatic vessel
   e. Nucleus of an endothelial cell lining a lymphatic vessel
   f. Interstitial connective tissue

Plate 32

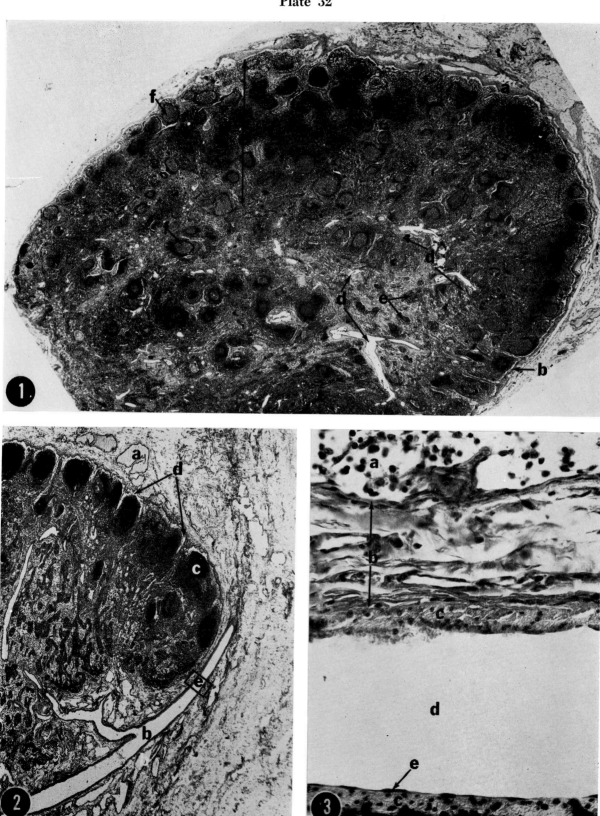

Plate 33

FIGURE 1. Hilus of a lymph node. (H&E X300)
    a. Connective tissue of the hilus containing many lymphatic vessels (at arrows)
    b. Lymph nodules
    c. Medullary cords
    d. Medullary region of an adjacent lymph node
FIGURE 2. Capsule and subcapsular sinus of a lymph node. (H&E X160)
    a. Capsule with adipose cells (at arrows)
    b. Subcapsular sinus of the cortex filled with lymphocytes
FIGURE 3. Cortical region of a lymph node. (H&E X360)
    a. Capsule
    b. Subcapsular sinus
    c. Lymph nodule
FIGURE 4. Reticular fibers in the capsule and cortical areas of a lymph node. (Reticular stain X300)
    a. Capsule
    b. Subcapsular sinus
    c. Reticular fibers

Plate 33

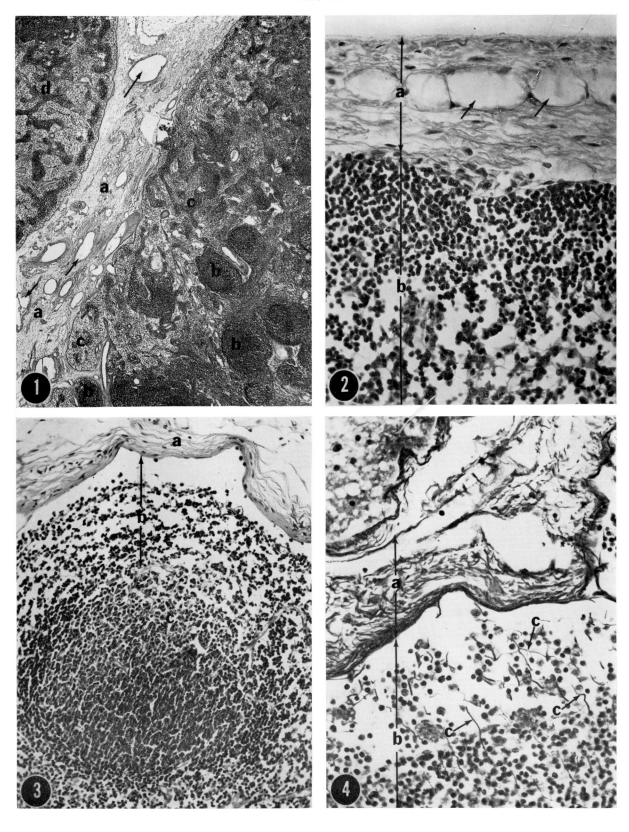

Plate 34

FIGURE 1. Medullary area of a lymph node. (H&E X210)
   a. Trabecula
   b. Trabecular veins
   c. Trabecular artery
FIGURE 2. Medullary area of a lymph node. (H&E X300)
   a. Medullary sinuses
   b. Trabecula
   c. Medullary cord
FIGURE 3. Medullary area of a lymph node. (Reticular stain X360)
   a. Reticular cells
   b. Reticular fibers
   c. Medullary sinuses
FIGURE 4. Medullary area of a lymph node. Compare with medullary
   lymphatic sinus, Figure 3. (H&E X300)
   a. Medullary blood vessels

Plate 34

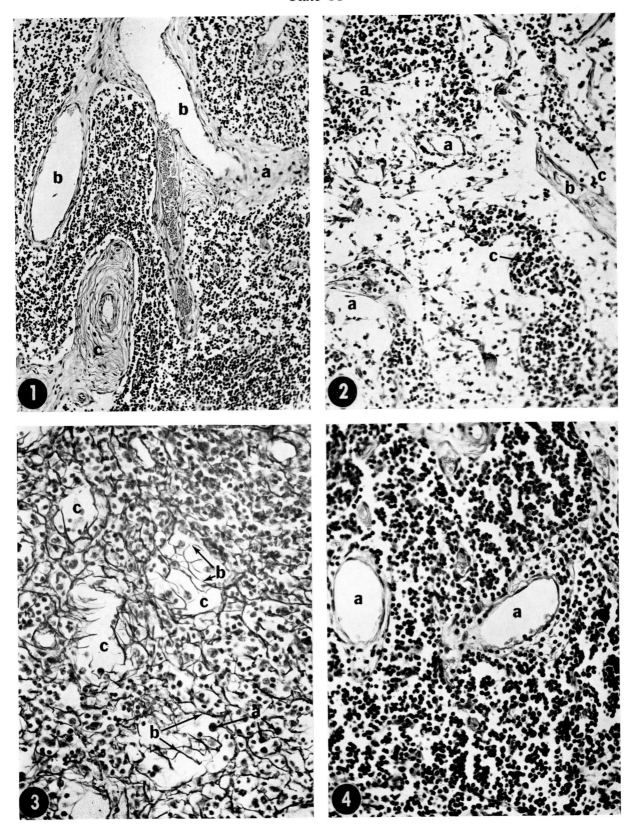

Plate 35

FIGURE 1. Aggregated lymph follicles (Peyer's patches in the ileum). (H&E X21)
   a. Mucosa of the ileum
   b. Muscularis mucosae
   c. Lymph nodules
   d. Efferent lymphatic vessels
   e. Area shown in Figure 2
   f. Submucosa

FIGURE 2. Aggregated lymph follicles. Area e, Figure 1. (H&E X110)
   a. Germinal center of lymph nodule
   b. Cortex of nodule
   c. Efferent lymphatic vessel

FIGURE 3. Solitary lymph follicle of the colon. (H&E X16)
   a. Lymph follicle
   b. Efferent lymphatic vessel
   c. Muscularis mucosae
   d. Lamina propria
   e. Blood vessels

FIGURE 4. Solitary lymph nodule in submucosa of the colon. (H&E X14)
   a. Lymph nodule
   b. Muscularis mucosae
   c. Intestinal mucosa
   d. Submucosa
   e. Efferent lymphatic vessels

Plate 35

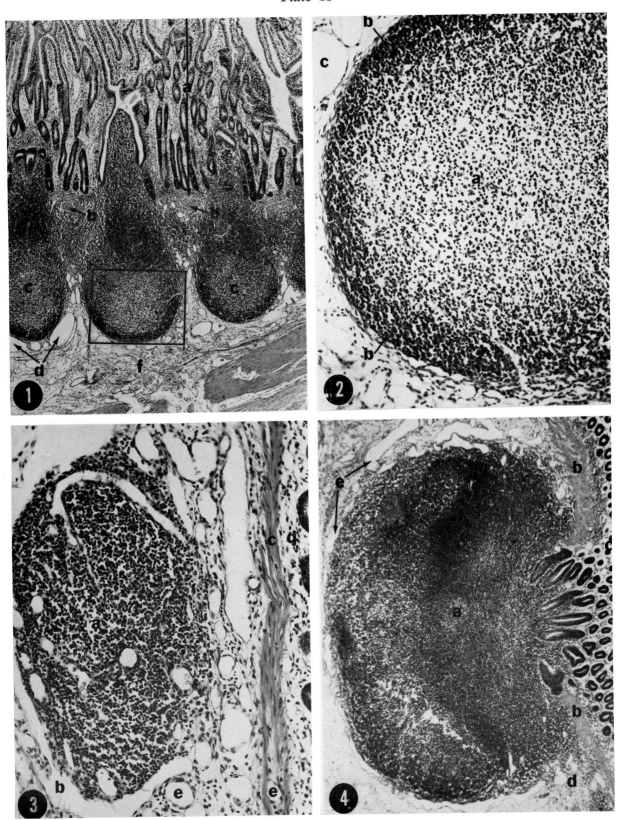

Plate 36

FIGURE 1. Palatine tonsil. (H&E X16)
  a. Stratified squamous epithelium
  b. Germinal centers of lymph nodules
  c. Tonsillar sinus
  d. Mucous glands
  e. Skeletal muscle
  f. Capsule

FIGURE 2. Tonsillar sinus. (H&E X140)
  a. Tonsillar sinus containing cellular debris
  b. Stratified squamous epithelium
  c. Lymphocytes infiltrating the surface epithelium

FIGURE 3. Capsule of the palatine tonsil. (H&E X150)
  a. Lymphatic tissue
  b. Efferent lymph capillaries
  c. Capsule

Plate 36

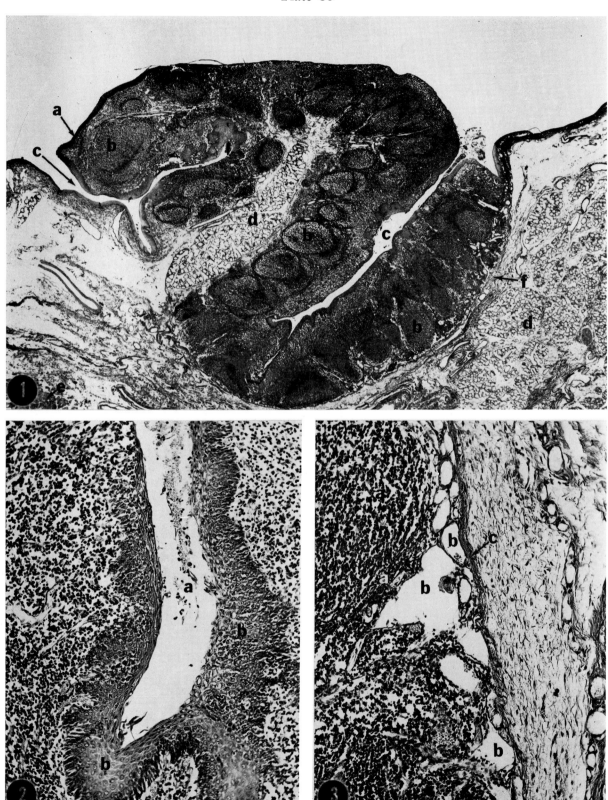

Plate 37

FIGURE 1. Thymus. Cross section, Level 5. (H&E X17)
   a. Cortex
   b. Medulla
   c. Trabecula
FIGURE 2. Portion of a thymic lobule. Cross section, Level 6. (H&E X320)
   a. Capsule
   b. Cortex
   c. Medulla
FIGURE 3. Reticular fibers of thymic interlobular trabecula. Longitudinal
   section, Level 7. (Reticular stain X140)
   a. Cortex
   b. Trabecula
   c. Reticular fibers
FIGURE 4. Cortex of the thymus. Notice relationship of blood vessels to
   reticular fiber distribution. Longitudinal section, Level 7. (Reticular
   stain X120)
   a. Blood vessels
   b. Reticular fibers

Plate 37

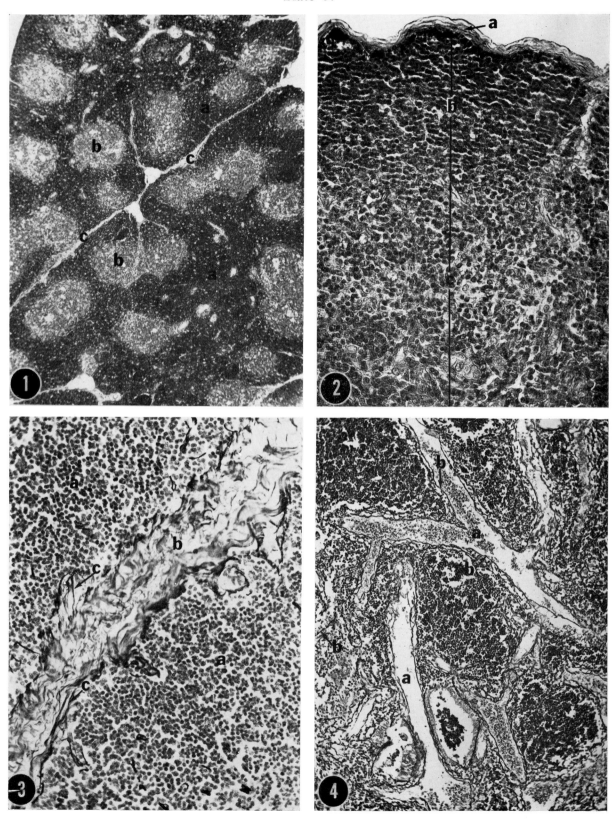

Plate 38

FIGURE 1. Medullary area of the thymus with its epithelial reticular cells. Longitudinal section, Level 7. (H&E X510)

FIGURE 2. Reticular fibers surrounding a medullary arteriole. Longitudinal section, Level 7. (Reticular stain X390)
   a. Reticular fibers
   b. Arteriole

FIGURE 3. Medullary area of the thymus. Longitudinal section, Level 7. (Thionine X510)
   a. Blood vessel
   b. Nerve

FIGURE 4. Recticular fibers distributed around blood vessels of the thymic medulla. A similar area is shown in the preceding figure. Longitudinal section, Level 7. (Reticular stain X510)
   a. Blood vessel
   b. Nerve
   c. Reticular fibers

Plate 38

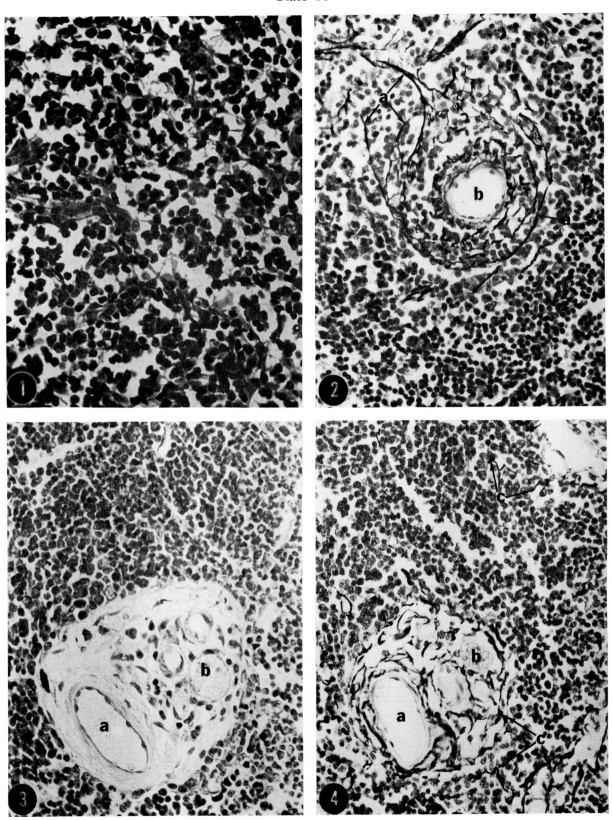

Plate 39

FIGURE 1. Thymic interlobular trabecula. Longitudinal section, Level 7. (H&E X180)
   a. Cortex
   b. Trabecula
   c. Blood vessels
   d. Adipose cells

FIGURE 2. Thymus. Longitudinal section, Level 7. (H&E X150)
   a. Medulla
   b. Cortex
   c. Hassall's corpuscles

FIGURE 3. Medulla of the thymus. Longitudinal section, Level 7. (H&E X705)
   a. Hassall's corpuscles
   b. Lymphocytes
   c. Epithelial reticular cells

FIGURE 4. Medulla of the thymus. Longitudinal section, Level 7. (Maximow Eosin Azure X990)
   a. Epithelial reticular cell
   b. Lymphocytes

Plate 39

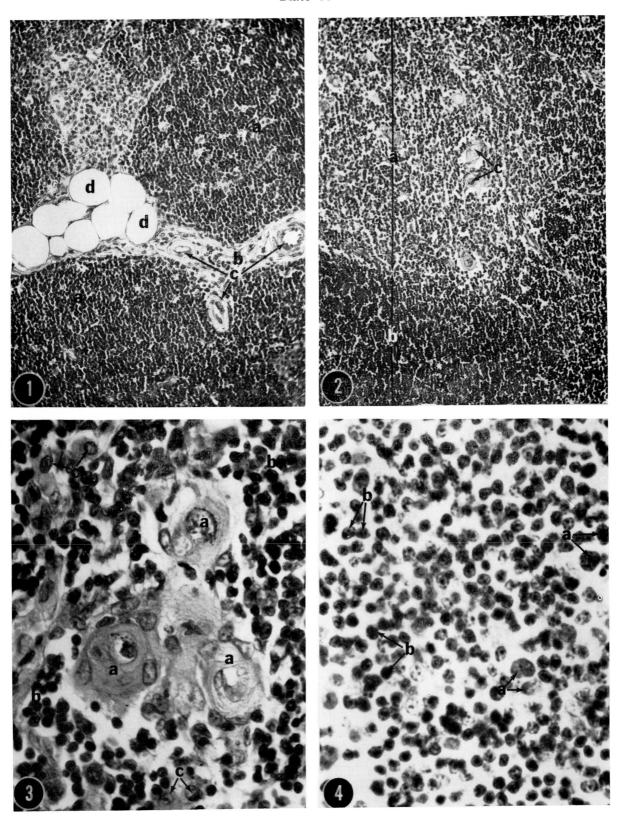

Chapter 4

Respiratory System

The anterior portion of the canine nasal cavity is a simple tube-shaped passage lined by stratified squamous epithelium. The most anterior portions, the vestibules, are filled in part by the expanded ends of the alar folds which deflect the incoming air to the ventral meatuses and subsequently to the dorsal and middle meatuses. The nasoturbinates, maxilloturbinates, and ethmoturbinates occupy a large portion of each nasal cavity. The maxillary turbinates are complex, convoluted, branched structures with a bony framework. The stratified squamous epithelium of the vestibule gradually changes into pseudostratified ciliated columnar epithelium in the respiratory portions of the nasal passage. The mucosa of the nasal septum and turbinates of the dog and guinea pig is characterized by pseudostratified ciliated columnar epithelium with goblet cells and serous glands, while in man and cat the glands are mixed.

Since the opening to the maxillary "sinus" has the same diameter as the nasal fossa, it is better termed maxillary recess. The frontal sinus is divided into lateral and medial parts which are lined with ciliated columnar epithelium. Many glands are present in the mucosa of the dog paranasal sinuses in contrast to man who has relatively few, small glands.

The dog has an extensive area of olfactory epithelium and an acute sense of smell, while man has a small olfactory area and is less sensitive to odors. According to some investigators the olfactory area of man is indistinguishable microscopically from that of the dog. Bowman's glands are serous in the guinea pig, dog and man and seromucous in the cat and rabbit.

The vomeronasal organ is made up of paired blind tubular diverticula in the base of the internasal septum. It is lined by ciliated columnar epithelium on its lateral wall and by olfactory epithelium on the medial wall. The mucosa contains glands, nerves and many vascular channels and is surrounded by an incomplete cartilagenous capsule in the dog. The structure is represented in the human fetus by a pit but is not present in the adult. Anteriorly, the lumen opens into the nasal fossa and communicates with the oral cavity by way of the nasopalatine duct. The nasopalatine duct is absent in ruminants, some rodents and primates.

The larynx is a muscular organ supported by a cartilagenous framework consisting of the epiglottic, thyroid, paired arytenoid, interarytenoid, sesamoid and cricoid cartilages to which the muscles are attached. The narrowest passage in the larynx is marked by the vocal and ventricular folds and the openings into the laryngeal saccules.

All mammals with a keen sense of smell have a well-developed epiglottis in contact with the soft palate. In the dog, it lies entirely below the soft palate. The epiglottic cartilage of all domestic animals and man is primarily elastic; however, in all species except the carnivores, it is indented with pits or contains perforations which are penetrated by glands, fat, blood vessels and nerve trunks. While the elastic cartilage of both cats and dogs is supplanted by adipose tissue, the replacement is much more extensive in the dog. The epiglottis of carnivores is thought to contain fewer taste buds and less glands than other animals.

The most outstanding feature of the carnivore trachea is the location of the trachealis muscles outside the dorsal cartilage free area. The muscle bundles are arranged transversely and attach to the perichondrium of the lateral side of the incomplete cartilagenous rings by elastic fibers. In the other domestic animals the muscle is located inside the tracheal cartilages and attaches to the inside of the rings, while in man the muscle occupies the space between the tips of the cartilage. The elastic tissue in the dog is loosely arranged and scattered through both the lamina propria and sub-mucosa, while in the cat it is concentrated in a more compact band near the epithelium. The pseudostratified ciliated columnar epithelium characteristic of the trachea is often replaced in the dorsal wall by areas of a transitional-type epithelium.

In comparison with man and other domestic and laboratory animals, the bronchial glands in the dog are small and relatively few in number. The horse and rat lack bronchial glands.

Engel (1958) has documented the unusual features of the dog lung. The transition of the terminal bronchiole into acini is not attained by the usual pattern. Instead, the terminal bronchus extends as a long alveolated tubule before terminating in acini. The lung of the dog "should not be used as a model of the mammalian lung."

RESPIRATORY SYSTEM

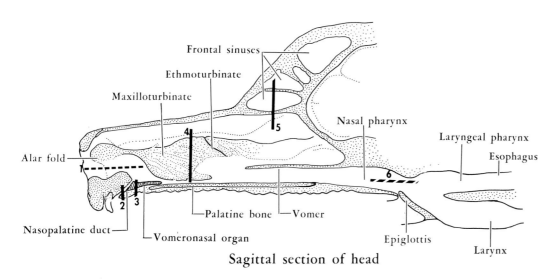

Frontal sinuses

Ethmoturbinate

Maxilloturbinate

Nasal pharynx

Laryngeal pharynx

Esophagus

Alar fold

Nasopalatine duct

Vomeronasal organ

Palatine bone — Vomer

Epiglottis

Larynx

Sagittal section of head

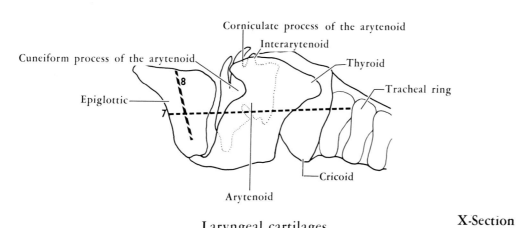

Corniculate process of the arytenoid

Interarytenoid

Cuneiform process of the arytenoid

Thyroid

Tracheal ring

Epiglottic

Cricoid

Arytenoid

Laryngeal cartilages

X-Section	——
Longitudinal	⟋⟋⟋
Frontal	------

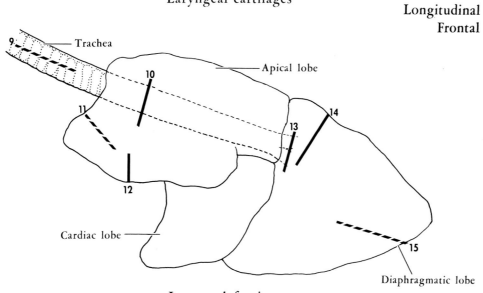

Trachea

Apical lobe

Cardiac lobe

Diaphragmatic lobe

Lungs - left view

Plate 40

Plate 41

FIGURE 1. Nasal vestibule and skin junction. Frontal section, Level 1. H&E X11)
  a. Plaque-like elevations on the planum nasale
  b. Nasal vestibule
  c. Stratified squamous epithelium
  d. Vascular lamina propria of the nasal vestibule
  e. Dorsal parietal cartilage (hyaline)
  f. Dermis
  g. Epidermis
FIGURE 2. Mucosa of the nasal vestibule. Frontal section, Level 1. (H&E X120)
  a. Stratified squamous epithelium
  b. Lamina propria
  c. Serous glands
  d. Ducts
  e. Artery
FIGURE 3. Nasal septum. Longitudinal section. (H&E X140)
  a. Pseudostratified ciliated columnar epithelium
  b. Lamina propria
  c. Blood vessels
  d. Serous glands
  e. Hyaline cartilage
FIGURE 4. Nasopalatine duct. Cross section, Level 2. (H&E X28)
  a. Nasopalatine duct
  b. Hyaline cartilage
  c. Vein
FIGURE 5. Maxilloturbinate. Cross section, Level 4. (H&E X36)
  a. Pseudostratified ciliated columnar respiratory epithelium
  b. Lamina propria
  c. Vascular plexus
  d. Bone
  e. Nasal meatus

Plate 41

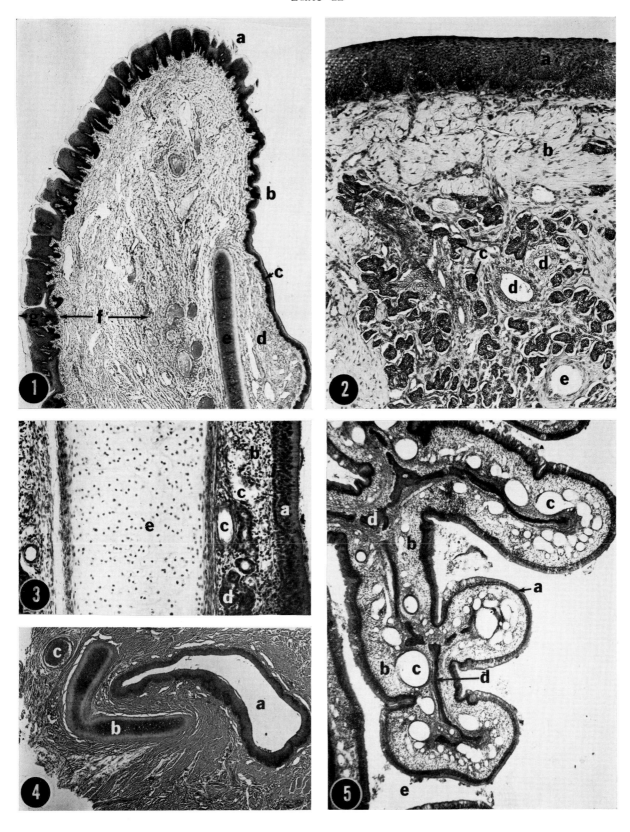

Plate 42

FIGURE 1. Vomeronasal organ. Cross section, Level 3. (H&E X39)
  a. Respiratory epithelium
  b. Olfactory epithelium
  c. Lamina propria
  d. Veins
  e. Serous glands
  f. Hyaline cartilage
  g. Unmyelinated nerve bundle
  h. Area seen in Figure 2

FIGURE 2. Glands of the vomeronasal organ. Cross section, Level 3. (H&E X185)
  a. Serous glands
  b. Ducts
  c. Veins

FIGURE 3. Respiratory mucosa of the nasal cavity. Cross section, Level 4. (H&E X120)
  a. Pseudostratified ciliated columnar epithelium
  b. Goblet cells
  c. Lamina propria
  d. Veins
  e. Turbinate bone

FIGURE 4. Olfactory mucosa. Cross section, Level 4. (H&E X630)
  a. Olfactory epithelium
  b. Supporting cells
  c. Neuroepithelial cells
  d. Basal cell layer
  e. Lamina propria
  f. Unmyelinated fibers of the olfactory nerve
  g. Veins
  h. Serous glands

Plate 42

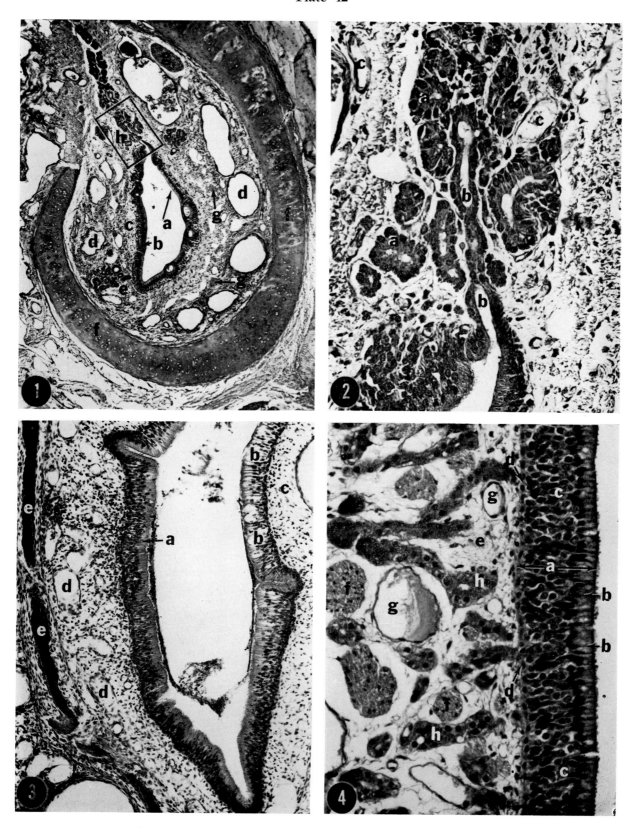

Plate 43

FIGURE 1. Nasopharynx. Longitudinal section, Level 6. (H&E X110)
  a. Pseudostratified ciliated columnar epithelium with numerous goblet cells
  b. Lamina propria
  c. Duct of a gland
  d. Seromucous glands
  e. Submucosa
  f. Skeletal muscle
  g. Pharyngeal glands

FIGURE 2. Glands of the nasopharynx. Longitudinal section, Level 6. (H&E X280)
  a. Mixed serous and mucous acini
  b. Serous acini
  c. Duct
  d. Blood vessels

FIGURE 3. Eustachian tube. Longitudinal section. (H&E X130)
  a. Lumen
  b. Pseudostratified ciliated columnar epithelium
  c. Mixed glands
  d. Elastic cartilage

FIGURE 4. Paranasal sinus. Cross section, Level 5. (H&E X330)
  a. Low ciliated columnar epithelium
  b. Lamina propria
  c. Periosteum
  d. Bone

Plate 43

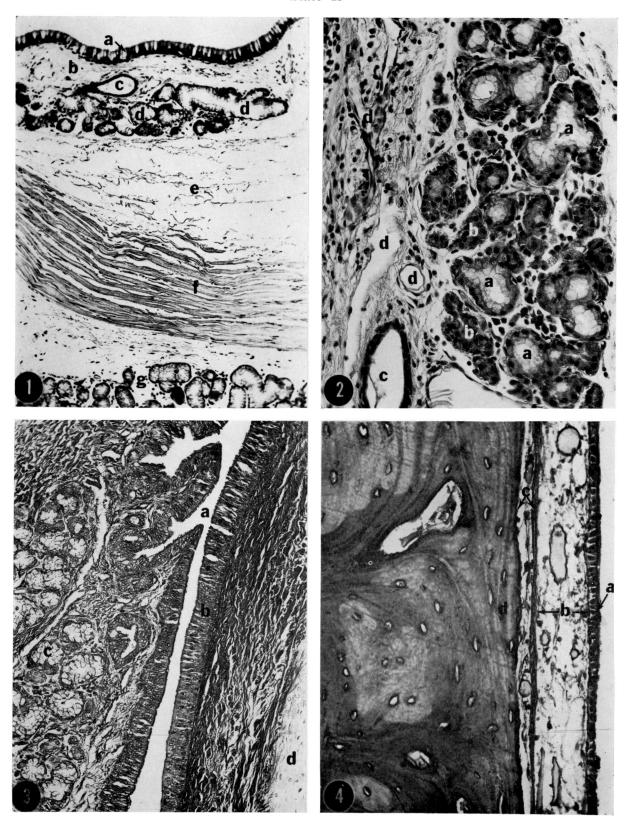

Plate 44

FIGURE 1. Larynx. Frontal section, Level 7. (H&E X6)
Note: as a result of oblique orientation of the section, the upper portion in the photograph is more ventral than the lower part.
a. Epiglottic cartilage (elastic)
b. Vestibule
c. Aryepiglottic fold
d. Laryngeal saccule
e. Ventricularis muscle
f. Cuneiform processes of arytenoid cartilage (elastic)
g. Glottis
h. Ventricular fold
i. Opening of laryngeal saccule
j. Vocal fold
k. Vocal ligament
l. Rima glottidis
m. Point of transition from stratified squamous to pseudostratified columnar epithelium
n. Infraglottic cavity
o. Vocalis muscle
p. Thyroarytenoideus muscle
q. Thyroid cartilage (hyaline)
r. Cricoarytenoideus muscle
s. Cricoid cartilage (hyaline)
t. Arytenoid cartilage (hyaline)
u. Laryngeal pharynx
v. Thyrohyoid bone
w. Glands of the dorsal wall of the laryngeal saccule
FIGURE 2. Epiglottis. Longitudinal section, Level 8. (H&E X24)
a. Pharyngeal cavity
b. Stratified squamous epithelium
c. Lamina propria
d. Epiglottic cartilage with the elastic cartilage partially replaced by fat
e. Seromucous glands
FIGURE 3. Vocal fold of the larynx. Frontal section, Level 7. (H&E X24)
a. Stratified squamous epithelium
b. Lamina propria
c. Vocal ligament (preponderantly elastic connective tissue)
d. Skeletal muscle fibers of the vocalis muscle
e. Ducts of adjacent glands

Plate 44

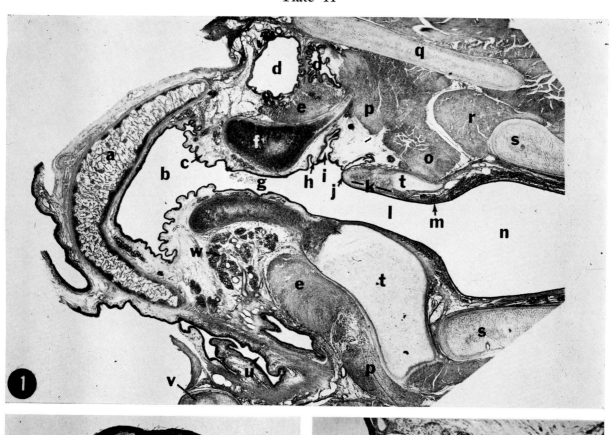

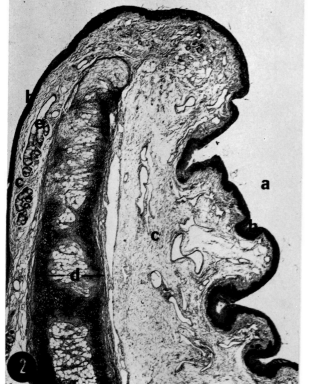

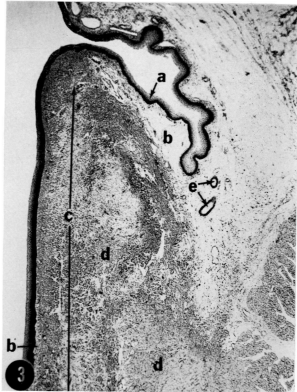

Plate 45

FIGURE 1. Laryngeal saccule. Frontal section, Level 7. (H&E X11)
  a. The lumen of the laryngeal saccule
  b. Stratified squamous epithelium
  c. Lamina propria
  d. Seromucous glands
  e. Adipose connective tissue
  f. Cuneiform cartilage
  g. Skeletal muscle (*musculus thyroarytenoideus*)
  h. Opening of laryngeal saccule into the cavity of the larynx
  i. Mucosal fold between the ventricular and vocal folds
  j. Vascular spaces

FIGURE 2. Wall of laryngeal saccule. Frontal section, Level 7. (H&E X160)
  a. Stratified squamous epithelium
  b. Lamina propria
  c. Seromucous glands
  d. Adipose connective tissue
  e. Vein

FIGURE 3. Trachea. Longitudinal section, Level 9. (H&E X12)
  a. Mucous membrane
  b. Cartilaginous rings in cross section (hyaline)
  c. Dense white fibrous connective tissue
  d. Adipose connective tissue
  e. Gland clusters

FIGURE 4. Tracheal mucosa. Longitudinal section, Level 9. (Weigert-Picric Acid X200)
  a. Pseudostratified ciliated columnar epithelium
  b. Basement membrane
  c. Lamina propria with elastic fibers (black)
  d. Dense collagenous tissue
  e. Vein
  f. Seromucous glands in the submucosa

Plate 45

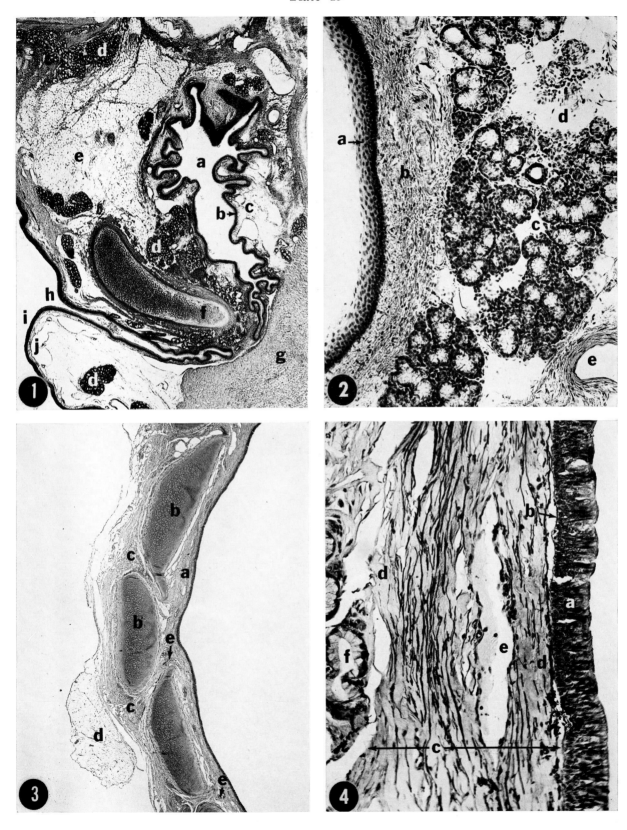

Plate 46

FIGURE 1. Trachea—dorsal wall. Cross section, Level 10. (H&E X12)
   a. Pseudostratified ciliated columnar epithelium
   b. Lamina propria
   c. Dorsal longitudinal fold
   d. Dorsal margin of the cartilaginous rings
   e. Submucosa
   f. Overlap of the cartilaginous rings (See Plate 45, Figure 3)
   g. Trachealis muscle (smooth)
   h. Adventitia

FIGURE 2. Primary bronchus. Cross section, Level 13. (H&E X27)
   a. Mucosa
   b. Smooth muscle
   c. Submucosa
   d. Cartilaginous plates (hyaline)
   e. Glands
   f. Adventitia
   g. Ganglion

FIGURE 3. Bronchial wall. Cross section, Level 14. (H&E X126)
   a. Pseudostratified ciliated columnar epithelium with goblet cells
   b. Lamina propria
   c. Smooth muscle
   d. Submucosa
   e. Serous glands
   f. Cartilage plate (hyaline)
   g. Adventitia

FIGURE 4. Bronchiole. Cross section, Level 12. (H&E X110)
   a. Pseudostratified ciliated columnar epithelium
   b. Lamina propria
   c. Smooth muscle
   d. Submucosa
   e. Serous glands
   f. Lymphatic tissue

Plate 46

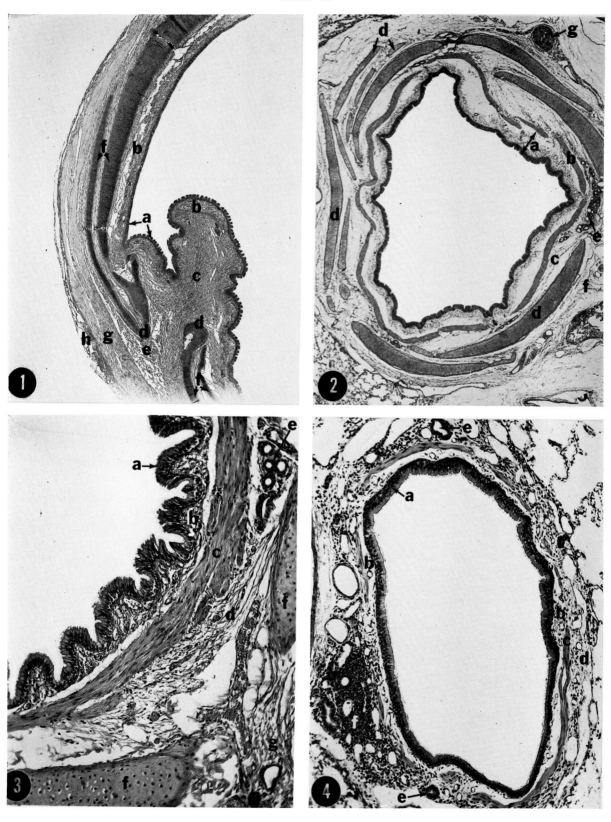

Plate 47

FIGURE 1. Lung. Longitudinal section, Level 15. (H&E X66)
  a. Terminal bronchiole
  b. Respiratory bronchiole
  c. Alveolar ducts
  d. Alveolar sac
  e. Alveoli

FIGURE 2. Lung. Cross section, Level 14. (H&E X320)
  a. Alveolar duct in longitudinal section
  b. Cuboidal epithelium
  c. Smooth muscle
  d. Alveoli
  e. Capillaries engorged with blood

FIGURE 3. Alveolar wall. Longitudinal section, Level 11. (H&E X1000)
  a. Endothelial cells of the capillaries
  b. Alveolar epithelium
  c. Great alveolar or septal cell

FIGURE 4. Visceral pleura and adjacent alveoli. Cross section, Level 14. (H&E X240)
  a. Mesothelium of the pleura
  b. Subepithelial layer containing connective tissues, and blood and lymph vessels
  c. Alveoli
  d. Blood filled capillary

Plate 47

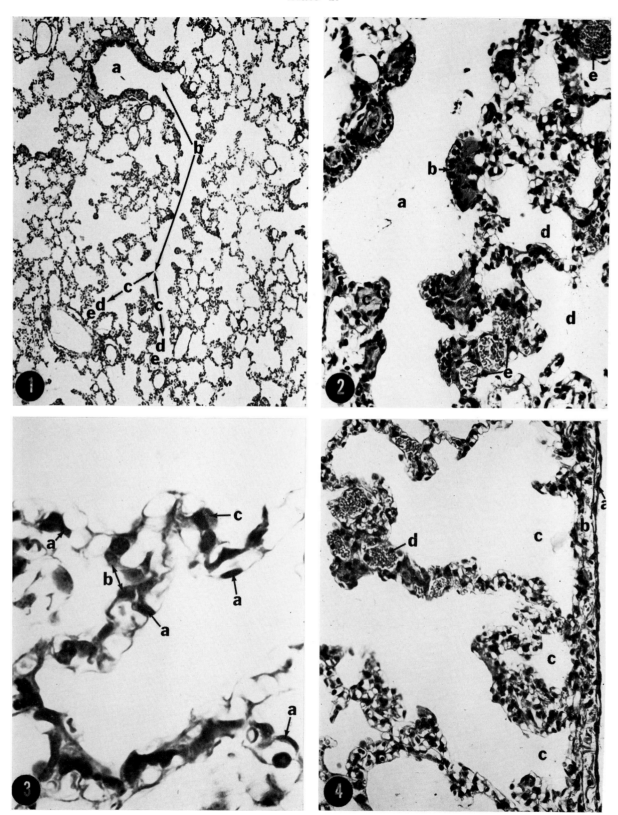

Chapter 5

Digestive System

The lyssa, found only in the tongue of carnivores, is a longitudinal, cordlike structure made up of adipose tissue, skeletal muscle fibers, blood vessels and nerves all ensheathed in collagenous fibers.

The foliate papillae of the tongue are fairly well developed in the dog, rudimentary in man, and best developed in the rabbit. They are composed of alternating parallel ridges separated by grooves and are situated on the lateral surface of the posterior part of the tongue. While the foliate and circumvallate papillae are quite different grossly, a single papilla often appears similar in histologic section, except that the gustatory furrows of the foliate papillae are more shallow than that of the vallate.

Conical papillae, located behind the V-shaped row of vallate papillae, are largest near the root of the tongue. Although they appear taller than the filiform papillae, their structure is similar.

The dog parotid salivary gland is primarily serous but contains occasional clusters of mucous acini. No definite mucous demilunes are present. According to some reports these clusters of mucous acini diminish with increasing age.

The mandibular salivary gland in the dog is composed of mucous acini with serous demilunes, while in man this gland is made up of purely serous secretory units with an occasional mixture of mucous and serous acini. Typical demilunes are usually not found.

The sublingual salivary gland in the dog is primarily serous but contains peculiar mucous tubular structures which connect directly to the intralobular striated ducts. In man the gland is mixed with more mucous than serous cells. Similar mucous tubular structures are also present in man. The presence of clusters of plasma cells between the acini of sublingual glands from purebred dogs has been reported elsewhere, and these cells were abundant in the glands from the beagle dog.

The zygomatic or orbital salivary gland constitutes a fourth major salivary gland found only in the dog and cat. The parenchyma of this gland consists of extremely long, branching mucous tubules. There are a few small, poorly developed serous demilunes.

The canine esophagus differs from that of man and other domestic animals in certain respects. Only the caudal portion of the dog esophagus has a well-developed muscularis mucosae, while in man it begins in the cranial portion at the level of the cricoid cartilage.

The tunica muscularis of the dog and ruminants is composed of skeletal muscle throughout its entire length. In the human esophagus the upper quarter is entirely skeletal muscle, in the middle portion, bundles of smooth muscle appear, and in the lower third only smooth muscle is found. In the horse and cat the transition from striated to smooth muscle takes place in the lower third to fifth of the esophagus, and in swine this change is nearer the cardia of the stomach.

Mucous glands are present throughout the entire length of the dog esophagus and are located in the submucosa with their ducts penetrating the muscularis mucosae in the caudal portion. In man the glands are of two types: the esophageal glands proper, and the esophageal cardiac glands. The esophageal glands proper are located in the submucosa and are distributed unevenly throughout the organ, while the esophageal cardiac glands are all confined to the lamina propria and are distinguishable into two groups, one in the cranial region, and the other in the caudal area near the cardia.

In swine the glands begin to decrease near the middle of the esophagus but may continue as single small glands as far as the cardia. The glands are confined to the pharyngo-esophageal area only in the horse, ruminants and cat.

The canine stomach, like that of other carnivores, has a lamina sub-glandularis located between the base of the gastric glands and the muscularis mucosae. In older animals there are two layers; an inner one, the stratum granulosum composed of cells, and an outer one, the stratum compactum made up of collagenous connective tissue. It is thought by some investigators that the latter layer offers protection against gastric wall perforations by bone splinters. Gland distribution in the stomach of carnivores is divided principally into fundic and pyloric regions. However, a transitional zone with cardiac glands containing a few parietal cells is present next to the cardia. The fundic gland mucosa is composed of a small lighter colored zone marked by a thin mucous membrane with deep gastric pits, and a larger, dark area characterized by a thick mucous membrane with shallow pits. In the light zone the glands contain fewer parietal than the true fundic glands of the darker zone.

The stomach of carnivores is similar to that of man. The stomach of the horse and pig is characterized by a rather large nonglandular area adjacent to the esophagus, lined by stratified squamous epithelium. In addition, swine have a well-developed cardiac gland area which includes the diverticulum ventriculi. The latter is especially rich in lymph nodules. The ruminant stomach is made up of three separate divisions collectively referred to as the forestomach, and a fourth segment, the abomasum, similar to the simple stomach of man and carnivores.

The histology of the dog small intestine does not differ markedly from that of man. The dog does not possess Paneth cells in the intestinal glands; however, the remaining cell types are all present. Duodenal glands (Brunner's glands) are present in the dog, but do not extend as far as they do in the human intestine.

The small intestine of dogs and other carnivores also has a lamina subglandularis composed of a cellular stratum granulosum and a homogenous stratum compactum interposed between the base of the glands of Lieberkühn and the muscularis mucosae. In young animals the stratum compactum is not well developed. The muscularis mucosae is relatively thick in the dog but otherwise not much different from that of other species.

The distribution and position of the Peyer's patches is somewhat different in the dog. They are often seen in the duodenum and jejunum as well as in the ileum, and as a rule they are positioned laterally and medially instead of opposite the mesenteric attachment as in other animals. In the dog they are visible from the outside, but this is not true in man or other domestic animals.

The outstanding feature of the canine large intestine is the presence of a well-developed diverticulum of the proximal portion, the cecum, which is not present in the human large intestine. The dog also lacks haustra, taenia coli and a vermiform process which are well developed in man.

In the dog there are tubuloalveolar anal glands at the recto-anal junction which secrete a lipid material. No such glands are present in man. Sebaceous circumanal glands occur at the junction of the anus and the perianal skin. These with the anal sacs and their associated anal sac glands are discussed and illustrated in the chapter on the integument.

DIGESTIVE SYSTEM

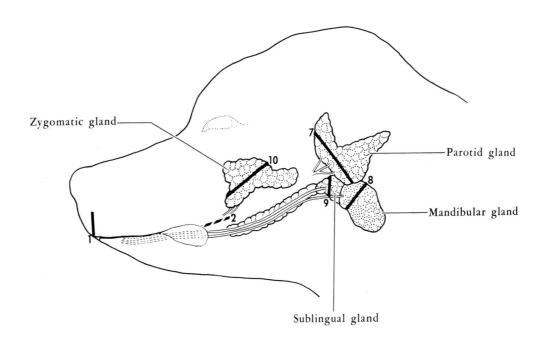

Zygomatic gland

Parotid gland

Mandibular gland

Sublingual gland

X-Section ——
Longitudinal ━ ━ ━
Frontal - - - - - -

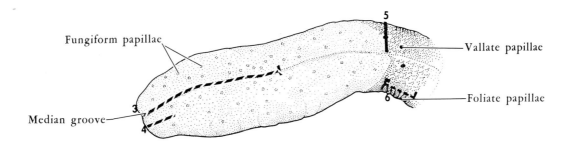

Fungiform papillae

Vallate papillae

Foliate papillae

Median groove

Tongue

Plate 48

Plate 49

FIGURE 1. Upper lip. Cross section, Level 1. (H&E X12)
a. Junction of the skin and the oral side of the lip
b. Tactile hair
c. Oral side of the lip
d. Lamina propria

FIGURE 2. Oral side of the upper lip. Cross section, Level 1. (H&E X310)
a. Keratinized stratified squamous epithelium
b. Lamina propria
c. Arteriovenous anastomoses

FIGURE 3. Buccal wall. Longitudinal section, Level 2. (H&E X22)
a. Stratified squamous epithelium
b. Lamina propria
c. Buccal glands
d. Area seen in Figure 4

FIGURE 4. Buccal glands. Longitudinal section, Level 2. (H&E X110)
a. Intralobular duct
b. Mucous acini with serous demilunes
c. Blood vessels in the intralobular connective tissue

Plate 49

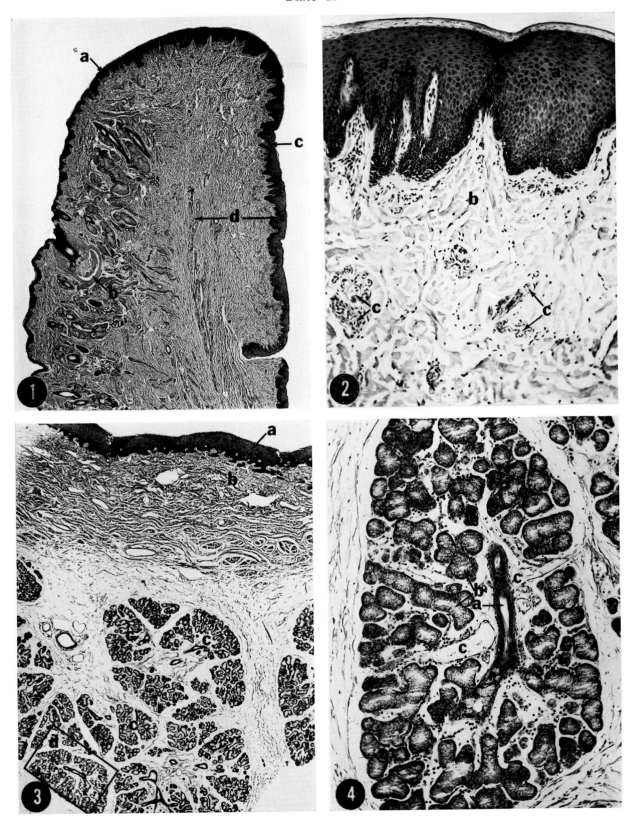

Plate 50

FIGURE 1. Tongue. Longitudinal section, Level 3. (H&E X16)
  a. Dorsal surface
  b. Ventral surface
  c. Lyssa composed of adipose and collagenous tissue
  d. Filiform papilla
  e. Fungiform papilla
  f. Intrinsic muscle of the tongue

FIGURE 2. Dorsal surface of the tongue. Longitudinal section, Level 3. (H&E X110)
  a. Fungiform papilla
  b. Keratinized stratified squamous epithelium
  c. Primary papilla of the lamina propria with secondary papillae at arrows
  d. Bundles of skeletal muscle

FIGURE 3. Ventral surface of the tongue. Longitudinal section, Level 3. (H&E X110)
  a. Stratified squamous epithelium
  b. Lamina propria containing blood vessels at arrows
  c. Intrinsic muscles of the tongue with the muscle fibers extending in three planes

Plate 50

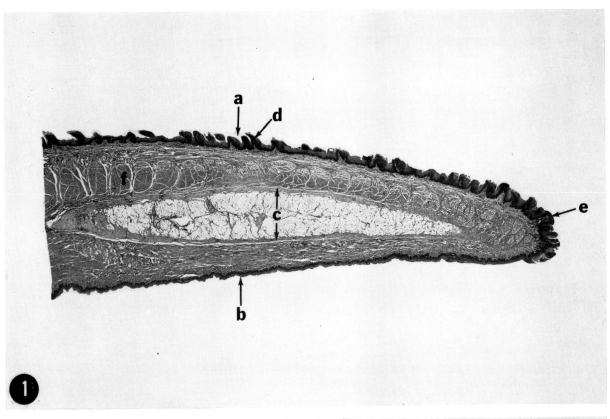

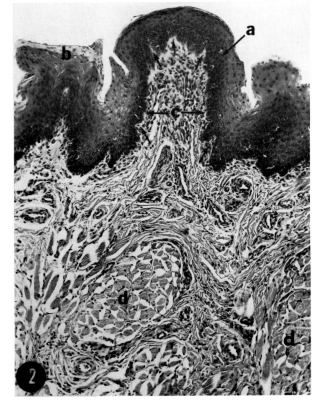

Plate 51

FIGURE 1. Filiform papillae. Longitudinal section, Level 4. (H&E X105)
- a. Keratinized stratified squamous epithelium
- b. Primary epithelial papilla
- c. Secondary epithelial papilla with "threadlike" processes
- d. Primary papillae of the lamina propria
- e. Secondary papillae of the lamina propria

FIGURE 2. Fungiform papilla. Longitudinal section, Level 4. (H&E X110)
- a. Stratified squamous epithelium with three taste buds at arrows
- b. Primary papilla of the lamina propria
- c. Secondary papillae of the lamina propria
- d. Filiform papilla with primary and secondary epithelial papillae

FIGURE 3. Vallate papilla. Cross section, Level 5. (H&E X48)
- a. Nonkeratinized stratified squamous epithelium
- b. Taste buds
- c. Primary papilla of the lamina propria
- d. Secondary papillae of the lamina propria
- e. Gustatory furrow
- f. Excretory duct entering the furrow
- g. Serous glands (von Ebner) embedded in the muscular and adipose tissue

FIGURE 4. Foliate papillae. Frontal section, Level 6. (H&E X40)
- a. Nonkeratinized stratified squamous epithelium
- b. Taste buds
- c. Primary papilla of the lamina propria
- d. Secondary papillae of the lamina propria
- e. Excretory duct of the serous glands entering the gustatory furrow
- f. Serous glands

Plate 51

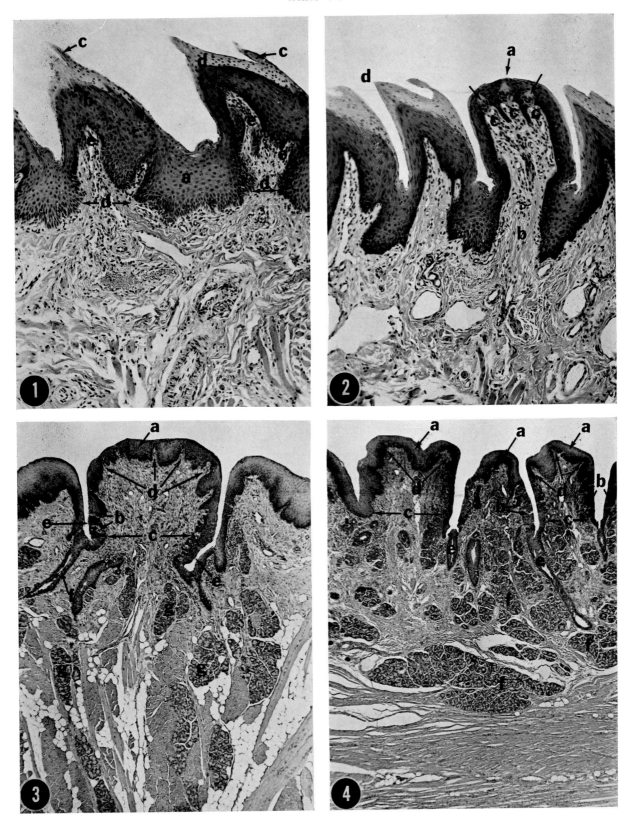

Plate 52

FIGURE 1. Fungiform papilla. Level 4. (H&E X220)
  a. Stratified squamous epithelium
  b. Taste buds (notice taste pore on far left at arrow)
  c. Primary papilla of the lamina propria
  d. Secondary papillae of the lamina propria
FIGURE 2. Conical papilla. Level 6. (H&E X110)
  a. Keratinized stratified squamous epithelium
  b. Secondary epithelial papilla
  c. Primary papilla of the lamina propria
FIGURE 3. Foliate papilla. Level 6. (H&E X110)
  a. Nonkeratinized stratified squamous epithelium
  b. Taste buds
  c. Primary papilla of the lamina propria
  d. Secondary papillae of the lamina propria
  e. Serous glands
FIGURE 4. Taste buds. Level 5. (H&E X1000)
  a. Taste pores
  b. Neuroepithelial cells
  c. Sustentacular cells

Plate 52

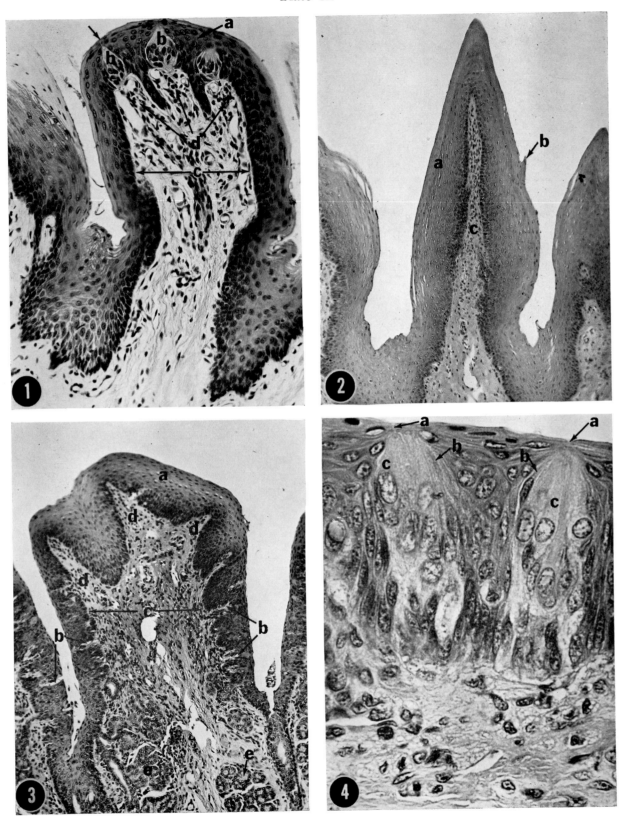

Plate 53

FIGURE 1. Parotid salivary gland. Level 7. (H&E X36)
  a. Collagenous connective tissue septa
  b. Interlobular ducts
  c. Intralobular salivary ducts
  d. Gland parenchyma composed primarily of serous acini
FIGURE 2. Parotid salivary gland. Level 7. (H&E X240)
  a. Intralobular salivary duct
  b. Serous acini
  c. Cluster of mucous acini seen only occasionally throughout the gland
     parenchyma (notice serous demilunes)
  d. Interlobular collagenous tissue
FIGURE 3. Interlobular duct in the parotid salivary gland. Level 7. (H&E
  X230)
  a. Stratified cuboidal epithelium lining the duct
  b. Interlobular connective tissue containing blood vessels (at arrows)
FIGURE 4. Junction of the intralobular duct with a serous acinus. Level 7.
  (H&E X450)
  a. Intralobular salivary duct
  b. Intercalated duct leaving an acinus (see arrow)
  c. Serous acini

Plate 53

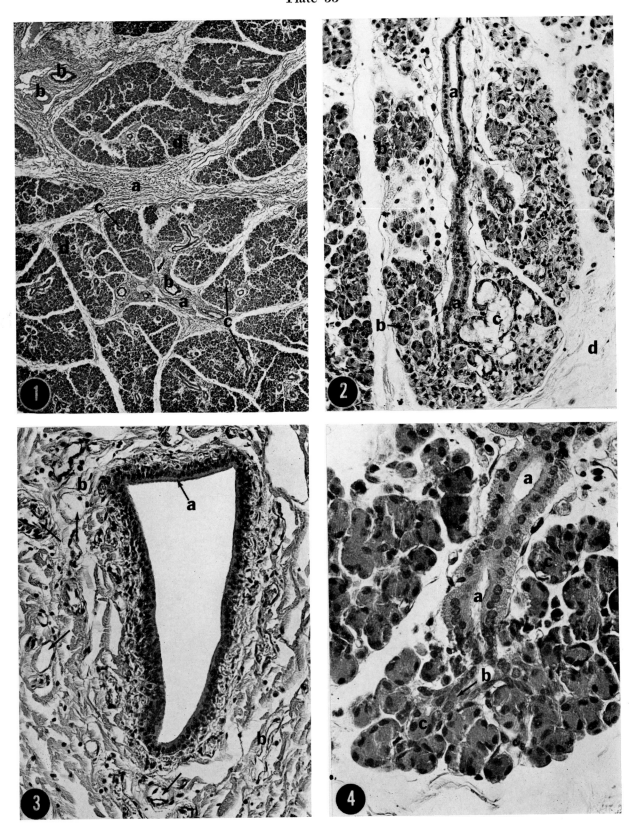

Plate 54

FIGURE 1. Mandibular salivary gland. Level 8. (H&E X35)
    a. Thin connective tissue capsule
    b. Interlobular ducts
    c. Intralobular ducts
    d. Gland parenchyma composed of mucous acini with serous demilunes
FIGURE 2. Mandibular salivary gland. Level 8. (H&E X220)
    a. Intralobular salivary ducts
    b. Mucous acini
    c. Serous demilunes (at arrows)
FIGURE 3. Interlobular duct in the mandibular salivary gland. Level 8. (H&E X200)
    a. Stratified columnar epithelium
    b. Interlobular connective tissue
FIGURE 4. Mandibular salivary gland. Level 8. (H&E X435)
    a. Intralobular salivary duct
    b. Intercalated duct connecting the acinus to the intralobular duct
    c. Mucous acini
    d. Serous demilunes

Plate 54

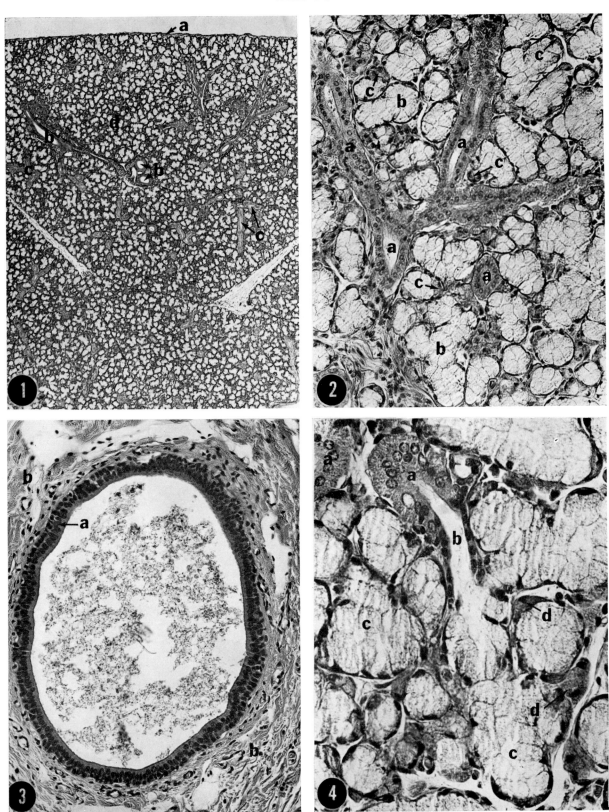

Plate 55

FIGURE 1. Sublingual salivary gland. Level 9. (H&E X35)
   a. Capsule
   b. Interlobular connective tissue
   c. Interlobular excretory duct
   d. Serous acini
   e. Mucous tubular structures
FIGURE 2. Sublingual salivary gland. Level 9. (H&E X220)
   a. Intralobular salivary duct
   b. Serous acini
   c. Mucous acinus
   d. Clusters of plasma cells located in the interstitial tissue
FIGURE 3. Interlobular excretory duct in the sublingual salivary gland. Level 9. (H&E X210)
   a. Stratified cuboidal epithelium
   b. Interlobular connective tissue
FIGURE 4. Sublingual salivary gland. Level 9. (H&E X435)
   a. Intralobular duct
   b. Mucous tubular structures connecting serous acini to the intralobular salivary duct
   c. Serous acini
   d. Cluster of plasma cells located in the interstitial tissue

Plate 55

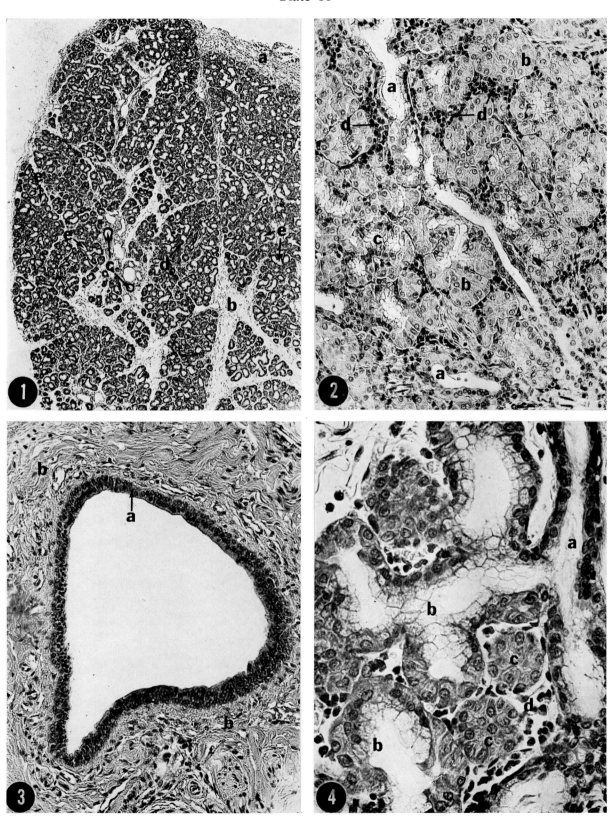

Plate 56

FIGURE 1. Sublingual salivary gland. Level 9. (Periodic Acid-Schiff X435)
  a. Serous acini with PAS positive granules lining the intercellular canaliculi
  b. Mucous tubular structures which reacted positively with PAS
  c. Clusters of plasma cells located between the acini
FIGURE 2. Sublingual salivary gland. Level 9. (Periodic Acid-Schiff X770)
  a. PAS positive granules lining the intercellular canaliculi of the serous acini
  b. Cluster of plasma cells located between the acini
FIGURE 3. Mandibular salivary gland. Level 8. (Periodic Acid-Schiff X425)
  a. Intralobular salivary duct with PAS positive material in the apical portion of the cells
  b. Mucous acini demonstrating an intense reaction with PAS
FIGURE 4. Sublingual salivary gland. Level 9. (H&E X206)
  a. Plasma cells seen between the acini. Notice the typical chromatin pattern in the plasma cells.

Plate 56

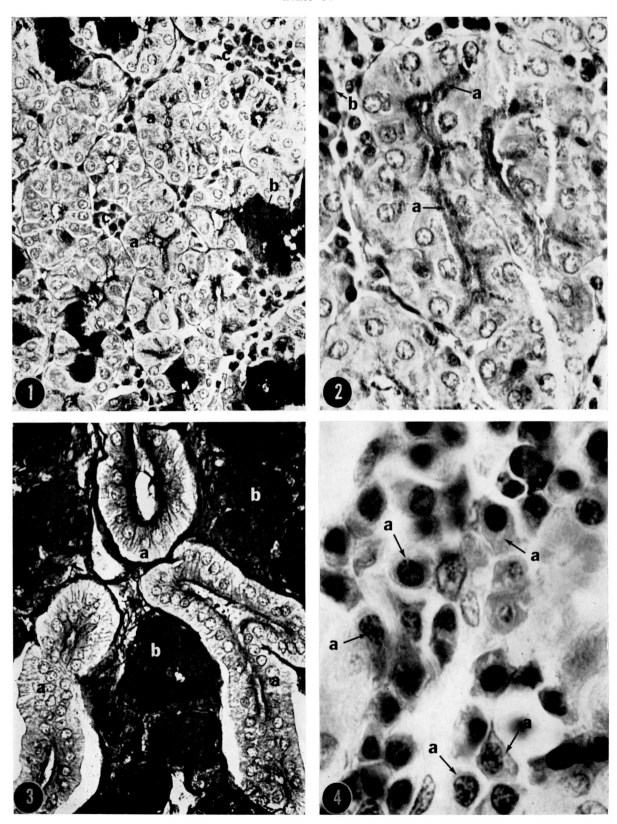

Plate 57

FIGURE 1. Zygomatic salivary gland. Level 10. (H&E X35)
   a. Interlobular connective tissue
   b. Intralobular salivary ducts
   c. Mucous acini of the gland parenchyma

FIGURE 2. Zygomatic salivary gland. Level 10. (H&E X220)
   a. Intralobular salivary ducts
   b. Mucous acini
   c. Serous demilunes

FIGURE 3. Interlobular excretory duct in the zygomatic salivary gland. Level 10. (H&E X210)
   a. Stratified cuboidal epithelial cells
   b. Interlobular connective tissue

FIGURE 4. Zygomatic salivary gland parenchyma. Level 10. (H&E X435)
   a. Intralobular salivary duct
   b. Mucous tubule terminating in the duct
   c. Mucous acini
   d. Serous demilunes

Plate 57

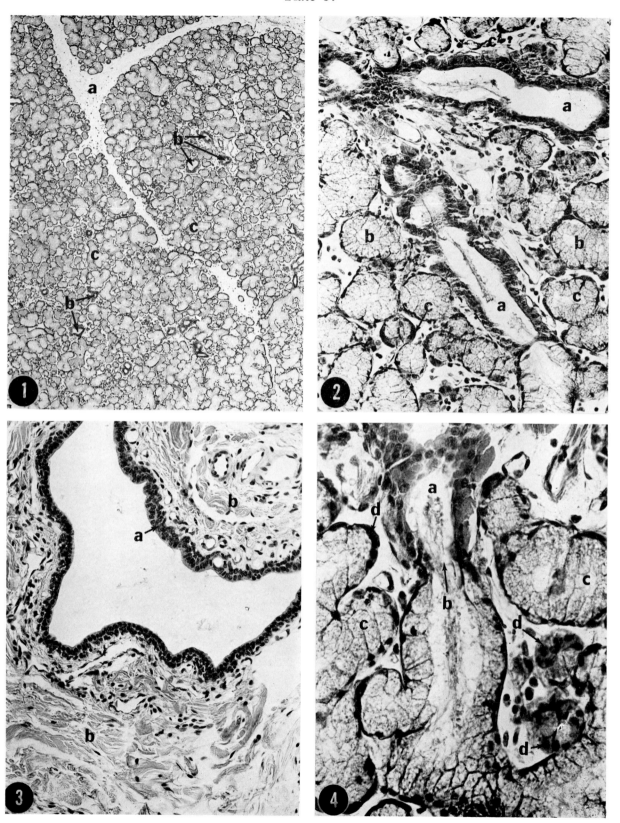

DIGESTIVE SYSTEM

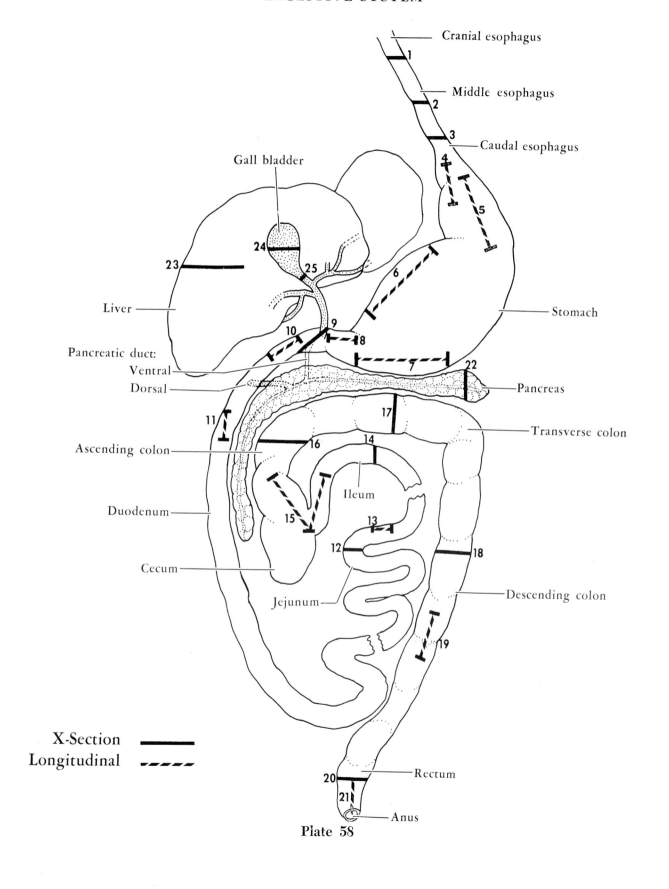

Cranial esophagus

Middle esophagus

Caudal esophagus

Gall bladder

Liver

Pancreatic duct:

Ventral

Dorsal

Stomach

Pancreas

Transverse colon

Ascending colon

Duodenum

Ileum

Cecum

Jejunum

Descending colon

Rectum

Anus

X-Section

Longitudinal

Plate 58

Plate 59

FIGURE 1. Cranial region of the esophagus. Cross section, Level 1. (H&E X21)
    a. Nonkeratinized stratified squamous epithelium
    b. Lamina propria
    c. Mucous glands with ducts (at arrows)
    d. Submucosa
    e. Blood vessels
    f. Skeletal muscle of the tunica muscularis
    g. Adventitia

FIGURE 2. Middle region of the esophagus. Cross section, Level 2. (H&E X21)
    a. Nonkeratinized stratified squamous epithelium
    b. Lamina propria
    c. Submucosa containing mucous glands. Notice duct at arrow
    d. Skeletal muscle of the tunica muscularis
    e. Adventitia

FIGURE 3. Caudal region of the esophagus. Cross section, Level 3 (H&E X21)
    a. Nonkeratinized stratified squamous epithelium
    b. Lamina propria
    c. Muscularis mucosae composed of isolated bundles of longitudinal smooth muscle fibers
    d. Submucosa containing mucous glands with ducts penetrating the muscularis mucosae at arrows
    e. Blood vessels
    f. Skeletal muscle of the tunica muscularis
    g. Serosa

FIGURE 4. Esophagus-stomach junction. Longitudinal section, Level 4. (H&E X33)
    a. Nonkeratinized stratified squamous epithelium of the esophagus
    b. Simple columnar epithelium of the stomach
    c. Cardiac glands
    d. Muscularis mucosae
    e. Esophageal glands in the submucosa extending into the cardia
    f. Smooth muscles of the tunica muscularis

Plate 59

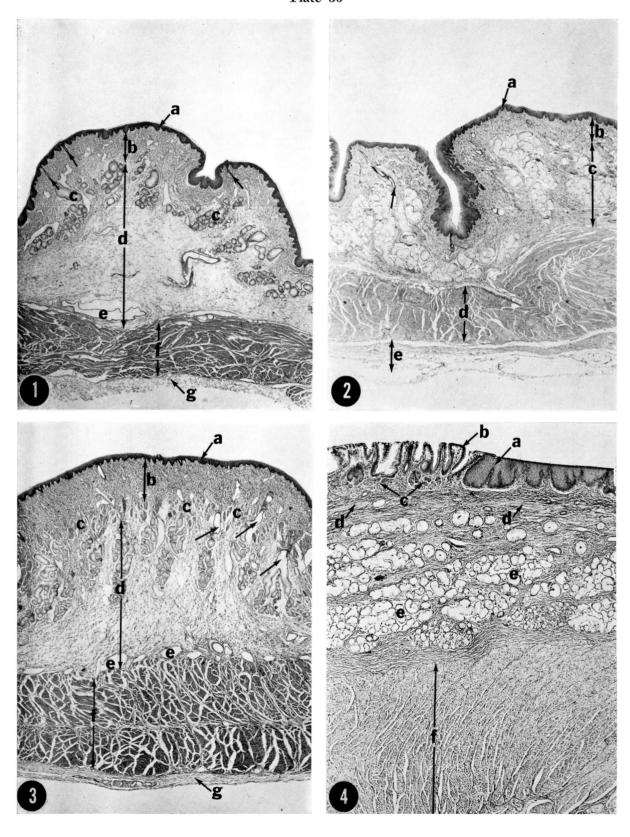

Plate 60

FIGURE 1. Caudal region of the esophagus. Longitudinal section, Level 4. (H&E X150)
   a. Nonkeratinized stratified squamous epithelium
   b. Excretory duct penetrating the epithelium
   c. Lamina propria
   d. Muscularis mucosae
   e. Mucous glands in the submucosa
   f. Submucosa

FIGURE 2. Caudal region of the esophagus. Cross section, Level 3. (H&E X130)
   a. Nonkeratinized stratified squamous epithelium
   b. Excretory duct of the submucosal gland
   c. Lamina propria
   d. Muscularis mucosae
   e. Submucosa

FIGURE 3. Tunica muscularis of the esophagus near the esophagus-stomach junction. Longitudinal section, Level 4. (H&E X120)
   a. Skeletal muscle bundles in the inner circular layer
   b. Smooth muscle bundles in the inner circular layer
   c. Myenteric ganglionic plexus (Auerbach) between the two layers of the tunica muscularis
   d. Outer longitudinal layer of the tunica muscularis

FIGURE 4. Tunica muscularis near the esophagus-stomach junction. Longitudinal section, Level 4. (H&E X120)
   a. Smooth muscle of the inner circular layer
   b. Myenteric ganglionic plexus (Auerbach) between the two muscle layers
   c. Smooth muscle of the outer longitudinal layer

Plate 60

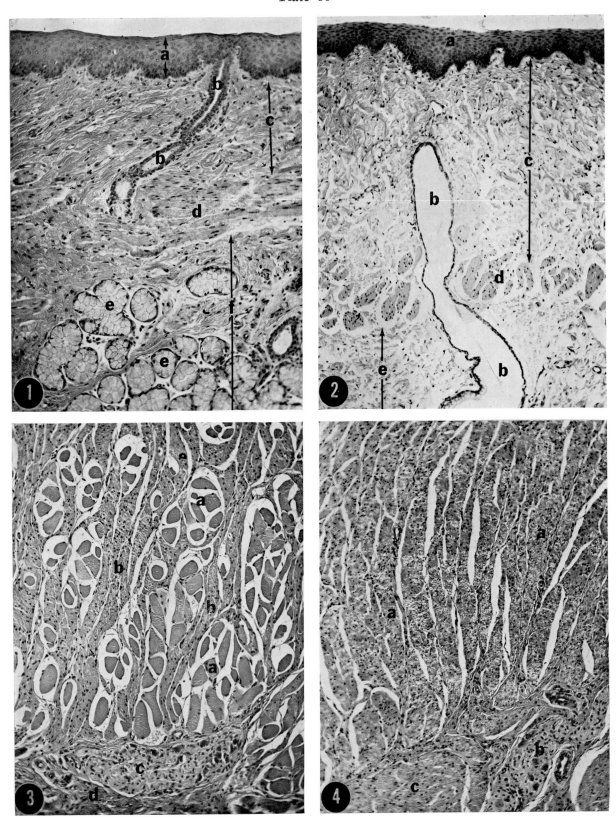

Plate 61

FIGURE 1. Cardiac region of the stomach. Longitudinal section, Level 4. (H&E X140)
  a. Simple columnar epithelium
  b. Lamina propria
  c. Cardiac glands
  d. Muscularis mucosae

FIGURE 2. Intermediate zone of the fundic region in stomach. Longitudinal section, Level 5. (H&E X140)
  a. Simple columnar epithelium
  b. Gastric pits
  c. Neck of the fundic glands
  d. Body of the fundic glands
  e. Muscularis mucosae

FIGURE 3. Fundic region of the stomach. Longitudinal section, Level 6. (H&E X140)
  a. Simple columnar epithelium
  b. Gastric pits
  c. Neck of the fundic glands
  d. Body of the fundic glands
  e. Muscularis mucosae with ascending fibers (at arrows)

FIGURE 4. Pyloric region of the stomach. Cross section, Level 7. (H&E X140)
  a. Simple columnar epithelium
  b. Gastric pits
  c. Pyloric glands
  d. Ascending muscle fibers from the muscularis mucosae
  e. Muscularis mucosae

Plate 61

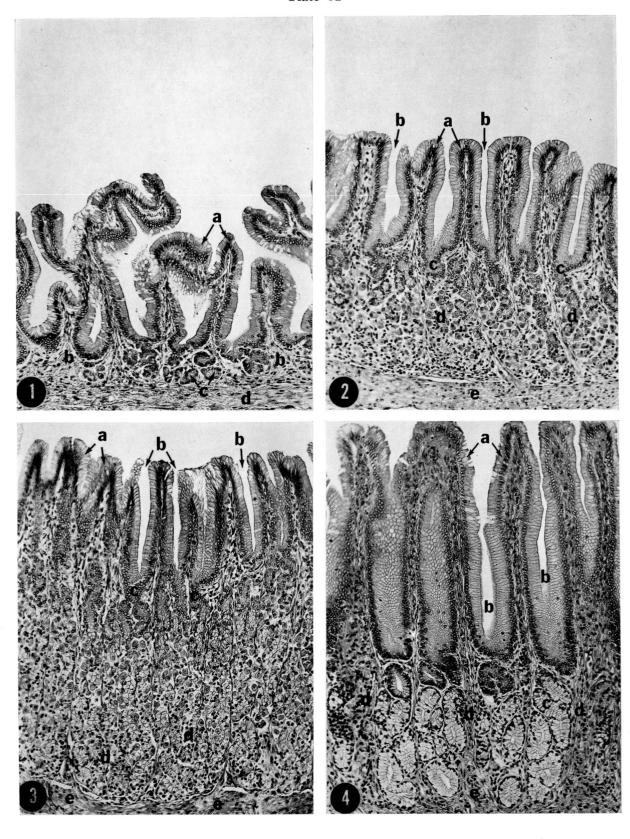

Plate 62

FIGURE 1. Surface cells of the gastric mucosa. Longitudinal section, Level 5. (H&E X700)
    a. Mucous secreting columnar epithelial cells with the nuclei at the base
    b. Surface modification of the cell membrane
    c. Lamina propria

FIGURE 2. Cardiac glands. Longitudinal section, Level 4. (H&E X700)
    a. Mucous acini of the tubuloalveolar cardiac glands
    b. Neck region of a cardiac gland (stains more eosinophilic)
    c. Parietal cells

FIGURE 3. Fundic glands. Longitudinal section, Level 6. (H&E X700)
    a. Parietal cells
    b. Chief cells
    c. Lumen of the glands

FIGURE 4. Pyloric glands. Cross section, Level 7. (H&E X700)
    a. Mucous secreting cells
    b. Stohr's cells
    c. Lumen of the glands
    d. Lamina propria

Plate 62

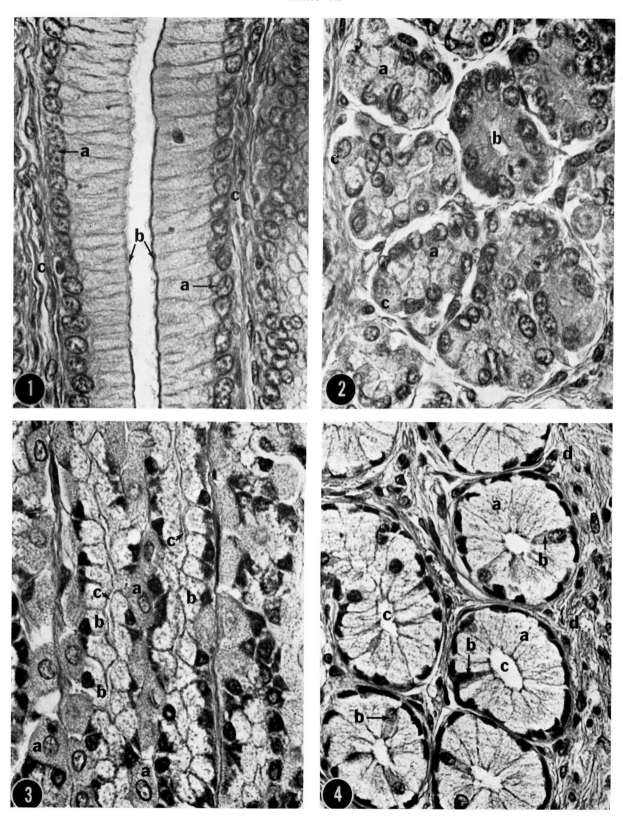

Plate 63

FIGURE 1. Mucosa of the fundic stomach. Longitudinal section, Level 6. (PAS stain X590)
   a. Mucous neck cells
   b. Parietal cells
   c. Chief cells

FIGURE 2. Muscularis mucosae in the pyloric stomach. Cross section, Level 7. (H&E X350)
   a. Base of pyloric glands
   b. Inner layer of the muscularis mucosae
   c. Outer layer of the muscularis mucosae
   d. Submucosa

FIGURE 3. Mucosa of the fundic stomach. Cross section, Level 7. (H&E X180)
   a. Fundic glands
   b. Lymph nodule
   c. Inner circular layer of the muscularis mucosae with fibers ascending into the lamina propria
   d. Outer longitudinal layer of the muscularis mucosae

FIGURE 4. Tunica muscularis of the stomach. Cross section, Level 7. (H&E X160)
   a. Circular layer with contraction bands at arrows
   b. Cell bodies in a myenteric plexus (Auerbach)
   c. Nerve fibers in a myenteric plexus (Auerbach)
   d. Outer longitudinal layer of the tunica muscularis

Plate 63

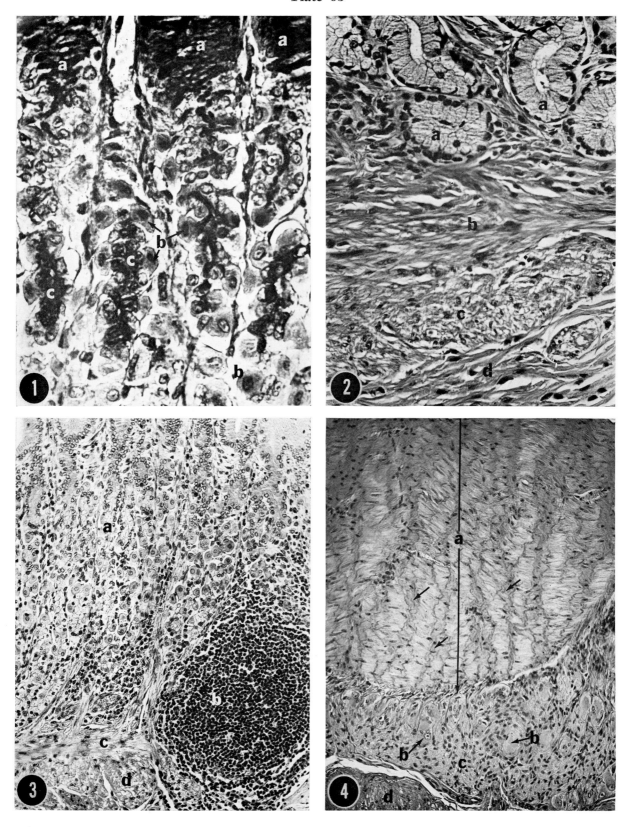

Plate 64

FIGURE 1. Pyloric duodenal junction. Longitudinal section, Level 8. (H&E X25)
  a. Pyloric stomach
  b. Duodenum
  c. Cross section of the crypts of Lieberkühn
  d. Brunner's glands extending through the muscularis mucosae (at arrows)
  e. Submucosa
  f. Tunica muscularis
  g. Tunica serosa

FIGURE 2. Duodenum. Longitudinal section, Level 10. (H&E X25)
  a. Tunica mucosa
  b. Muscularis mucosae
  c. Submucosa with Brunner's glands
  d. Tunica muscularis
  e. Tunica serosa

FIGURE 3. Duodenum from an area without Brunner's glands. Longitudinal section, Level 11. (H&E X25)
  a. Tunica mucosa
  b. Muscularis mucosae
  c. Submucosa
  d. Tunica muscularis
  e. Tunica serosa

FIGURE 4. Duodenum at the level of the major duodenal papilla. Cross section, Level 9. (H&E X16)
  a. Tunica mucosa
  b. Muscularis mucosae
  c. Submucosa
  d. Common bile duct in the duodenal papilla
  e. Inner circular muscle of the tunica muscularis

Plate 64

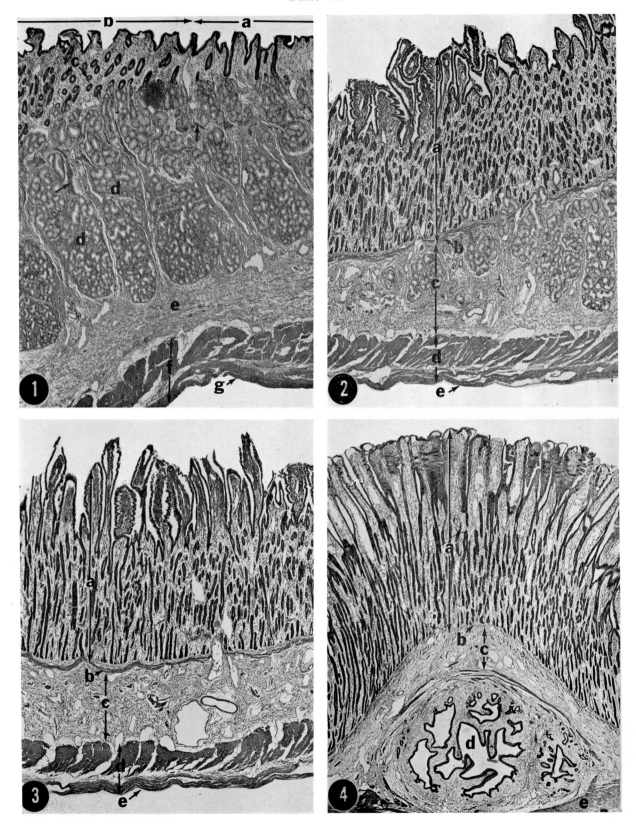

Plate 65

FIGURE 1. Jejunum. Cross section, Level 12. (H&E X32)
  a. Tunica mucosa
  b. Villi
  c. Crypts of Lieberkühn opening between the villi
  d. Muscularis mucosae
  e. Submucosa
  f. Tunica muscularis
  g. Tunica serosa
  h. Lymphatic vessel

FIGURE 2. Jejunum illustrating a plica circularis. Longitudinal section, Level 13. (H&E X34)
  a. Tunica mucosa
  b. Muscularis mucosae
  c. Submucosal core of the plica circularis
  d. Tunica muscularis
  e. Tunica serosa

FIGURE 3. Ileum. Cross section, Level 14. (H&E X34)
  a. Tunica mucosa
  b. Muscularis mucosae
  c. Lymph nodules of a Peyer's patch penetrating the muscularis mucosae
  d. Submucosa with numerous blood and lymphatic vessels
  e. Tunica muscularis
  f. Tunica serosa

FIGURE 4. Muscularis mucosae of the ileum. Cross section, Level 14. (H&E X350)
  a. Base of the crypts of Lieberkühn
  b. Stratum granulosum
  c. Inner circular layer of the muscular mucosae
  d. Outer longitudinal layer of the muscularis mucosae
  e. Submucosal connective tissue
  f. Submucosal ganglionic plexus (Meissner) with cell bodies at arrows

Plate 65

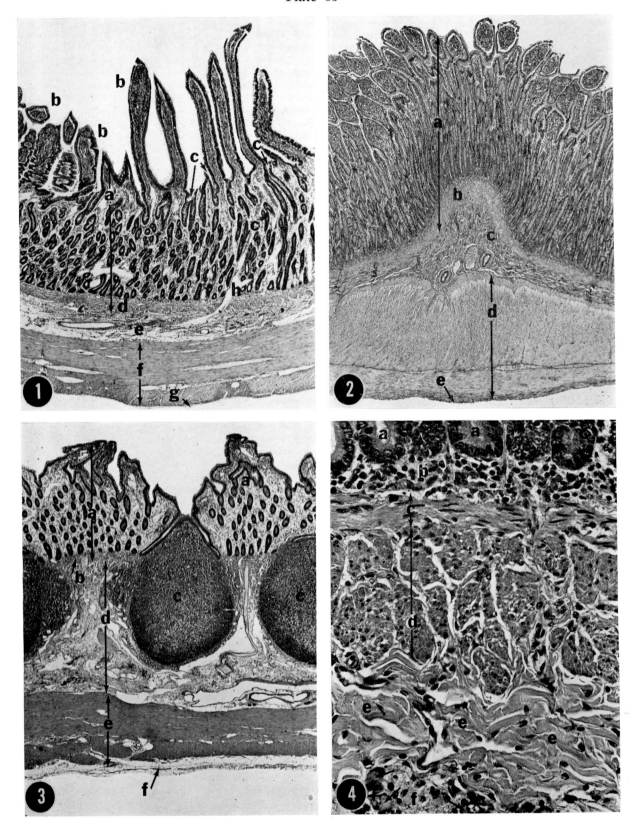

Plate 66

FIGURE 1. Jejunum. Cross section, Level 12. (H&E X140)
 a. Crypts of Lieberkühn lined with columnar epithelium and goblet
    cells
 b. Lamina propria filled with numerous plasma cells
 c. Muscularis mucosae
FIGURE 2. Crypts of Lieberkühn of the jejunum. Cross section, Level 12.
 (H&E X680)
 a. Simple columnar epithelium
 b. Goblet cells
 c. Lamina propria containing numerous plasma cells
 d. Lumen of the glands
FIGURE 3. Crypts of Lieberkühn of the jejunum. Cross section, Level 12.
 (H&E X110)
 a. Opening of a crypt of Lieberkühn between two villi
 b. Lamina propria
FIGURE 4. Tunica muscularis of the jejunum. Cross section, Level 12. (H&E
 X290)
 a. Inner circular layer
 b. Myenteric plexus (Auerbach) with ganglion cells at arrows
 c. Outer longitudinal layer

Plate 66

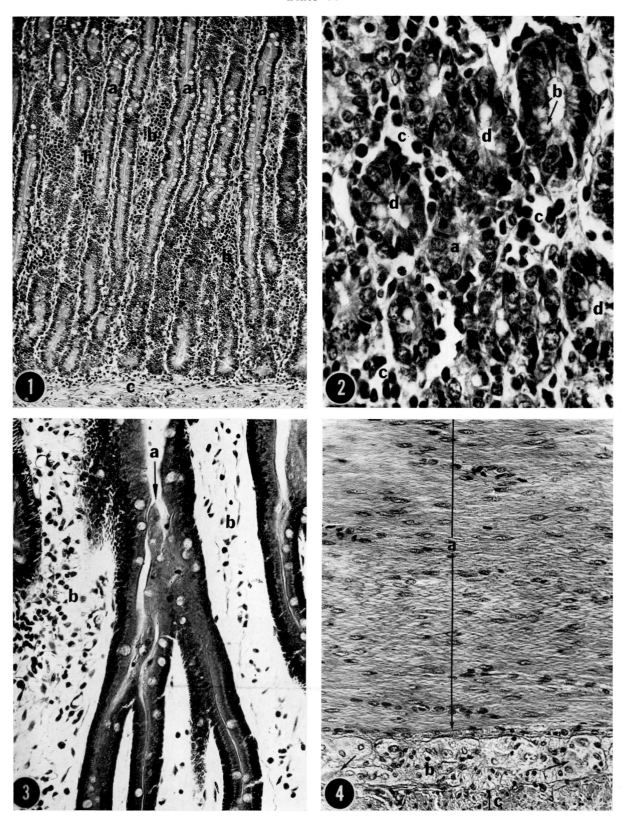

Plate 67

FIGURE 1. Villus in longitudinal section. (H&E X320)
    a. Simple columnar epithelium
    b. Goblet cells
    c. Capillaries
    d. Smooth muscle fibers
    e. Lacteal
FIGURE 2. Villus in cross section. (H&E X320)
    a. Simple columnar epithelium
    b. Goblet cells
    c. Capillaries
    d. Lacteal
    e. Lamina propria
FIGURE 3. Villus (H&E X970)
    a. Simple columnar epithelium with microvilli (at arrow)
    b. Goblet cell
    c. Capillaries
    d. Smooth muscle fibers
    e. Lumen of a lacteal with endothelial cells (at arrows)
FIGURE 4. Villus (H&E X1700)
    a. Microvilli of the simple columnar epithelium
    b. Capillary
    c. Smooth muscle fibers

Plate 67

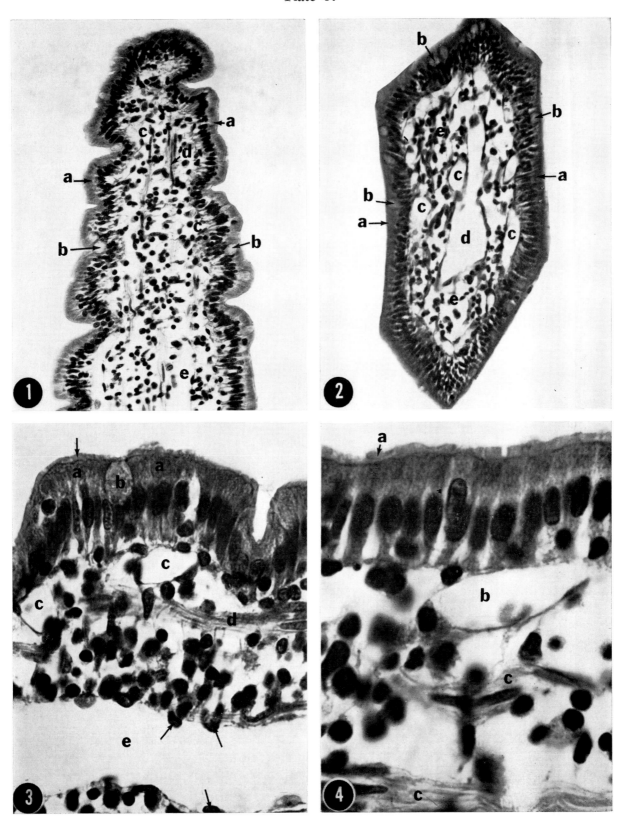

Plate 68

Figure 1. Ileoceco-colic junction. Longitudinal section, Level 15. (H&E X3)
  a. Lumen of the cecum
  b. Lumen of the ileum
  c. Lumen of the colon
  d. Aggregated lymph nodules (Peyer's patch)

Figure 2. Colon. Cross section, Level 16. (H&E X14)
  a. Tunica mucosa with intestinal glands
  b. Muscularis mucosae
  c. Submucosa containing numerous blood vessels and lymph nodules
  d. Tunica muscularis
  e. Tunica serosa

Figure 3. Colon illustrating a longitudinal fold. Cross section, Level 17. (H&E X8)
  a. Tunica mucosa
  b. Muscularis mucosae
  c. Submucosa containing numerous blood and lymphatic vessels
  d. Tunica muscularis
  e. Tunica serosa

Figure 4. Cecum. Longitudinal section. (H&E X40)
  a. Tunica mucosa
  b. Muscularis mucosae interrupted by lymph nodules
  c. Submucosa
  d. Tunica muscularis
  e. Tunica serosa

Plate 68

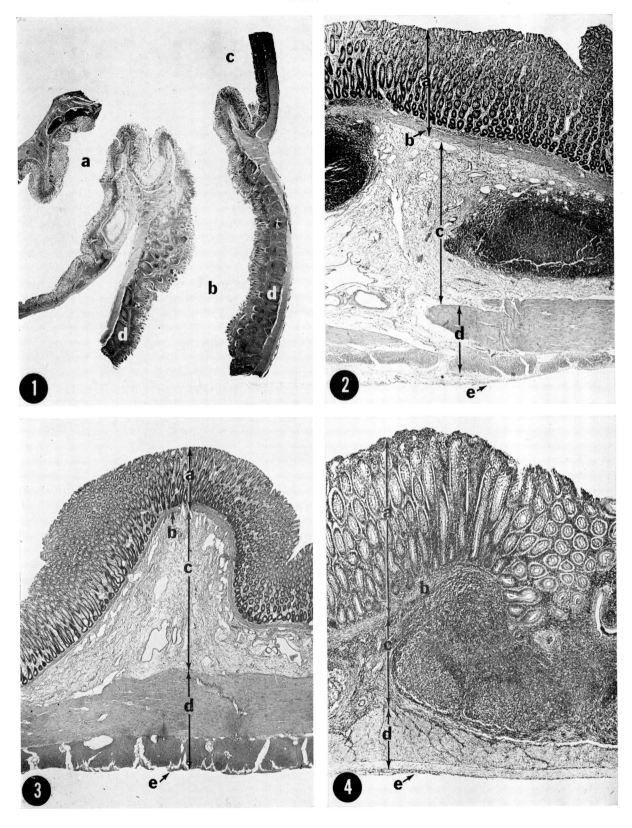

Plate 69

FIGURE 1. Ascending colon. Cross section, Level 16. (H&E X130)
  a. Simple columnar epithelium and goblet cells (at arrows)
  b. Lamina propria
  c. Base of the crypts of Lieberkühn
  d. Muscularis mucosae

FIGURE 2. Transverse colon. Cross section, Level 17. (H&E X130)
  a. Simple columnar epithelium
  b. Goblet cells
  c. Lamina propria
  d. Base of the crypts of Lieberkühn
  e. Muscularis mucosae

FIGURE 3. Descending colon. Cross section, Level 18. (H&E X130)
  a. Simple columnar epithelium
  b. Goblet cells
  c. Lamina propria
  d. Base of the crypts of Lieberkühn
  e. Muscularis mucosae

FIGURE 4. Rectum. Longitudinal section, Level 21. (H&E X130)
  a. Simple columnar epithelium with numerous goblet cells
  b. Lamina propria
  c. Base of the crypts of Lieberkühn
  d. Muscularis mucosae
  e. Submucosa

Plate 69

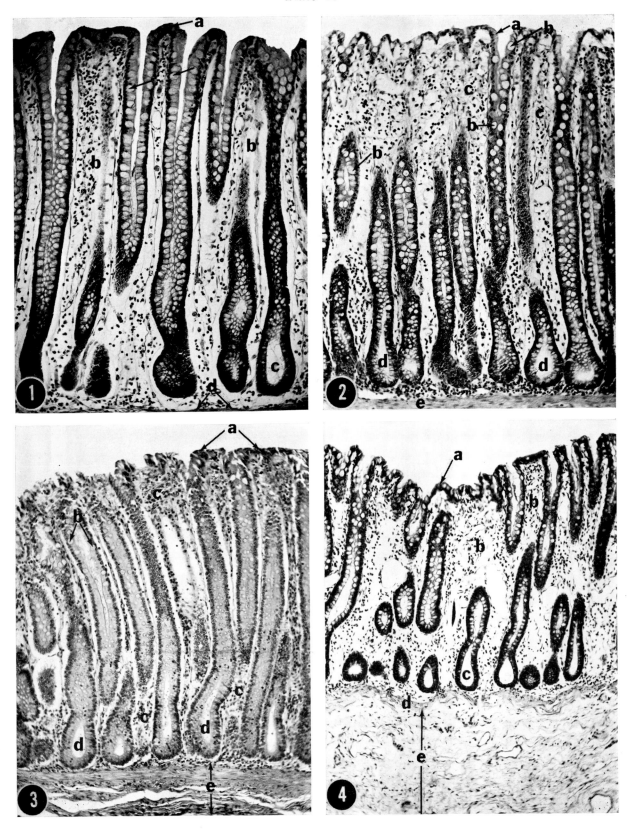

Plate 70

FIGURE 1. Colon. Longitudinal section, Level 19. (H&E X350)
    a. Base of the crypts of Lieberkühn
    b. Lamina propria
    c. Muscularis mucosae
    d. Submucosa
    e. Submucosal plexus (Meissner)

FIGURE 2. Tunica muscularis of the colon. Longitudinal section, Level 19. (H&E X230)
    a. Inner circular layer
    b. Myenteric plexus (Auerbach) with cell bodies at arrows
    c. Outer longitudinal layer
    d. Contraction bands

FIGURE 3. Recto-anal junction. Longitudinal section, Level 21. (H&E X73)
    a. Rectum
    b. Anus
    c. Anal glands

FIGURE 4. Anal glands. Longitudinal section, Level 21. (H&E X275)
    a. Lumen of the ducts
    b. Serous acini

Plate 70

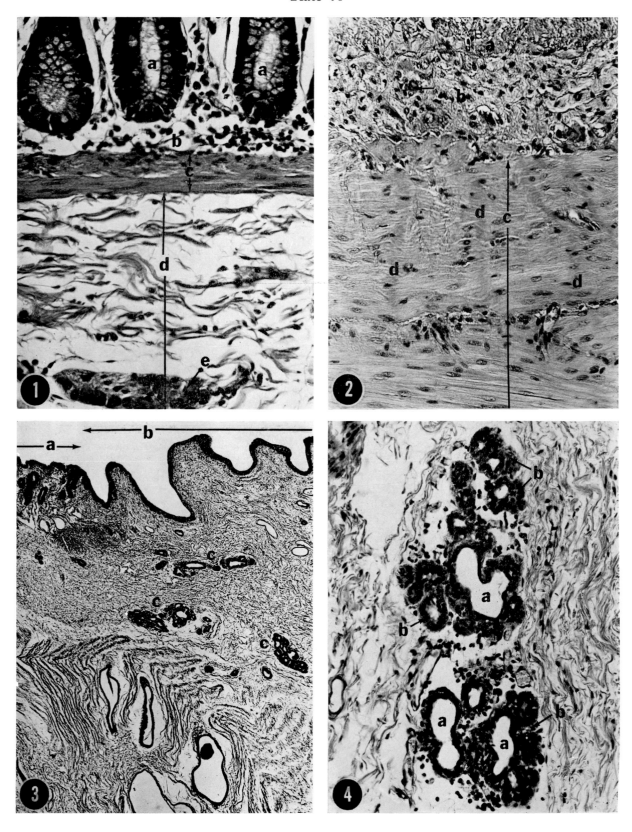

Plate 71

FIGURE 1. Pancreas. Level 22. (H&E X38)
   a. Capsule
   b. Interlobular duct
   c. Gland parenchyma
   d. Islets of Langerhans
FIGURE 2. Excretory duct of the pancreas. Level 22. (H&E X375)
   a. Simple columnar epithelium
   b. Connective tissue of the duct
   c. Pancreatic acini
FIGURE 3. Pancreas. Level 22. (H&E X650)
   a. Excretory duct
   b. Intercalated duct leaving an acinus (see arrow at upper right) and entering the excretory duct (lower left)
   c. Secretory acini containing centroacinar cells at arrows
FIGURE 4. Islets of Langerhans and associated structures. Level 22. (H&E X790)
   a. Cells of the Islets of Langerhans
   b. Secretory acinus with centroacinar cell at arrow
   c. Sero-zymogen granules at the apex of the acinar cells

Plate 71

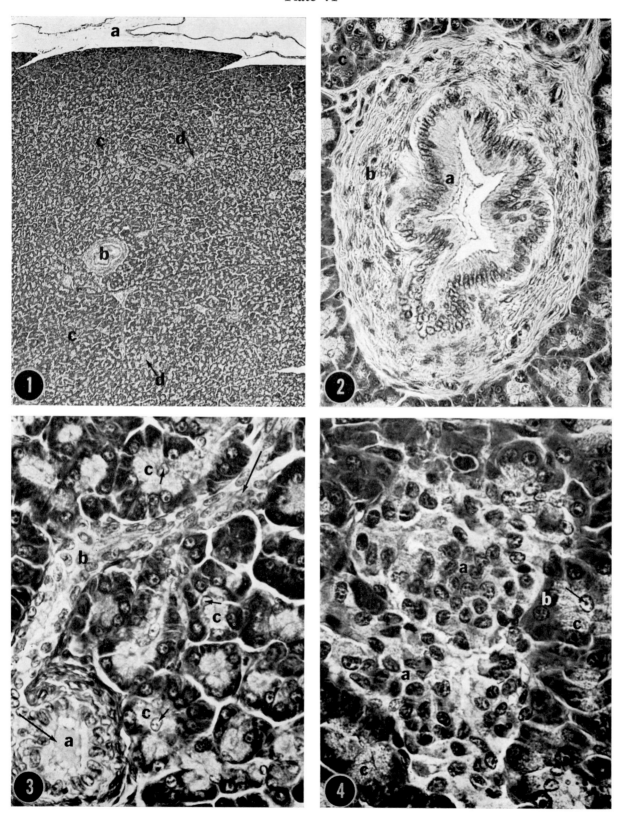

Plate 72

FIGURE 1. Liver. Level 23. (H&E X46)
    a. Portal areas at the periphery of the liver lobules
    b. Central veins

FIGURE 2. Portal area. Level 23. (H&E X290)
    a. Interlobular branch of the portal vein
    b. Interlobular branch of the hepatic artery
    c. Interlobular bile duct
    d. Lymphatic vessel

FIGURE 3. Periphery of the liver. Level 23. (H&E X400)
    a. Mesothelium
    b. Capsule
    c. Nuclei of liver cells
    d. Sinusoids
    e. Endothelial cell of a sinusoid
    f. Bile canaliculus

FIGURE 4. Liver. Level 23. (H&E X1500)
    a. Sinusoid
    b. Von Küpffer cells
    c. Endothelial cell of a sinusoid
    d. Bile canaliculi

Plate 72

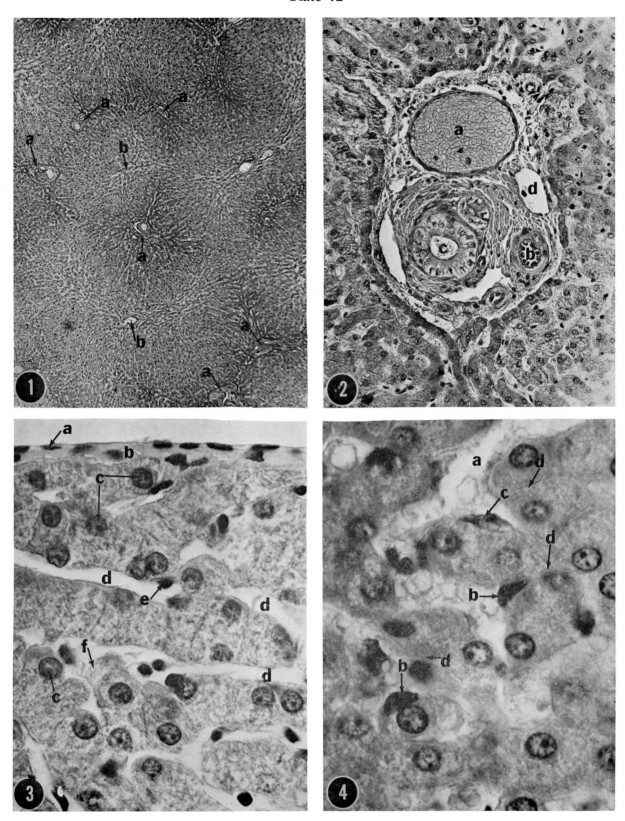

Plate 73

FIGURE 1. Liver. Level 23. (Reticular stain X400)
   a. Hepatic cells
   b. Reticular fibers located between the hepatic cells and the cells lining the sinusoids
   c. Sinusoids

FIGURE 2. Central vein. Level 23. (H&E X300)
   a. Lumen of the central vein
   b. Endothelium
   c. Sinusoids opening into the central vein

FIGURE 3. Sublobular vein. Level 23. (H&E X210)
   a. Lumen of the sublobular vein
   b. Central vein joining the sublobular vein
   c. Endothelium

FIGURE 4. Sublobular vein. Level 23. (H&E X110)
   a. Lumen of the vein filled with blood
   b. Lymphatic vessels

Plate 73

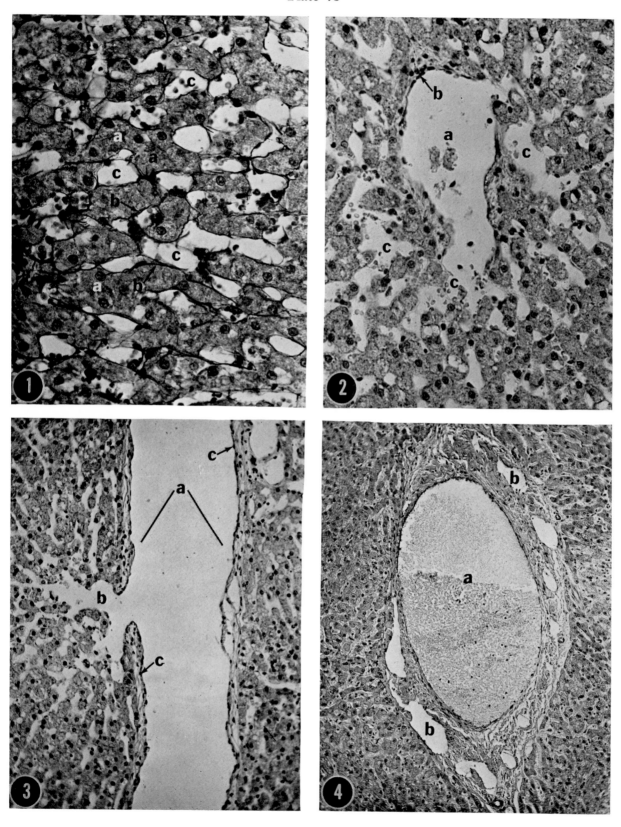

Plate 74

FIGURE 1. Gall bladder. Level 24. (H&E X97)
   a. Simple columnar epithelium
   b. Lamina propria
   c. Rokitansky-Aschoff sinuses
   d. Muscle layer
   e. Perimuscular connective tissue
FIGURE 2. Gall bladder mucosa. Level 24. (H&E X480)
   a. Simple columnar epithelium with prominent microvilli
   b. Lamina propria
FIGURE 3. Gall bladder with mucosal folds. Level 24. (H&E X280)
   a. Simple columnar epithelium
   b. Lamina propria
   c. Rokitansky-Aschoff sinuses
FIGURE 4. Wall of the cystic duct. Level 25. (H&E X200)
   a. Simple columnar epithelium
   b. Lamina propria with numerous blood vessels
   c. Serosa

Plate 74

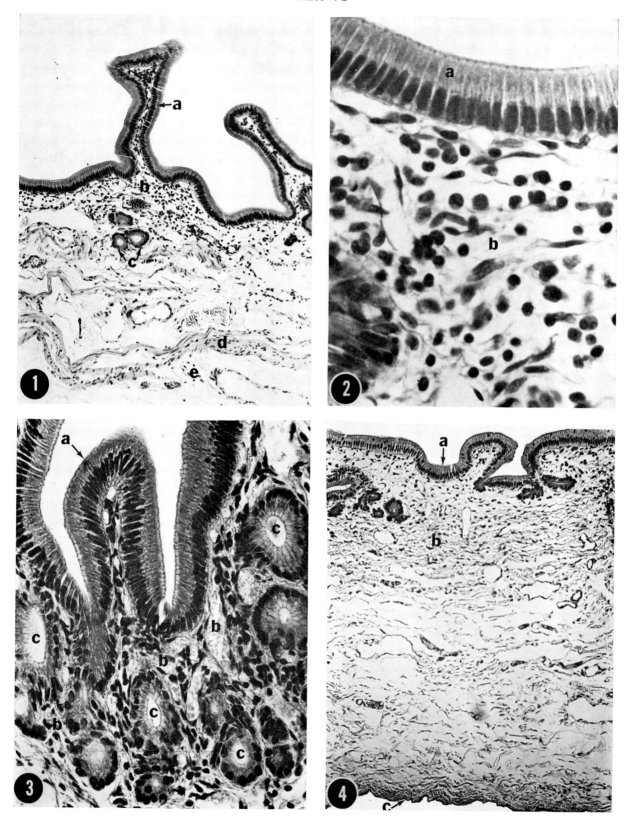

Chapter 6

Urinary System

The capsule of the kidney of the dog has the least smooth muscle of any of the domestic animals except the cat which has none. The renal corpuscles of the carnivore tend to be more spherical than those of the other domestic animals. As in the horse, pig and cat, the juxtamedullary renal corpuscles of the dog are larger than those in the cortical region, while the reverse is true in the ox. The number of juxtaglomerular cells is increased in the goat and dog. The general structure of the uriniferous tubule of all domestic animals is similar to that of the human species. A distinctive feature of the carnivore proximal convoluted tubule is the presence of fat droplets, located distally in the dog but confined to the initial segment in cats. These six-month-old beagle dogs did not show this characteristic very well, and MacNider (1945) reported that four-month-old pups do not deposit lipids in the proximal convoluted tubule; but lipid deposition does increase in older dogs. Among the domestic animals the diameter of the papillary duct is smallest in the dog and largest in the horse. While several of the domestic animals have transitional epithelium extending into the papillary duct, the dog has only simple columnar epithelium. The dog and cat kidneys are distinguished by large stellate veins which are located immediately under or in the edge of the capsule in the cat and a short distance away from the capsule in the dog (Yadava and Calhoun, 1958).

The mucous glands characteristic of the kidney, pelvis and ureter of the horse are not present in any of the other domestic animals.

The urinary bladder of the dog is almost completely invested by the peritoneum which covers a relatively thick subserous layer. The carnivore bladder has a low epithelial lining.

The pelvic urethra of the male dog, like that of man, is divided into prostatic and membranous segments, while the cat urethra is composed of preprostatic, prostatic and postprostatic portions. Since the disseminate prostate of the other domestic animals extends throughout the length of the pelvic urethra, it is not generally referred to as prostatic and membraneous urethra in these species. The dosal aspect of the proximal portion of the carnivore urethra contains two layers of smooth muscle, an outer longitudinal and an inner circular, while the ventrolateral wall has an additional inner longitudinal layer making three layers. The membraneous portion is marked by an intermingled skeletal muscle layer which encircles the uretha. Proximal to the os penis, the urethra becomes embedded in the ventral groove of the corpus cavernosum penis. In the glans the os penis partially surrounds the dorsal wall of the urethra. The epithelial lining of the male urethra is transitional near the bladder, changing to

159

admixtures of stratified cuboidal or stratified columnar and transitional. The muscularis of the proximal female urethra contains an inner circular layer with scattered outer longitudinal bundles. As the urethra joins the vagina (female reproductive system, Plate 84), the smooth muscle is gradually replaced by three layers of skeletal muscle, inner and outer scattered longitudinal bundles with a thick middle circular layer. The epithelial lining of the female urethra is transitional near the bladder, changing to stratified cuboidal or stratified columnar and finally to stratified squamous near the urethral opening.

URINARY SYSTEM

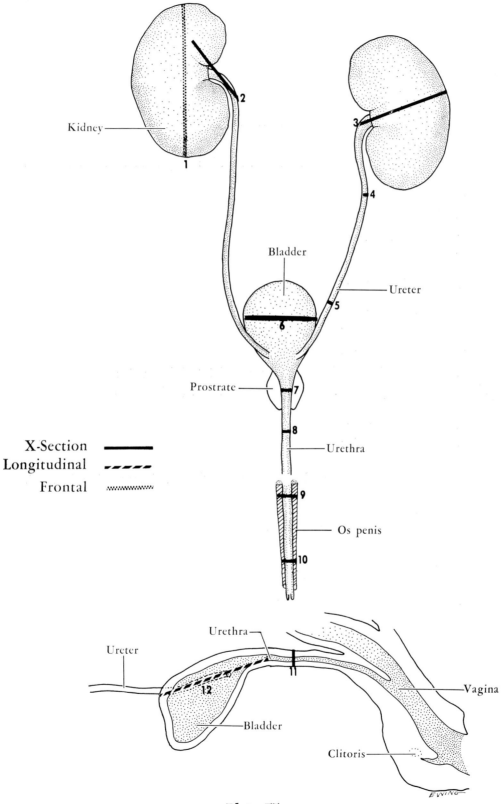

Kidney

Bladder

Ureter

Prostrate

X-Section
Longitudinal
Frontal

Urethra

Os penis

Urethra

Ureter

Vagina

Bladder

Clitoris

Plate 75

Plate 76

FIGURE 1. Kidney cortex and medulla. Median longitudinal section. (H&E X13)
    a. Capsule
    b. Cortex
    c. Medullary rays
    d. Medulla
    e. Pelvis
    f. Interlobar artery
    g. Arcuate artery
    h. Interlobular artery
    i. Stellate veins
    j. Interlobular veins
    k. Junction of interlobular, arcuate and interlobar veins

FIGURE 2. Kidney cortex. Cross section, Level 3. (H&E X16)
    a. Capsule
    b. Renal corpuscles
    c. Interlobular veins
    d. Interlobular artery

FIGURE 3. Kidney capsule and adjacent parenchyma. Cross section, Level 3. (H&E X250)
    a. Capsule
    b. Collagenous connective tissue
    c. Smooth muscle
    d. Trabecula
    e. Distal convoluted tubules
    f. Proximal convoluted tubules

Plate 76

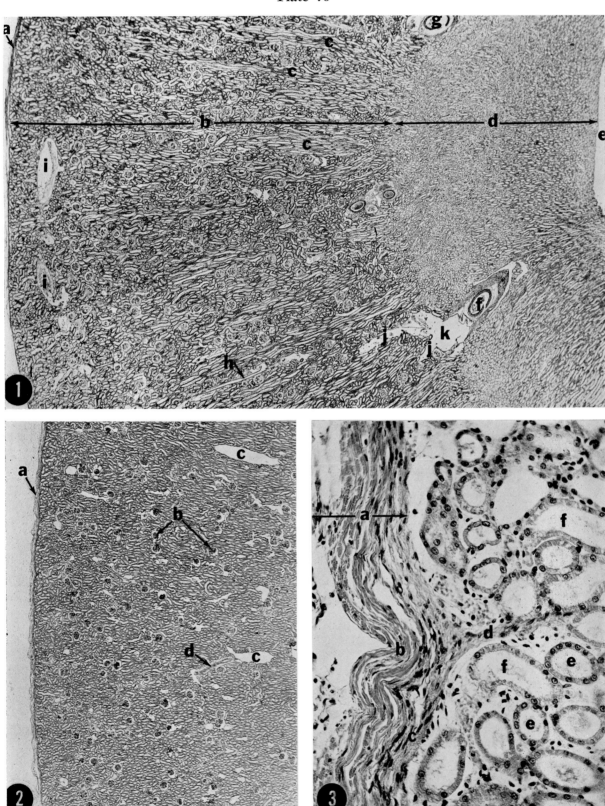

Plate 77

FIGURE 1. Renal corpuscle and related structures. (H&E X340)
  a. Proximal convoluted tubules
  b. Distal convoluted tubules
  c. Interstitial cells
  d. Parietal layer of the renal corpuscle
  e. Visceral layer of the renal corpuscle
  f. Glomerular capillaries
  g. Afferent arteriole
  h. Efferent arteriole
  i. Macula densa
  j. Distal portion of proximal convoluted tubule containing fat droplets

FIGURE 2. Renal corpuscle. (H&E X230)
  a. Distal convoluted tubules
  b. Proximal convoluted tubules
  c. Interstitial cells
  d. Parietal layer of the renal corpuscle
  e. Visceral layer of the renal corpuscle
  f. Glomerular capillaries
  g. Intralobular artery
  h. Afferent arterioles
  i. Macula densa

FIGURE 3. Renal corpuscle. (H&E X450)
  a. Distal convoluted tubule
  b. Proximal convoluted tubules
  c. Interstitial cells
  d. Parietal layer of the renal corpuscle
  e. Visceral layer of the renal corpuscle
  f. Glomerular capillaries
  g. Afferent arteriole
  h. Macula densa
  i. Juxtaglomerular cells

FIGURE 4. Renal corpuscle. (H&E X340)
  a. Proximal convoluted tubule
  b. Distal convoluted tubules
  c. Parietal layer of the renal corpuscle extended into the promixal convoluted tubule at the renal pole
  d. Visceral layer of the renal corpuscle
  e. Glomerular capillary
  f. Afferent arteriole
  g. Macula densa

Plate 77

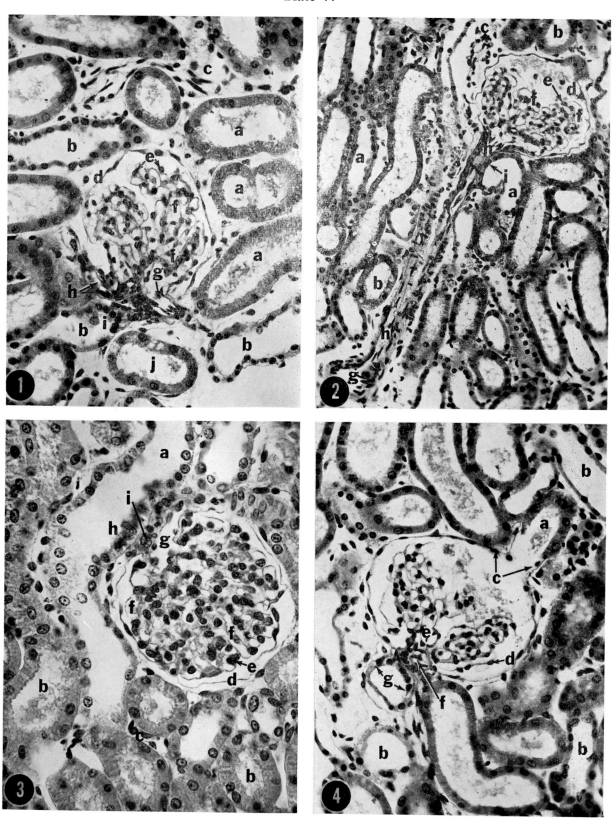

Plate 78

FIGURE 1. Proximal convoluted tubules after Carnoy's fixation. Notice that the cells are tall forming a stellate lumen. The brush borders are not as distinct as in Figure 2. (H&E X970)

FIGURE 2. Proximal convoluted tubules after perfusion with a mercurial fixative. (H&E X970)
   a. Brush borders
   b. Basal striations

FIGURE 3. Distal convoluted tubules after Carnoy's fixation. (H&E X970)
   a. Macula densa
   b. Juxtaglomerular apparatus
   c. Afferent artery

FIGURE 4. Distal convoluted tubules after perfusion with a mercurial fixative (H&E X970)

Plate 78

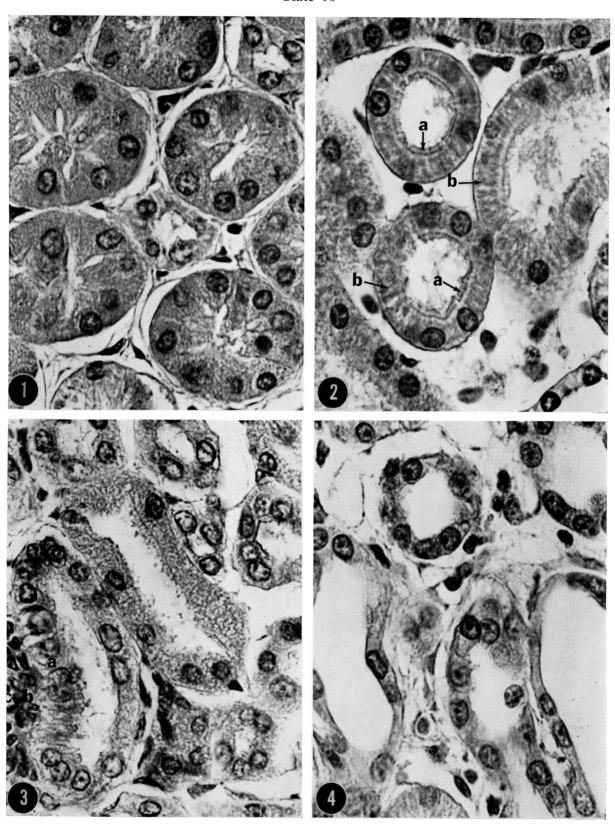

Plate 79

FIGURE 1. Collecting tubules separated by interstitial tissue. Cross section, Level 3. (H&E X145)
  a. Collecting tubules
  b. Interstitial tissue
  c. Capillaries

FIGURE 2. Medulla. Frontal section, Level 1. (H&E X310)
  a. Descending limb of Henle's loop
  b. Ascending limb of Henle's loop
  c. Collecting tubule
  d. Capillaries
  e. Thin segment of Henle's loop

FIGURE 3. Pelvis of the kidney. Cross section, Level 3. (H&E X21)
  a. Papillary ducts opening into the pelvis
  b. Pelvis
  c. Ureter

FIGURE 4. Wall of the pelvis. Level 1. (H&E X270)
  a. Transitional epithelium
  b. Lamina propria
  c. Capillaries
  d. Smooth muscle

Plate 79

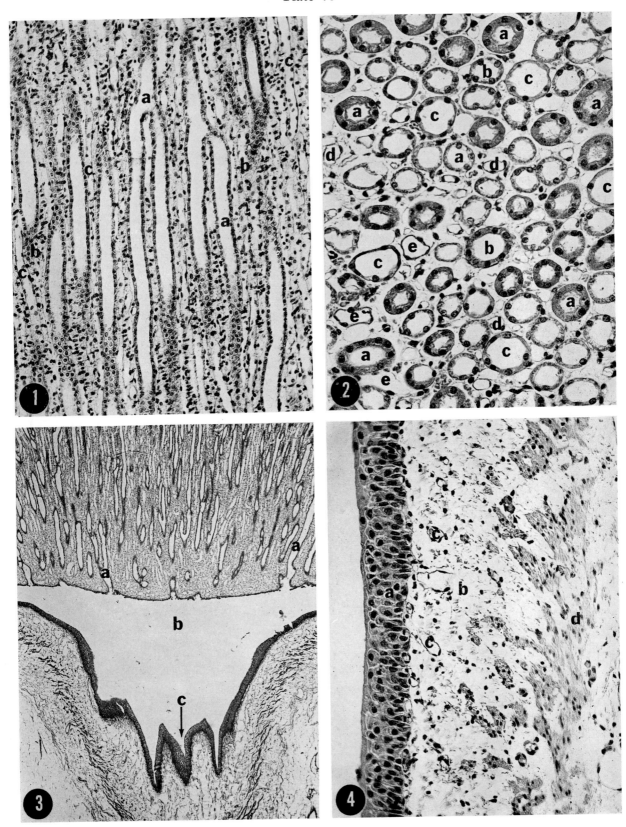

Plate 80

FIGURE 1. Interlobular vessels in the cortex. Cross section, Level 3. (H&E X54)
  a. Interlobular artery
  b. Interlobular veins
FIGURE 2. Arcuate vessels. Cross section, Level 2. (H&E X105)
  a. Arcuate artery
  b. Arcuate vein
  c. Interlobular veins
FIGURE 3. Stellate vein in the kidney cortex. Cross section, Level 3. (H&E X105)
  a. Capsule
  b. Cortex of the kidney with proximal and distal convoluted tubules
  c. Stellate vein
FIGURE 4. Vasa recta in the medulla. Frontal section, Level 1. (H&E X410)
  a. Collecting tubules
  b. Ascending venous limbs of the vasa recta
  c. Descending arterial limbs of the vasa recta

Plate 80

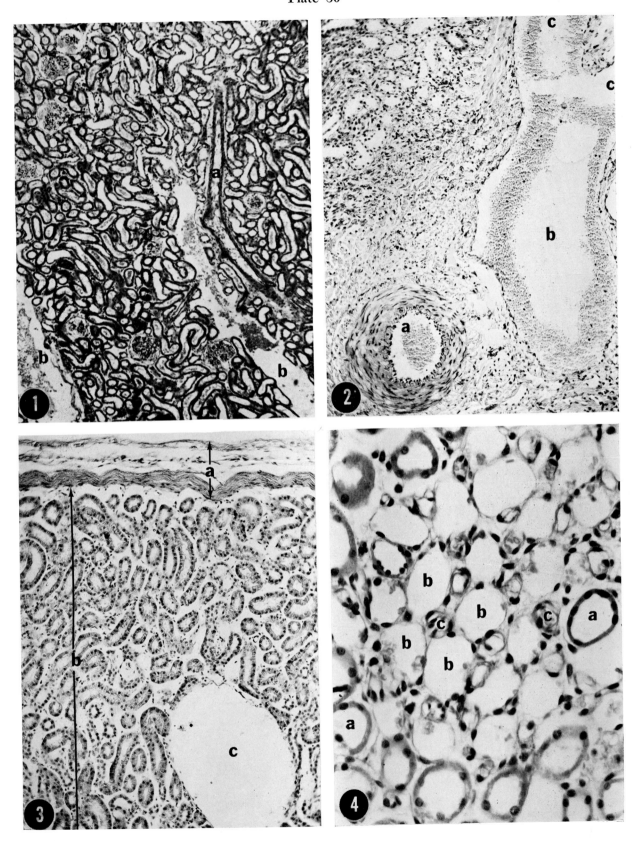

Plate 81

FIGURE 1. Ureter. Cross section, Level 4. (H&E X38)
    a. Transitional epithelium
    b. Lamina propria
    c. Submucosa
    d. Tunica muscularis
    e. Serosa
    f. Adipose tissue
    g. Vein
    h. Artery

FIGURE 2. Ureter. Cross section, Level 5. (H&E X110)
    a. Transitional epithelium
    b. Lamina propria
    c. Submucosa
    d. Inner longitudinal smooth muscle
    e. Middle circular smooth muscle
    f. Outer longitudinal smooth muscle
    g. Collagenous fibers of the serosa

FIGURE 3. Ureter near urinary bladder. Longitudinal section, Level 12. (H&E X170)
    a. Transitional epithelium
    b. Lamina propria
    c. Scanty smooth muscle of the tunica muscularis
    d. Loose connective tissue of the serosa

FIGURE 4. Ureter penetrating the urinary bladder wall. Longitudinal section, Level 12. (H&E X53)
    a. Muscle of the bladder wall
    b. Ureter
    c. Ureter lumen
    d. Submucosa of the bladder
    e. Urinary bladder mucosa with scattered muscularis mucosae fibers at arrows
    f. Urinary bladder lumen

Plate 81

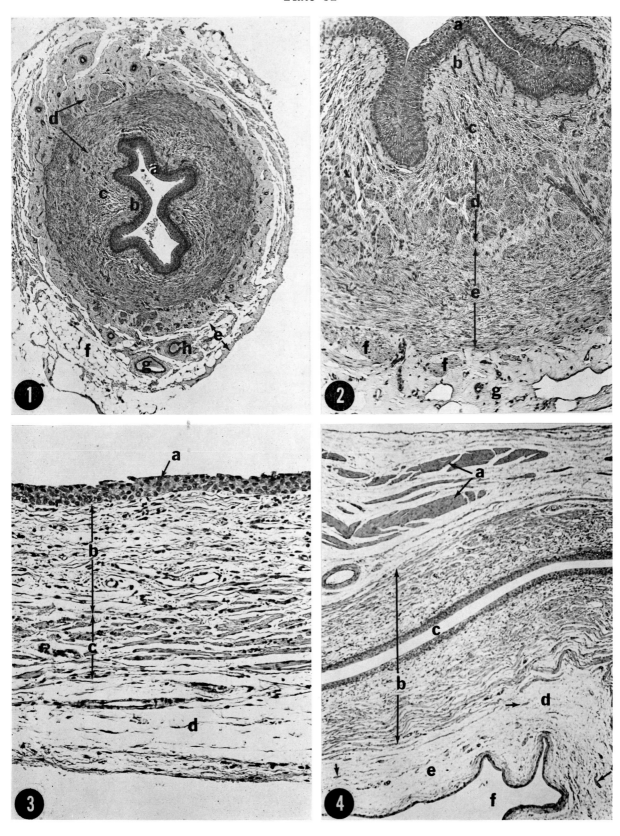

Plate 82

FIGURE 1. Urinary bladder and ureter. Notice that the serosa invests the bladder and ureter. Longitudinal section, Level 12. (H&E X11)
  a. Ureter
  b. Bladder wall
  c. Bladder lumen
  d. Serosa extending around the ureter and investing most of the bladder

FIGURE 2. Urinary bladder. Cross section, Level 6. (H&E X55)
  a. Transitional epithelium
  b. Lamina propria
  c. Artery
  d. Inner longitudinal smooth muscle
  e. Middle circular smooth muscle
  f. Outer longitudinal smooth muscle
  g. Serosa

FIGURE 3. Urinary bladder. Longitudinal section, Level 12. (H&E X232)
  a. Transitional epithelium
  b. Lamina propria
  c. Scattered bundles of the muscularis mucosae
  d. Inner longitudinal smooth muscle
  e. Nerve trunk

FIGURE 4. Urethra, female (proximal). Cross section, Level 11. (H&E X110)
  a. Lumen lined by transitional epithelium
  b. Lamina propria
  c. Venous plexuses
  d. Circular smooth muscle
  e. Scattered longitudinal muscle bundles
  f. Adventitia

Plate 82

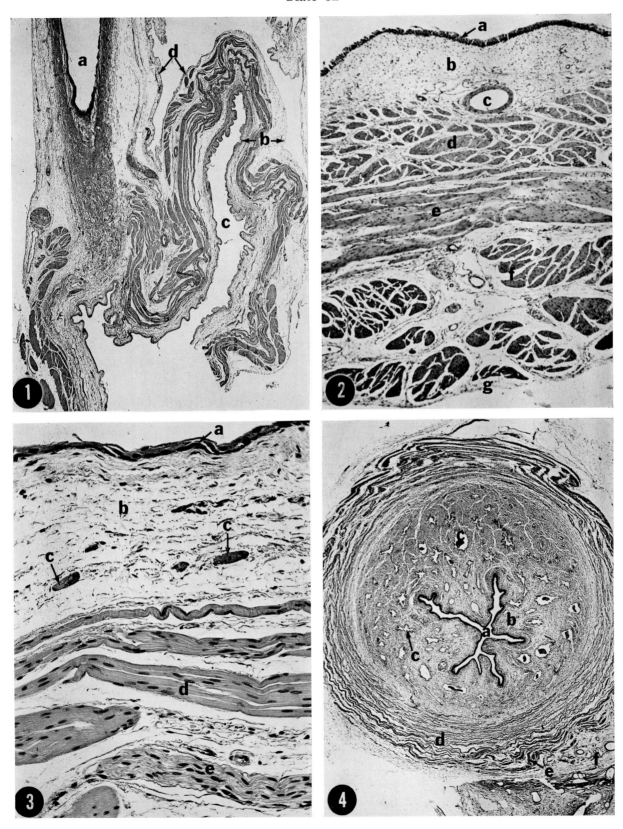

Plate 83

FIGURE 1. Prostatic urethra. Cross section, Level 7. (H&E X32)
    a. Lumen of the urethra
    b. Transitional epithelium
    c. Lamina propria
    d. Prostate glands and ducts

FIGURE 2. Membranous urethra. Cross section. Level 8. (H&E X45)
    a. Lumen of the urethra lined with transitional and stratified columnar epithelium
    b. Corpus cavernosum urethrae
    c. Skeletal muscle
    d. Adventitia

FIGURE 3. Penile urethra of the bulbus glandis (see Fig. 3, Plate 103) Cross section, Level 9. (H&E X33)
    a. Lumen of the urethra lined with transitional and stratified columnar epithelium
    b. Lamina propria
    c. Corpus cavernosum urethrae
    d. Branches of the dorsal artery of the penis
    e. Os penis

FIGURE 4. Penile urethra of the pars longa glandis (see Fig. 4, Plate 103) Cross section, Level 10. (H&E X23)
    a. Lumen of the urethra lined with transitional and stratified columnar epithelium
    b. Lamina propria
    c. Corpus cavernosum urethrae
    d. Circular collagenous connective tissue bundles
    e. Adventitia
    f. Os penis

Plate 83

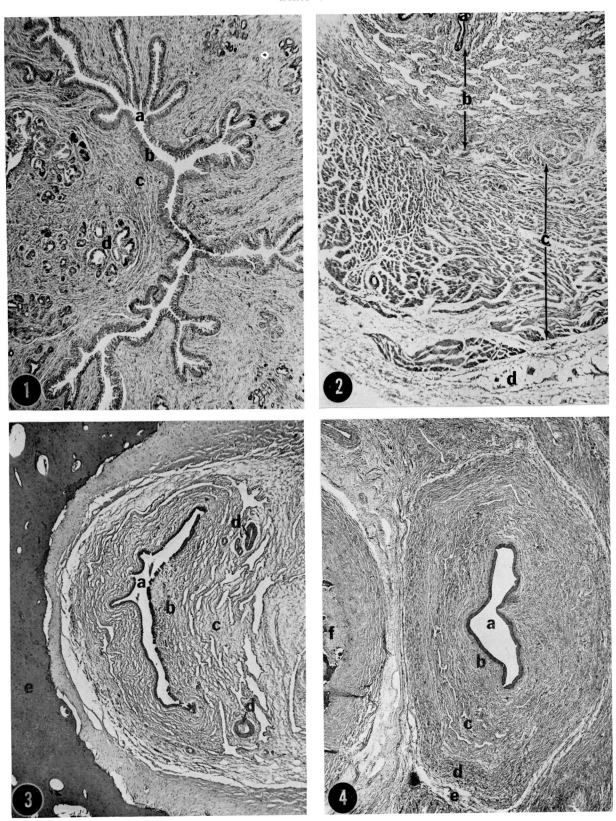

Chapter 7

Female Reproductive System

The ovary of the dog and sow protrudes into a peritoneal sac, the ovarian bursa, which partially surrounds the ovary. There is a small orifice, 5 to 10 mm long, caudoventral to the kidney, through which the ova are discharged into the infundibulum of the oviduct. With the exception of the mare, the ovary of the dog, other domestic animals and man is divided into a cortex and medulla. The ovarian follicle of the dog and other carnivores is similar to that in the human ovary except for an occasional polyoocyte follicle.

The ovarian stroma in the dog contains conspicuous clusters of polygonal shaped interstitial cells. This cell type is either absent or present in very small numbers in the human ovary.

The wall of each ovarian bursa contains the oviduct, which follows a more or less tortuous course from the orifice of the bursa to the opening into the uterine horn. Histologically, the oviduct is similar to that found in man.

The canine uterus, as well as the uteri of other domestic animals consists of two horns, a body and a neck or cervix. The uterine horns lie within the abdomen and unite at the body. The uterine wall is similar in most animals; however, there are a few differences worth mentioning. The uterine glands in the lamina propria show much less branching in carnivores than in man. The stratum vasculare, located between the inner circular and outer longitudinal layers of the myometrium, is very well developed in the dog but often indistinct in the human uterus.

The neck of the uterus or cervix differs from the body of the uterus in several respects. It is lined by a tall columnar epithelium containing mucus-secreting cells. The inner circular and outer longitudinal smooth muscle layers contain an abundance of elastic tissue and the vascular layer seen in the body of the uterus is absent. The high mucosal folds which characterize the cervix of other domestic animals are lacking in the dog. Only in carnivores do the glands of the cervical mucosa extend to the level of the external os.

In the dog, as it does in all animals, the vaginal epithelium reflects the cyclic changes during the estrus cycle; however, there is true cornification of the superficial cells during estrus. In man these are not completely cornified, but the cells do contain kerotohyalin granules.

The dog does not possess the major vestibular glands of Bartholin, as seen in man. The absence of these glands correlates with the absence of the bulbourethral gland in the male dog, since the vestibular glands are considered to be a homologue of these glands. The dog does have small lobular glands located deep in the vestibular wall near the constrictor muscle.

FEMALE REPRODUCTIVE SYSTEM

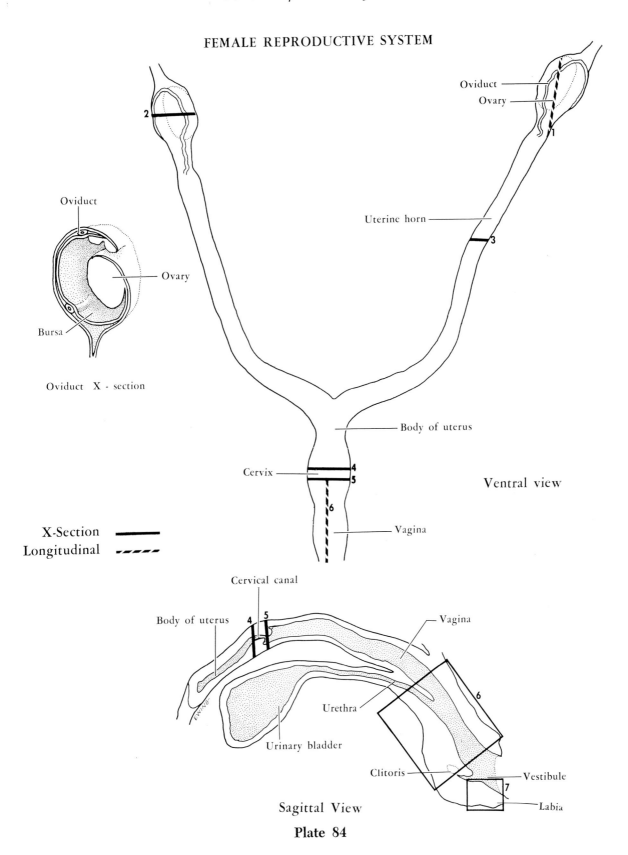

Oviduct

Ovary

Uterine horn

Oviduct

Ovary

Bursa

Oviduct X - section

Body of uterus

Cervix

Ventral view

X-Section

Longitudinal

Vagina

Cervical canal

Body of uterus

Vagina

Urethra

Urinary bladder

Clitoris

Vestibule

Labia

Sagittal View

Plate 84

Plate 85

FIGURE 1. Ovary within the ovarian bursa. Longitudinal section, Level 1. (H&E X16)
- a. Ovarian bursa
- b. Mesovarium
- c. Ovarian medulla
- d. Ovarian cortex
- e. Oviduct within the mesosalpinx

FIGURE 2. Ovarian cortex. Longitudinal section, Level 1. (H&E X270)
- a. Ovarian epithelium
- b. Tunica albuginea
- c. Ovarian follicles
- d. Connective tissue stroma

FIGURE 3. Ovarian medulla. Longitudinal section, Level 1. (H&E X270)
- a. Connective tissue stroma
- b. Interstitial cell mass
- c. Blood vessels

Plate 85

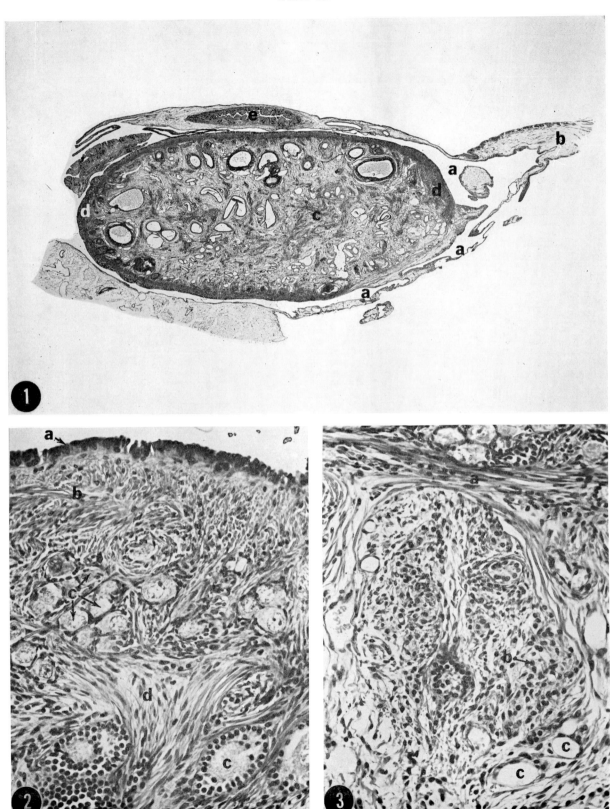

Plate 86

FIGURE 1. Primary follicle. Level 1. (H&E X710)
  a. Oocyte with prominent nucleus
  b. Flattened follicular cells
  c. Ovarian stroma

FIGURE 2. Secondary follicle. Level 1. (H&E X270)
  a. Primary oocyte with prominent nucleus and zona pellucida (at arrow)
  b. Multilayered follicular cells
  c. Ovarian stroma with numerous blood vessels

FIGURE 3. Secondary follicle with developing antrum. Level 1. (H&E X270)
  a. Primary oocyte with prominent nucleus and nucleolus. Notice the zona pellucida (at arrow).
  b. Cells of the cumulus oophorous
  c. Antrum
  d. Membrana granulosa cells
  e. Thecal cells

FIGURE 4. Secondary follicle with well developed antrum. Level 1. (H&E X170)
  a. Primary oocyte (the first meiotic division occurs after ovulation in the dog)
  b. Cells of the cumulus oophorous
  c. Antrum
  d. Membrana granulosa
  e. Thecal cells

Plate 86

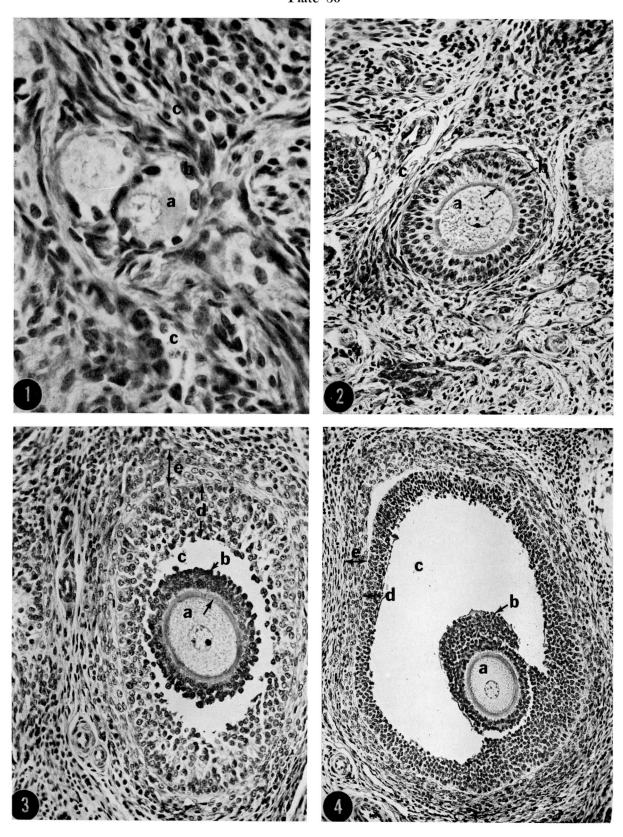

Plate 87

FIGURE 1. Primary oocyte within a mature follicle. Level 1. (H&E X540)
  a. Nucleus
  b. Nucleolus
  c. Cytoplasm
  d. Zona pellucida
  e. Corona radiata cells penetrating the zona pellucida
FIGURE 2. Follicular wall. Level 1. (H&E X710)
  a. Membrana granulosa
  b. Theca interna
  c. Theca externa
FIGURE 3. Polyoocyte follicle. Level 1. (H&E X270)
  a. Oocytes
  b. Granulosa cells
  c. Early formation of the antrum
  d. Thecal cells
FIGURE 4. Atretic follicle (advanced). Level 1. (H&E X170)
  a. Degenerated oocyte
  b. Granulosa cells
  c. Follicular cavity filled with fibroblasts, wandering cells, and capillaries
  d. Prominent hyaloid membrane
  e. Ovarian stroma

Plate 87

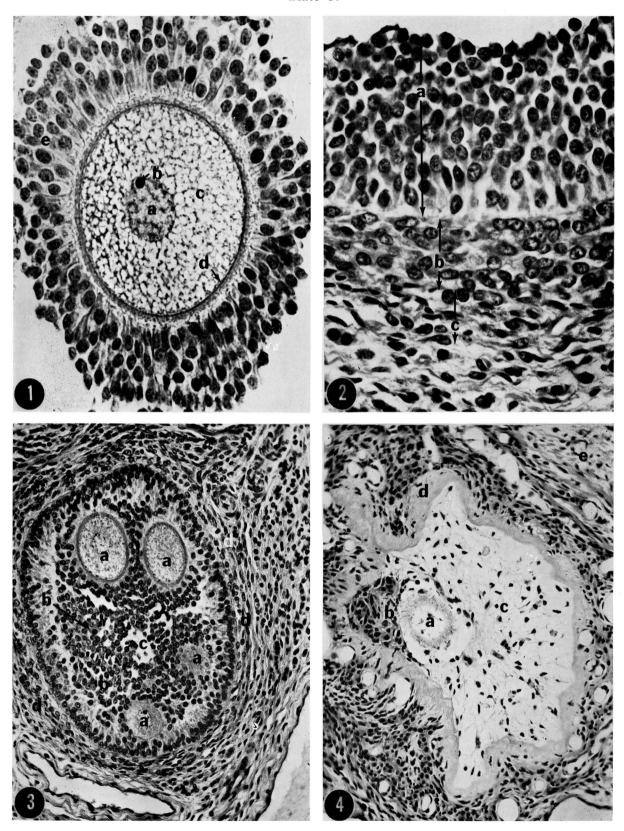

Plate 88

FIGURE 1. Ovarian stroma. Level 1. (H&E X270)
  a. Clusters of interstitial cells
  b. Connective tissue stroma
  c. Blood vessels
FIGURE 2. Ovarian stroma. Level 1. (H&E X930)
  a. Interstitial cells. Notice foamy cytoplasm due to lipid accumulation.
  b. Capillary
FIGURE 3. Rete ovarii. Level 1. (H&E X450)
  a. Ducts of the rete ovarii
  b. Blood vessels
  c. Ovarian stroma

Plate 88

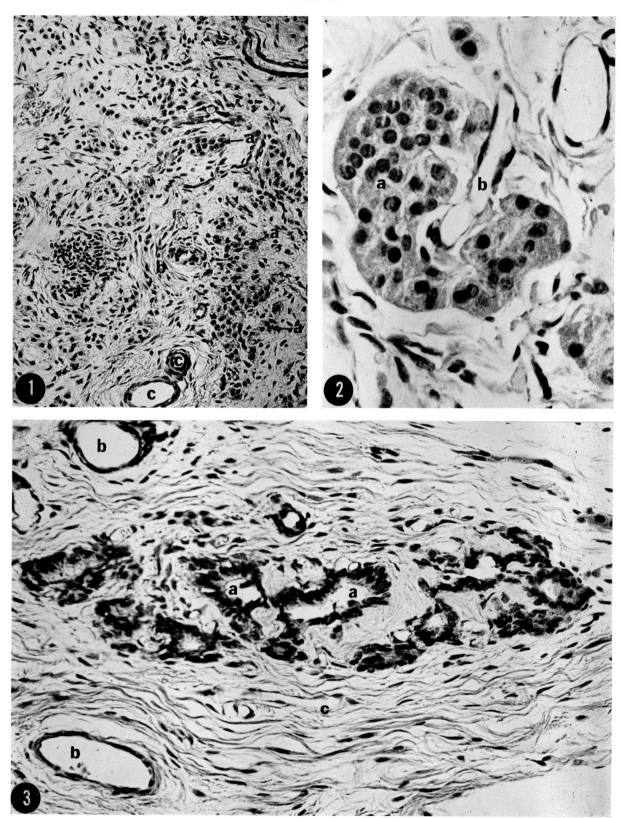

Plate 89

FIGURE 1. Oviduct. Cross section, Level 2. (H&E X97)
    a. Lumen of the oviduct
    b. Longitudinal mucosal folds
    c. Circular muscle coat
    d. Mesosalpinx
    e. Mesothelium

FIGURE 2. Oviduct. Cross section, Level 2. (H&E X315)
    a. Simple low columnar epithelium
    b. Vascular lamina propria
    c. Epithelial lined recesses of the lumen
    d. Circular smooth muscle
    e. Serosa

FIGURE 3. Oviduct mucosa. Cross section, Level 2. (H&E X710)
    a. Simple, low columnar epithelium
    b. Lamina propria
    c. Capillary
    d. Epithelial lined recesses of the lumen

Plate 89

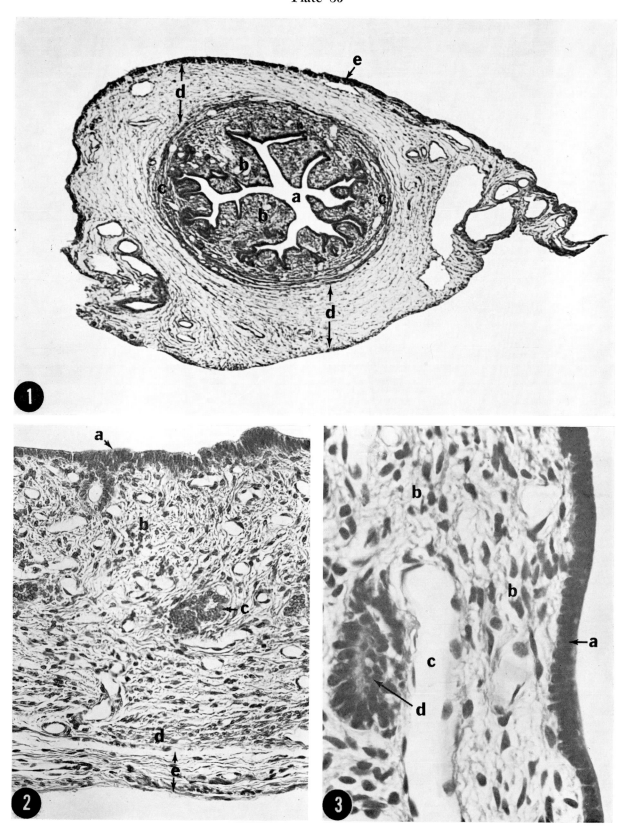

Plate 90

FIGURE 1. Uterine horn. Cross section, Level 3. (H&E X36)
   a. Endometrium
   b. Myometrium
   c. Perimetrium
   d. Mesometrium
FIGURE 2. Uterine wall. Cross section, Level 3. (H&E X170)
   a. Endometrium lined with simple columnar epithelium
   b. Uterine gland
   c. Circular layer of the myometrium
   d. Vascular layer of the myometrium
   e. Thin longtitudinal layer of the myometrium
   f. Perimetrium
FIGURE 3. Uterine mucosa. Cross section, Level 3. (H&E X600)
   a. Simple columnar epithelium (anestrum)
   b. Lamina propria
   c. Uterine glands

Plate 90

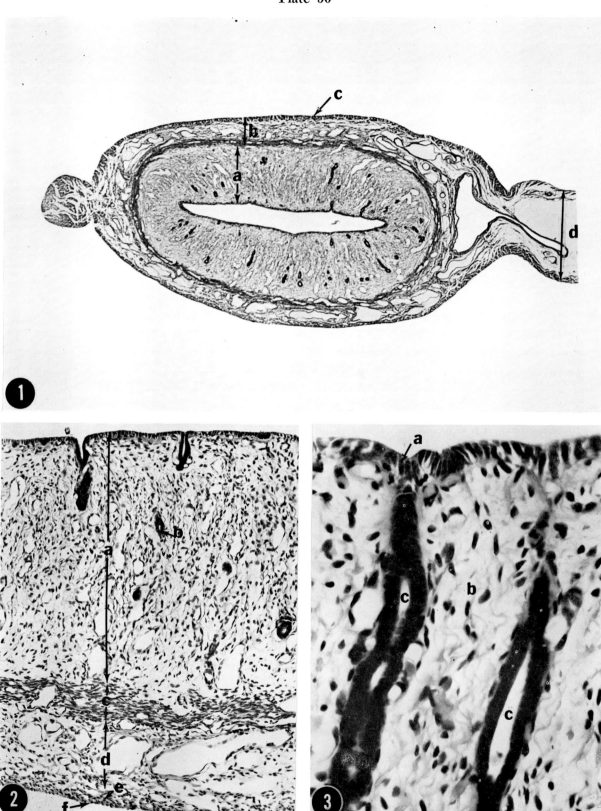

Plate 91

FIGURE 1. Prevaginal portion of the uterine cervix. Cross section anterior to the internal uterine orifice, Level 4. (H&E X19)
  a. Dorsal aspect
  b. Smooth muscle fibers
  c. Dorsal uterine wall anterior to the cervical canal (area seen in Fig. 2)
  d. Lumen of the body of the uterus dorsal to the prevaginal portion of the cervix
  e. Prevaginal portion of the cervix (area seen in Fig. 3)
  f. Ventral aspect of the cervix
  g. Middle uterine artery
  h. Middle uterine vein
  i. Mesometrium

FIGURE 2. Dorsal uterine wall anterior to the cervical canal (area at c in Fig. 1). Cross section, Level 4. (H&E X120)
  a. Stratified cuboidal epithelium
  b. Lamina propria (notice absence of glands during prepuberty)
  c. Myometrium (smooth muscle)
  d. Perimetrium

FIGURE 3. Ventral wall of the prevaginal portion of the uterine cervix (area at e in Fig. 1.) Cross section, Level 4. (H&E X120)
  a. Stratified columnar epithelium
  b. Lamina propria (notice absence of glands)
  c. Smooth muscle fibers
  d. Blood vessels

Plate 91

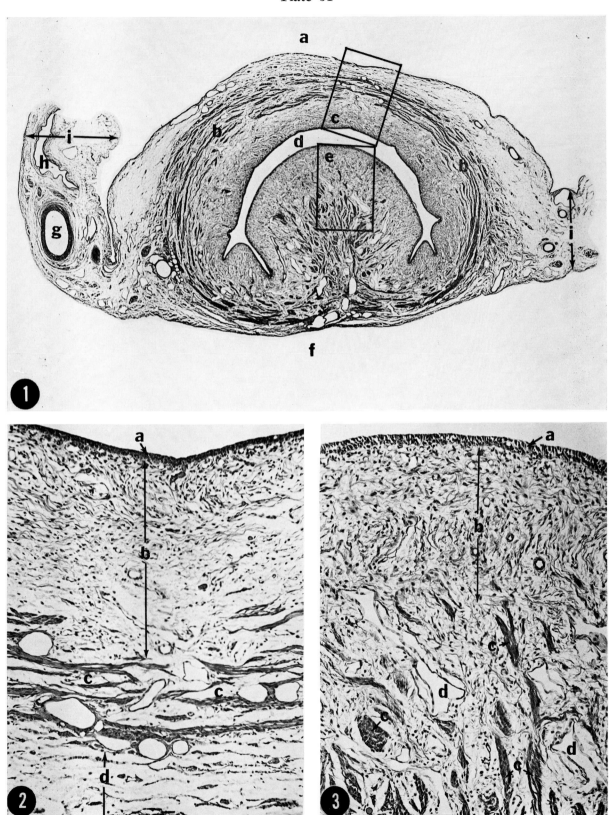

Plate 92

FIGURE 1. Vaginal portion of the cervix. Cross section posterior to the external uterine orifice, Level 5. (H&E X17)
  a. Dorsal aspect of the cervix
  b. Smooth muscle fibers of the vaginal portion of the cervix
  c. Vaginal portion of the cervix (area seen in Fig. 3)
  d. Fornix of the vagina
  e. Fornix of the vagina (area seen in Fig. 2)
  f. Ventral aspect
FIGURE 2. Fornix of the vagina (area e in Fig. 1). Cross section, Level 5. (H&E X180)
  a. Stratified squamous epithelium
  b. Blood vessels of the lamina propria
  c. Smooth muscle
FIGURE 3. Wall of the vaginal portion of the uterine cervix (area c in Fig. 1). Cross section, Level 5. (H&E X180)
  a. Stratified squamous epithelium
  b. Blood vessels of the lamina propria
  c. Smooth muscle fibers

Plate 92

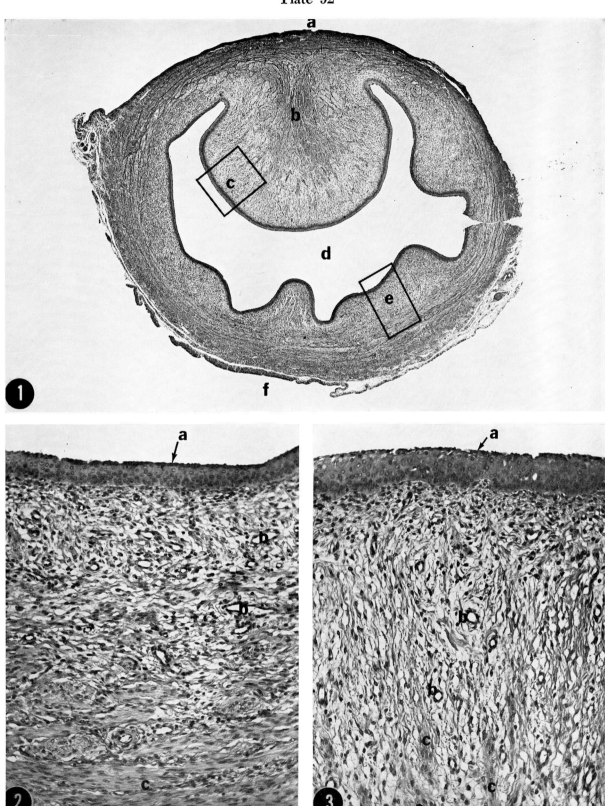

Plate 93

FIGURE 1. Vagina, urethra, and vestibule. Longitudinal section, Level 6. (H&E X9)
- a. Vagina
- b. Vestibule
- c. Vaginal epithelium
- d. Urethral orifice
- e. Clitoris
- f. Ventral vaginal wall (area seen in Fig. 2)

FIGURE 2. Ventral vaginal wall. Longitudinal section, Level 6. (H&E X110)
- a. Stratified squamous epithelium
- b. Vascular lamina propria (notice blood vessels at arrows)
- c. Smooth muscle

FIGURE 3. Vaginal mucosa. Level 6. (H&E X425)
- a. Epithelium characteristic of anestrus. During estrus this proliferates into stratified squamous epithelium.
- b. Lamina propria
- c. Bundles of collagenous connective tissue
- d. Blood vessels

Plate 93

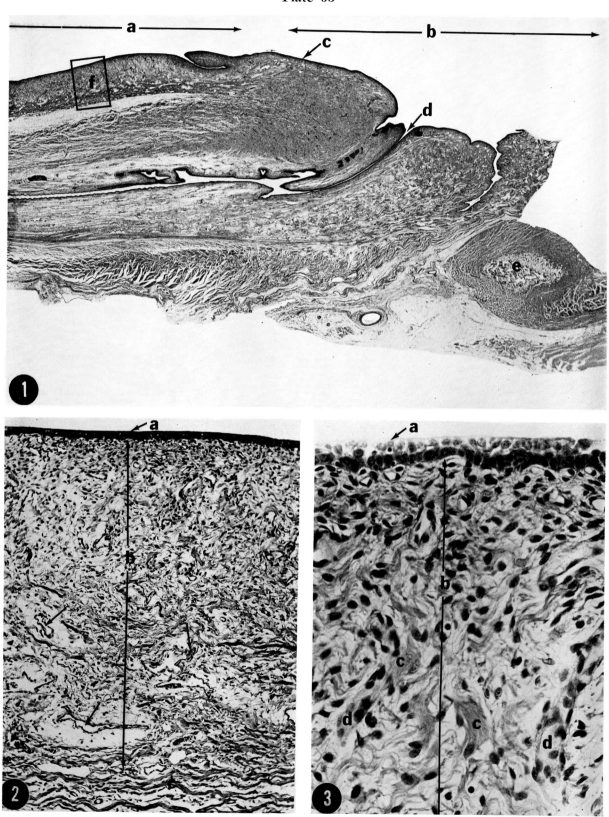

Plate 94

FIGURE 1. Wall of the vestibule. Longitudinal section, Level 6. (H&E X38)
    a. Stratified squamous epithelium
    b. Lamina propria
    c. Simple tubuloalveolar vestibular glands
    d. Erectile tissue of the vestibular bulb

FIGURE 2. Vestibular mucosa. Longitudinal section, Level 6. (H&E X310)
    a. Stratified squamous epithelium
    b. Vascular lamina propria

FIGURE 3. Vestibular glands. Longitudinal section, Level 6. (H&E X310)
    a. Duct of the gland
    b. Secretory acini of the gland

FIGURE 4. Clitoris. Longitudinal section, Level 6 (H&E X120)
    a. Erectile tissue of the glans clitoridis
    b. Tunica albuginea
    c. Corpus clitoridis—composed mostly of fat

Plate 94

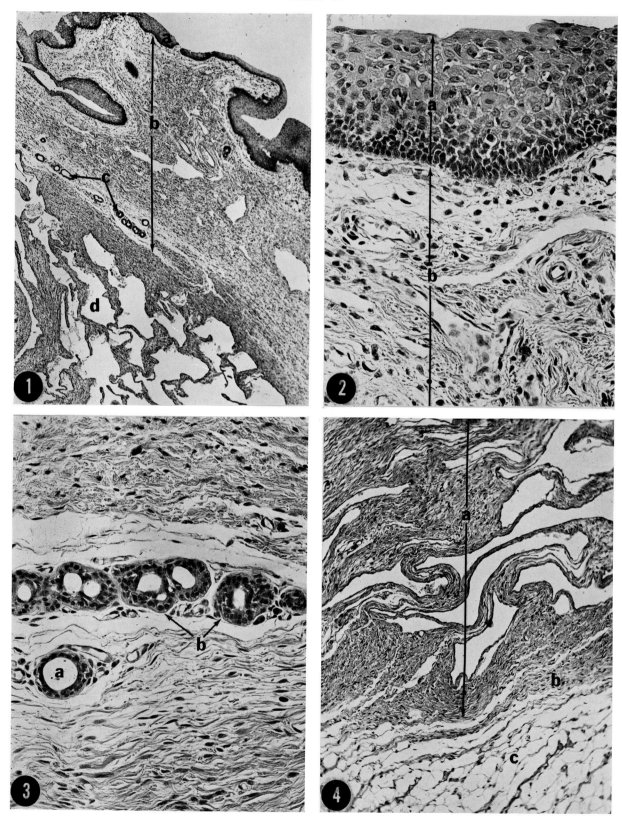

Plate 95

FIGURE 1. Labium of the vulva. Longitudinal section, Level 7. (H&E X23)
  a. Labial mucosa with stratified squamous epithelium
  b. Lymphatic vessels
  c. Integument (also see Plate 9, Figure 5)
  d. Hair follicles
  e. Tubular sweat glands
  f. Sebaceous glands
FIGURE 2. Mucosa of the vulva. Longitudinal section, Level 7. (H&E X110)
  a. Nonkeratinized stratified squamous epithelium
  b. Lamina propria
  c. Lymphatic vessels
  d. Blood vessels

Plate 95

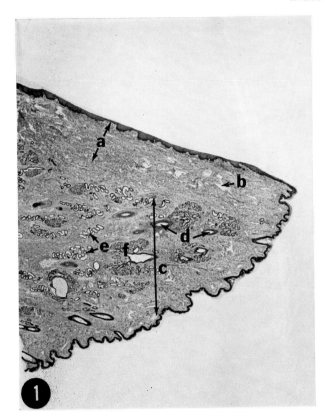

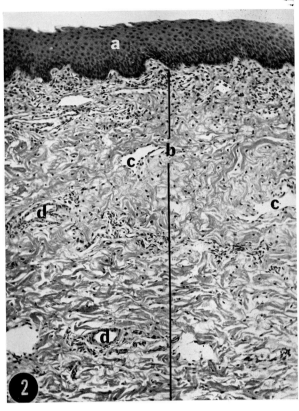

Chapter 8

Male Reproductive System

Except for the absence of the seminal vesicles and bulbourethral glands and the presence of an os penis, the male genital system of the dog is similar to that of other species.

The histology of the canine testis is not significantly different from that of man and other domestic animals. The vascular layer of the tunica albuginea, however, lies near the parenchyma, which is similar to the ram and man but different from the horse and boar where it is located in the middle of the tunic.

The smooth muscle fibers of the tunica muscularis of the dog's ductus deferens, like those of the stallion, bull and man, are interwoven and the layers are less distinct. This is in contrast to the boar and ram where the inner layer is predominantly circular and the outer longitudinal. The ampulla of the dog contains branched tubular glands which have sac-like dilations similar to man, bull, stallion and ram. The ampulla is absent in the cat.

The body of the dog prostate is large and completely surrounds the proximal portion of the urethra while the disseminate prostate is composed only of scattered small glands. This arrangement contrasts with the ruminant and swine prostate which consists mostly of disseminate glands that form a layer in the wall of the entire pelvic urethra.

The penis of the dog differs significantly from that of man and other domestic animals. The corpora cavernosa penis of the dog extends throughout the root and body but continues into the glans as an ossified terminal portion, the os penis. The median septum of the tunica albuginea is continuous throughout the body of the penis in the dog but is present only near the root of ruminants and boars. Smooth muscle fibers are more prevalent in the walls of the cavernous spaces in the dog than in man but not so abundant as in the stallion. The glans penis, the chief erectile structure of the dog penis, consists of two separate parts: the bulbus glandis, and the pars longa glandis. The bulbus glandis is a cavernous expansion of the corpus cavernosum urethrae and surrounds the proximal part of the os penis. It contains large venous sinuses between trabeculae which are rich in elastic tissue. The pars longa glandis, which is separated from the bulbus glandis by a thick layer of dense connective tissue, continues distally as a sheath for the corpus cavernosum urethrae and os penis.

MALE REPRODUCTIVE SYSTEM

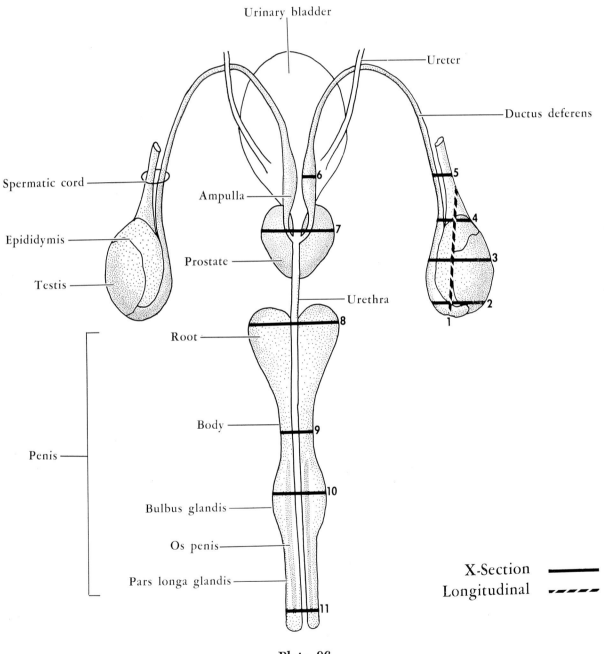

Plate 96

Plate 97

FIGURE 1. Testis and epididymis. Longitudinal section, Level 1. (H&E X5)
 a. Convoluted seminiferous tubules
 b. Rete testis
 c. Efferent ductules
 d. Head of the epididymis
 e. Body of the epididymis
 f. Tail of the epididymis
 g. Tunica albuginea
 h. Vascular portion of the spermatic cord

FIGURE 2. Capsule of the testis. Longitudinal section, Level 1. (H&E X150)
 a. Visceral layer of the tunica vaginalis
 b. Tunica albuginea
 c. Vein
 d. Convoluted seminiferous tubule

FIGURE 3. Septula testis. Longitudinal section, Level 1. (H&E X140)
 a. Tunica albuginea
 b. Artery
 c. Septula testis
 d. Convoluted seminiferous tubule

Plate 97

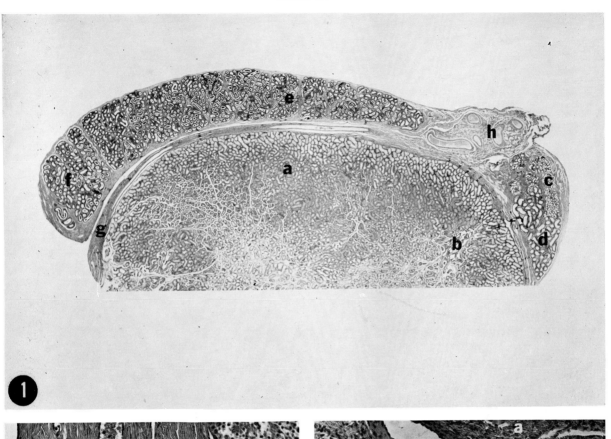

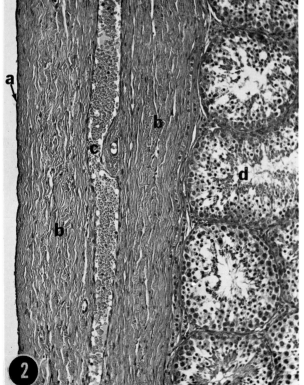

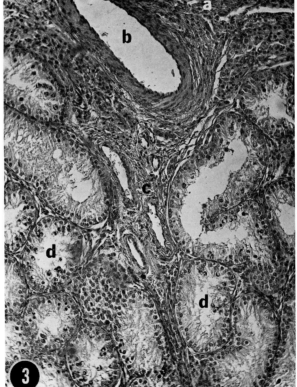

Plate 98

Convoluted seminiferous tubules in various stages of the "Cycle of the
Seminiferous Epithelium." (Stages I through VI) Cross section, Level 3.
(H&E X700)
a. Spermatids in an early stage of development
b. Spermatids in an intermediate stage of development
c. Spermatids in a late stage of development
d. Primary spermatocytes
e. Spermatogonia
f. Sustentacular cells (Sertoli)
g. Interstitial cells (Leydig)

Plate 98

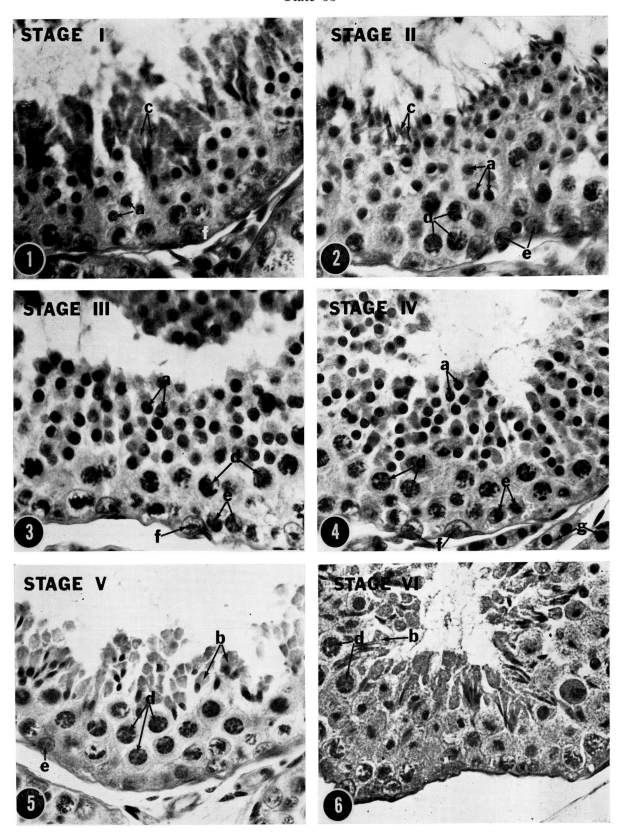

Plate 99

Figure 1. Testis. Cross section, Level 3. (H&E X870)
    a. Interstitial cells (Leydig)
    b. Nucleus of a sustentacular cell (Sertoli)
    c. Arteriole
Figure 2. Junction of a convoluted seminiferous tubule with a straight tubule. Level 3. (H&E X300)
    a. Convoluted seminiferous tubule
    b. Straight tubule lined with cuboidal epithelium
Figure 3. Rete testis. Cross section, Level 4. (H&E X220)
    a. Lumen of the rete testis lined with low cuboidal epithelium
    b. Connective tissue of the mediastinum testis
Figure 4. Spermatozoa. (Iron hematoxylin) (H&E X1970)

Plate 99

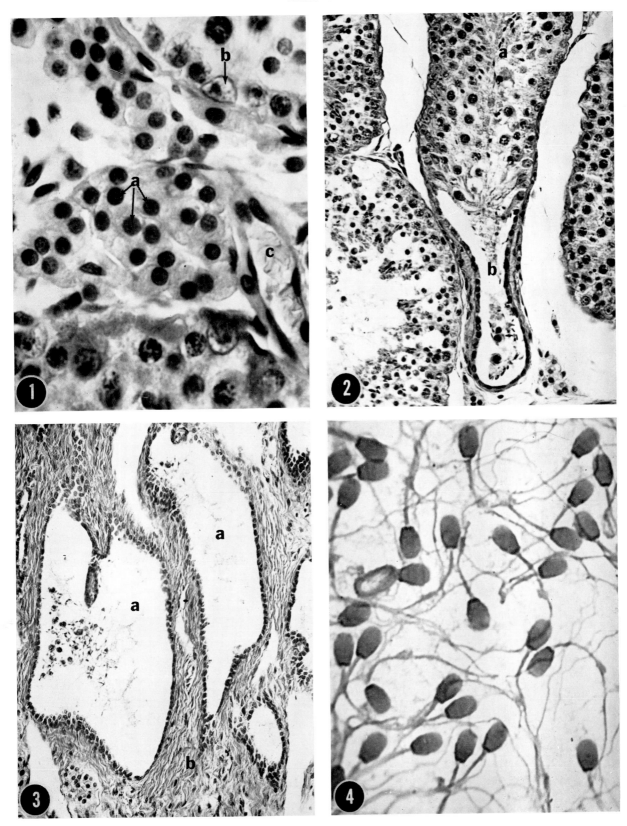

Plate 100

FIGURE 1. Efferent ductules. Cross section, Level 4. (H&E X275)
   a. Efferent ductules lined with simple columnar epithelium. Notice some ciliated cells at arrows.
   b. Stroma

FIGURE 2. Head of the epididymis. Cross section, Level 4. (H&E X275)
   a. Lumen of the duct lined with pseudostratified columnar epithelium with stereocilia at arrows
   b. Stroma

FIGURE 3. Body of the epididymis. Cross section, Level 3. (H&E X275)
   a. Lumen of the duct lined with pseudostratified columnar epithelium with stereocilia
   b. Spermatozoa
   c. Stroma

FIGURE 4. Tail of the epididymis. Cross section, Level 2. (H&E X275)
   a. Lumen of duct lined with pseudostratified columnar epithelium with stereocilia
   b. Spermatozoa
   c. Stroma

Plate 100

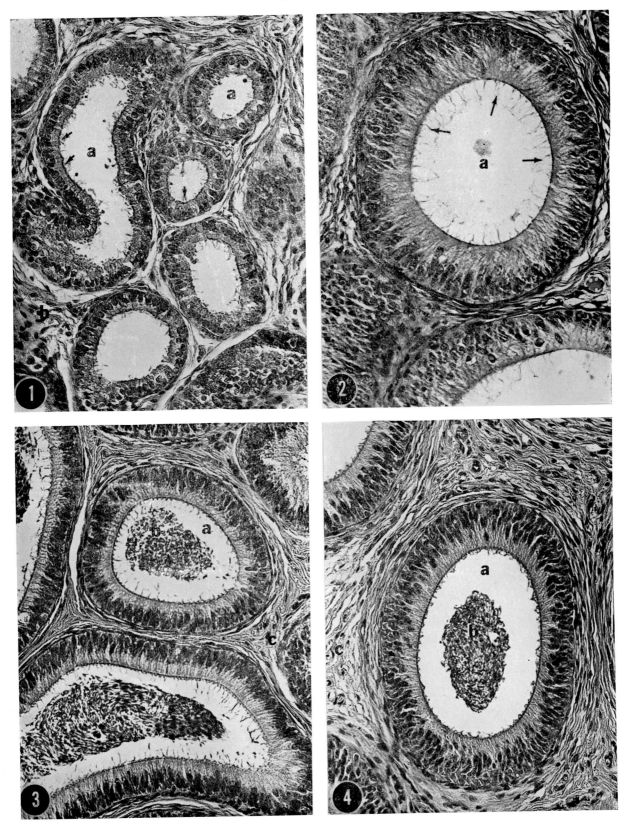

Plate 101

FIGURE 1. Spermatic cord. Cross section, Level 5. (H&E X11)
    a. External cremaster muscle (skeletal)
    b. Ductus deferens
    c. Vaginal cavity
    d. Parietal layer of the tunica vaginalis
    e. External spermatic fascia
    f. Testicular artery (cut through two convolutions)
    g. Pampiniform plexus of the testicular vein
    h. Internal cremaster muscle (smooth)

FIGURE 2. Ductus deferens. Cross section, Level 5. (H&E X200)
    a. Lumen
    b. Pseudostratified ciliated columnar epithelium
    c. Lamina propria
    d. Tunica muscularis

FIGURE 3. Ampulla of the ductus deferens. Cross section, Level 6. (H&E X125)
    a. Lumen
    b. Alveolus of the gland
    c. Tunica muscularis

FIGURE 4. Ampulla of the ductus deferens. Cross section, Level 6. (H&E X870)
    a. Lumen
    b. Simple columnar epithelium of a glandular alveolus
    c. Stroma

Plate 101

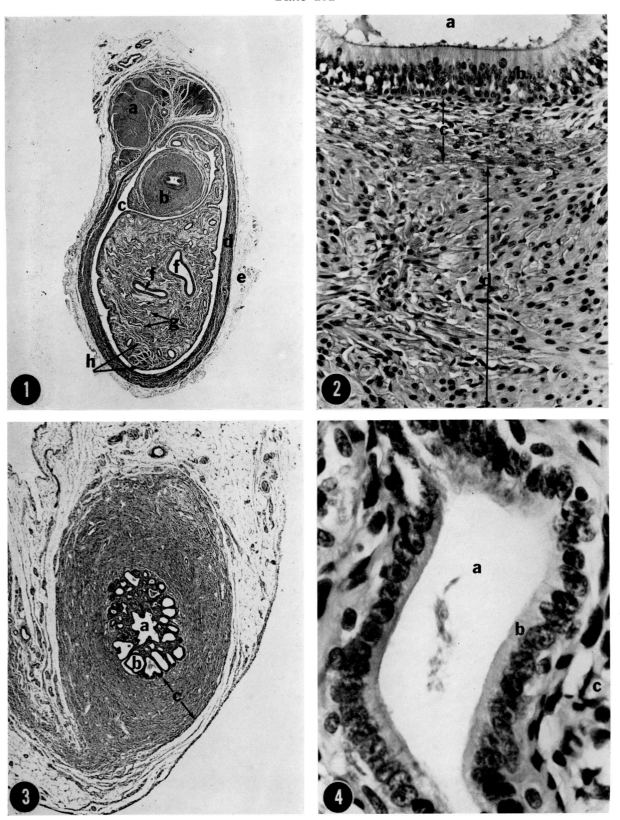

Plate 102

FIGURE 1. Prostate. Cross Section, Level 7. (H&E X7.5)
   a. Fibromuscular capsule
   b. Ductus deferentes
   c. Dorsal median septum
   d. Prostatic urethra
   e. Central fibrous zone
   f. Ventral median septum
   g. Lobule of the main prostatic gland
   h. Submucosal prostatic glands
   i. Fibromuscular septum
   j. Autonomic ganglia

FIGURE 2. Prostatic lobule. Cross section, Level 7. (H&E X40)
   a. Fibromuscular capsule
   b. Fibromuscular septum
   c. Tubuloalveolar secretory unit

FIGURE 3. Prostatic glandular tissue. Cross section, Level 7. (H&E X820)
   a. Lumen of secretory unit
   b. Basal epithelial cells
   c. Low columnar epithelial cells
   d. Clear cell
   e. Connective tissue stroma between secretory units

Plate 102

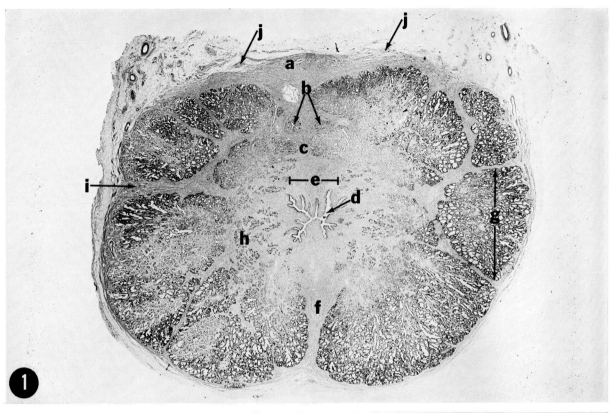

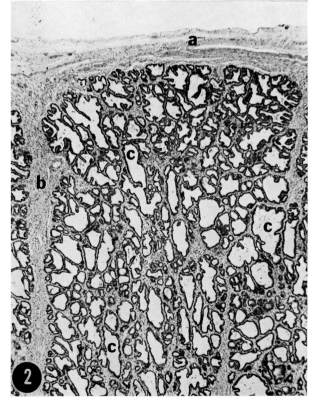

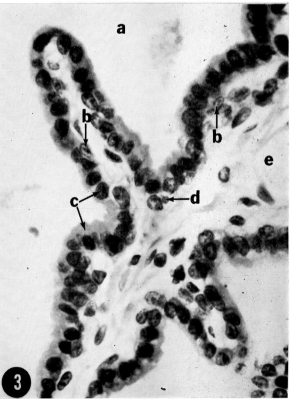

Plate 103

FIGURE 1. Root of the penis. Cross section, Level 8. (H&E X5)
    a. Dorsal arteries of the penis
    b. Dorsal veins of the penis
    c. Tunica albuginea
    d. Corpora cavernosa penis
    e. Urethra
    f. Corpus cavernosum urethrae
    g. Artery of the urethral bulb
    h. Bulbocavernosus muscle
    i. Ischiocavernosus muscle

FIGURE 2. Body of the penis. Cross section, Level 9. (H&E X5)
    a. Tunica albuginea
    b. Septum penis
    c. Corpora cavernosa penis
    d. Urethra
    e. Corpus cavernosum urethrae
    f. Retractor penis muscle (smooth)
    g. Dorsal vein of the penis
    h. Dorsal artery of the penis

FIGURE 3. Bulbus glandis of the penis. Cross section, Level 10. (H&E X5)
    a. Stratified squamous epithelium of the glans penis
    b. Dermis of the skin of the glans penis
    c. Subcutaneous connective tissue of the glans penis
    d. Bulbus glandis
    e. Os penis
    f. Corpus cavernosum urethrae (see Figure 3, Plate 83)
    g. Deep branch of the dorsal artery of the penis
    h. Superficial branch of the dorsal artery of the penis

FIGURE 4. Pars longa glandis of the penis. Cross section, Level 11. (H&E X5)
    a. Stratified squamous epithelium of the glans penis
    b. Pars longa glandis
    c. Fibrocartilagenous end of the os penis
    d. Urethra (see Figure 4, Plate 83)
    e. Corpus cavernosum urethrae
    f. Deep branch of the dorsal artery of the penis

Plate 103

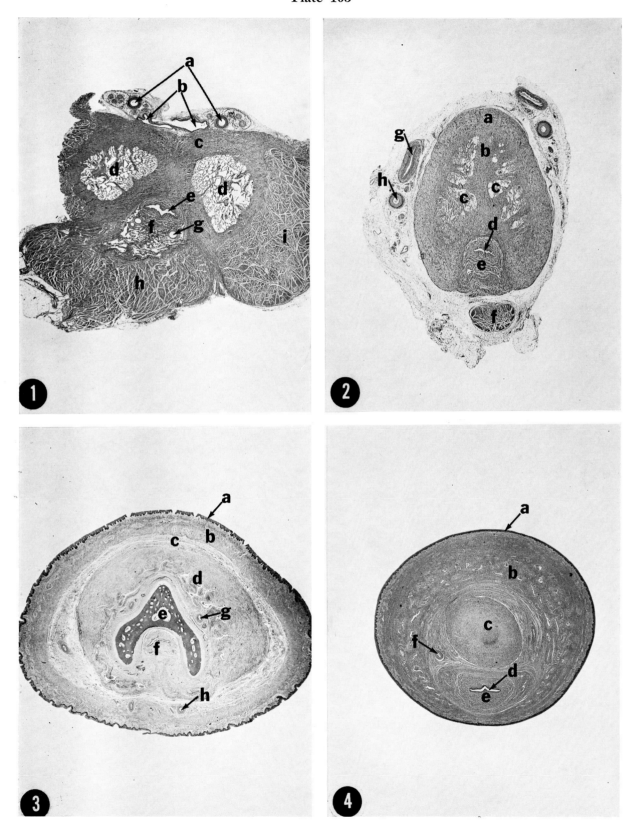

Chapter 9

Endocrine System

The adrenal gland of the dog, as in man and other domestic animals, is composed of a cortex and medulla which are distinct both developmentally and functionally. The entire gland is surrounded by a distinct capsule composed of connective tissue cells and fibers, smooth muscle fibers, blood vessels and nerves. From the inner layer of the capsule, connective tissue septae project inward to the corticomedullary junction. In the horse, swine and carnivore, the peripheral portion of the cell cords of the zona fasciculata become wider, forming arches, the zona arcuata, near the inner surface of the capsule. This arrangement corresponds to the zona glomerulosa seen in the human adrenal cortex.

The medullary cells are arranged in small, oval groups separated by loose connective tissue and blood vessels. Sympathetic ganglion cells are present in the adrenal medulla of the dog but are less frequently observed than in other domestic animals, especially the ruminant.

The thyroid gland of the dog consists of two separate lobes lying lateral to the trachea to which they are only loosely attached. The dog lacks the well-developed isthmus so characteristic of man. The size and histologic structure of the thyroid lobes vary not only with age, season and sex but also markedly with breeds. The inbreeding of dogs appears to result in a marked increase in the number of plasma cells in the interstitial connective tissue of the thyroid.

The two pairs of parathyroid glands of the dogs are found in association with the thyroid glands; in swine the parathyroid gland is embedded in the thymus. A well-developed connective tissue capsule separates the parathyroid gland from the thyroid gland. As in the ox the interstitial connective tissue may be heavy. In older dogs adipose tissue may develop in the capsule. The parenchyma of the parathyroid forms cords or clusters of cells which show no characteristic arrangement in any species. In dogs and cattle, as well as in the human species, both oxyphil and chief cells may be present. However, the chief cell is the only cell in young dogs and the oxyphil cells appear only in older presenile animals. While pacinian corpuscles have been reported in the parathyroid of dogs, none was seen in the sections.

The hypophysis, like the adrenal gland, is composed of two parts which are distinct developmentally and functionally. One, the pars buccalis, originates as a dorsal evagination of the stomodeum. The other, the pars nervosa, results from an outpocketing of the floor of the diencephalon. That portion of the pars buccalis which fuses with the pars nervosa is called the pars intermedia. In man and horse the anterior lobe is in close apposition to the pars intermedia, but in the dog a vestigial neurohypophyseal cleft persists separating the pars intermedia from the pars nervosa. The lumen of the infundibulum in the dog is variable in its extent and may extend down into the pars nervosa for a considerable distance as in the swine, or it may end before reaching the hypophysis as in ruminants.

The cells of the pars distalis are arranged in columns separated by large thin-walled vascular sinusoids. As many as six cell types have been described in the dog: two acidophils, one orange, the other red; two basophils, one blue and one purple; a chromophobe which stains indistinctly; and a sixth type, a large cell with a weak affinity for stains, sometimes referred to as the zeta cell. The proportion of acidophils to basophils is 11 to 1, and the number of basophils is much lower in dogs than in man. Cysts are more frequently seen in brachycephalic breeds than in mesocephalic breeds.

ENDOCRINE SYSTEM

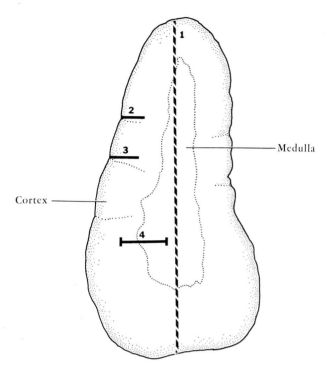

Medulla

Cortex

Adrenal

X-Section	——
Longitudinal	✕✕✕✕
Oblique	▬▬

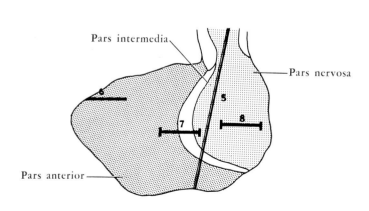

Pars intermedia

Pars nervosa

Pars anterior

Hypophysis

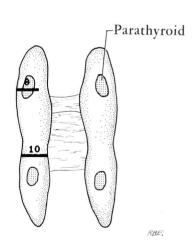

Parathyroid

Thyroid

Plate 104

Plate 105

FIGURE 1. Adrenal gland. Longitudinal section, Level 1. (H&E X15)
  a. Subperitoneal connective tissue
  b. Capsule
  c. Zona arcuata
  d. Zona fasciculata
  e. Zona reticularis
  f. Medulla
  g. Central vein of the medulla
  h. Autonomic ganglion
  i. Area seen in Figure 3

FIGURE 2. Cortex of adrenal gland. Cross section, Level 2. (Chromalum hematoxylin X120)
  a. Capsule
  b. Zona arcuata
  c. Zona fasciculata
  d. Cortical sinusoids

FIGURE 3. Adrenal septum extending inward from the capsule. Cross section, Level 2. (Chromalum hematoxylin X120)
  a. Septum
  b. Capsule
  c. Zona arcuata
  d. Zona fasciculata
  e. Cortical sinusoids

Plate 105

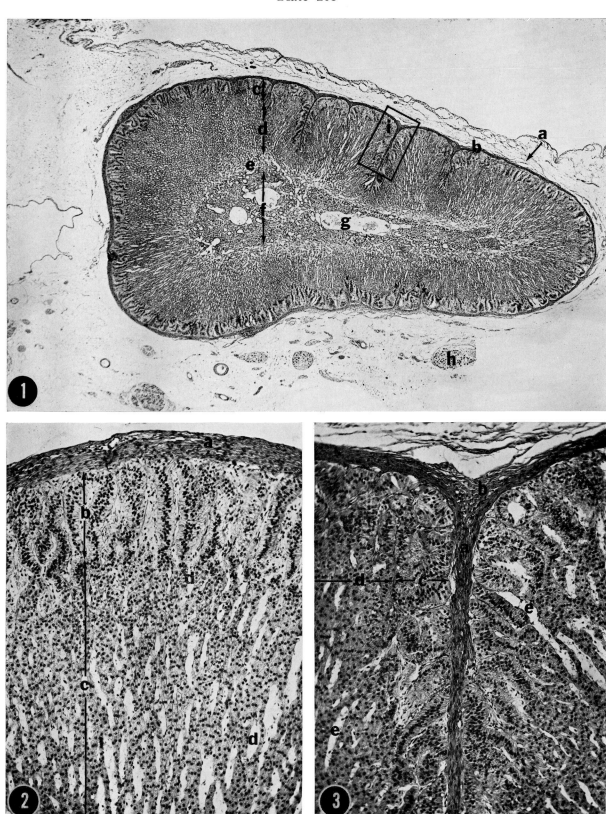

Plate 106

FIGURE 1. Capsule of the adrenal gland. Cross section, Level 2. (Chromalum hematoxylin X300)
   a. Subperitoneal connective tissue
   b. Arterioles
   c. Venule
   d. Capsule
   e. Zona arcuata

FIGURE 2. Adrenal cortex. Cross section, Level 2. (Chromalum hematoxylin X250)
   a. Capsule
   b. Zona arcuata
   c. Zone fasciculata
   d. Sinusoids
   e. Area seen in Figure 3

FIGURE 3. Adrenal cortex. Cross section, Level 2. (Chromalum hematoxylin X530)
   a. Capsule
   b. Parenchymal cells of zona arcuata
   c. Sinusoid

FIGURE 4. Adrenal cortex. Cross section, Level 3. (Chromalum hematoxylin X200)
   a. Parenchyma of zona fasciculata
   b. Sinusoids
   c. Parenchyma of zona reticularis

Plate 106

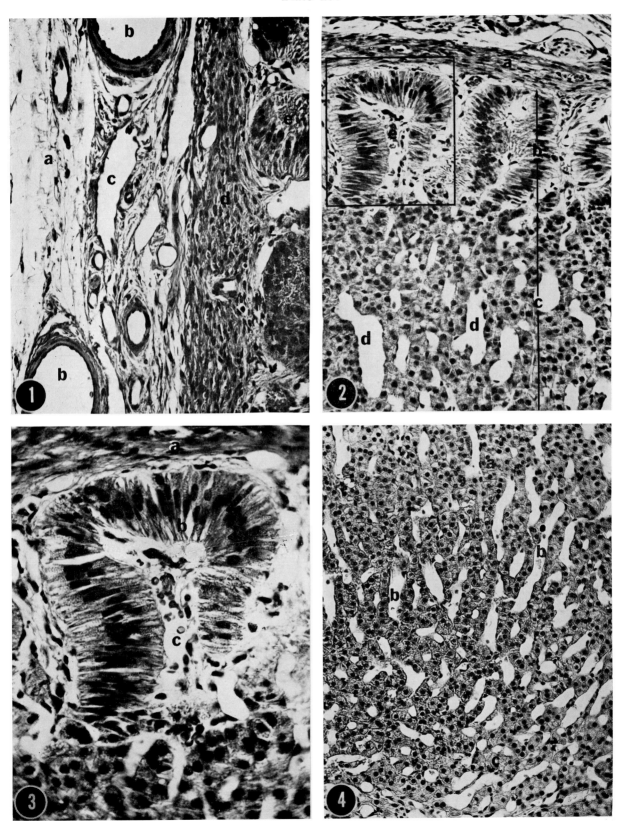

Plate 107

FIGURE 1. Adrenal medulla. Cross section, Level 4. (H&E X210)
  a. Medullary parenchyma
  b. Central vein
  c. Arterioles

FIGURE 2. Adrenal cortex and medulla. Cross section, Level 4. (H&E X175)
  a. Zona reticularis
  b. Medulla
  c. Medullary sinusoids
  d. Arteriole

FIGURE 3. Adrenal medulla. Cross section, Level 4. (H&E X185)
  a. Medullary parenchymal cells adjacent to vascular channels
  b. Sinusoids
  c. Central vein

FIGURE 4. Adrenal medulla. Cross section, Level 4. (H&E X325)
  a. Medullary parenchymal cells
  b. Sinusoid
  c. Arterioles

Plate 107

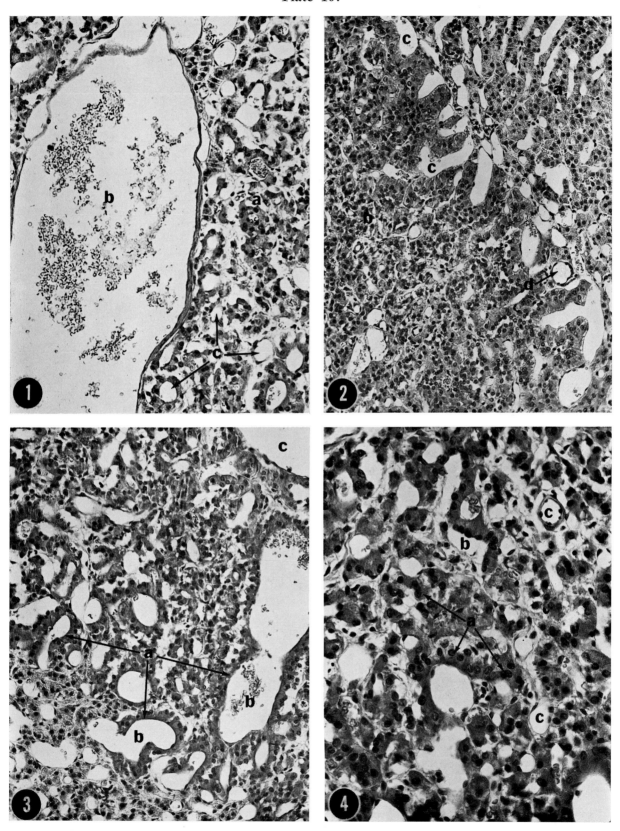

Plate 108

FIGURE 1. Hypophysis. Oblique section, Level 5. (H&E X15)
   a. Pars distalis
   b. Pars intermedia
   c. Pars nervosa
   d. Infundibulum
   e. Hypothalamus
FIGURE 2. Pars distalis. Cross section, Level 6. (McFarlane's trichrome X140)
   a. Sinusoid
   b. Parenchyma
FIGURE 3. Pars distalis. Cross section, Level 6. (McFarlane's trichrome X390)
   a. Chromophilic cells
   b. Chromophobic cells
   c. Sinusoids
FIGURE 4. Pars intermedia. Cross section, Level 7. (McFarlane's trichrome X175)
   a. Pars distalis
   b. Neurohypophyseal cleft
   c. Pars intermedia
   d. Pars nervosa
   e. Sinusoid

Plate 108

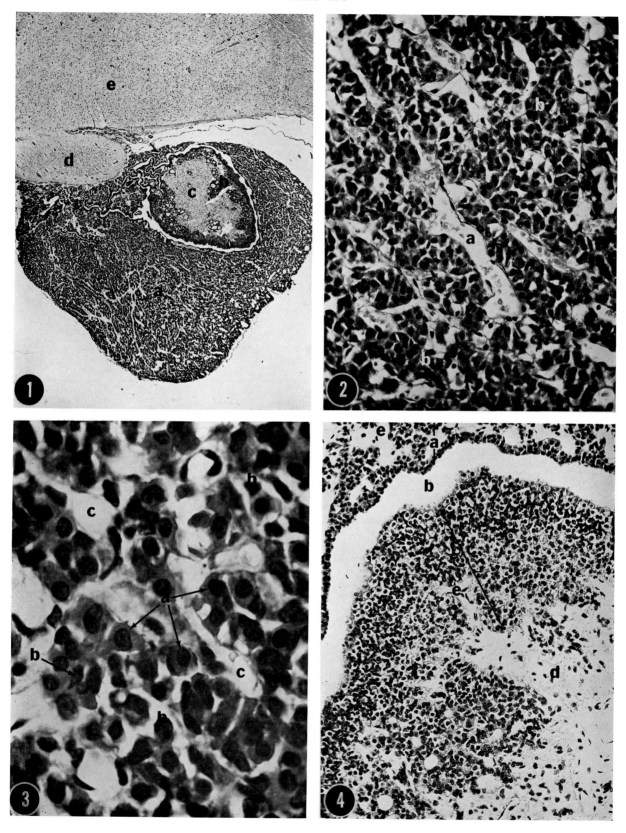

Plate 109

FIGURE 1. Pars intermedia. Cross section, Level 7. (McFarlane's trichrome X280)

    a. Neurohypophyseal cleft

    b. Pars intermedia

    c. Follicles of pars intermedia containing colloid

    d. Pars nervosa

FIGURE 2. Pars intermedia and pars nervosa. Cross section, Level 7. (McFarlane's trichrome X320)

    a. Pars intermedia

    b. Colloid containing follicles of pars intermedia

    c. Pars nervosa

    d. Sinusoid

FIGURE 3. Pars nervosa. Cross section, Level 8. (McFarlane's trichrome X330)

    a. Pars nervosa

    b. Pars intermedia

    c. Sinusoids

FIGURE 4. Pars nervosa. Cross section, Level 8. (McFarlane's trichrome X800)

    a. Pituicytes (cells of Herring)

Plate 109

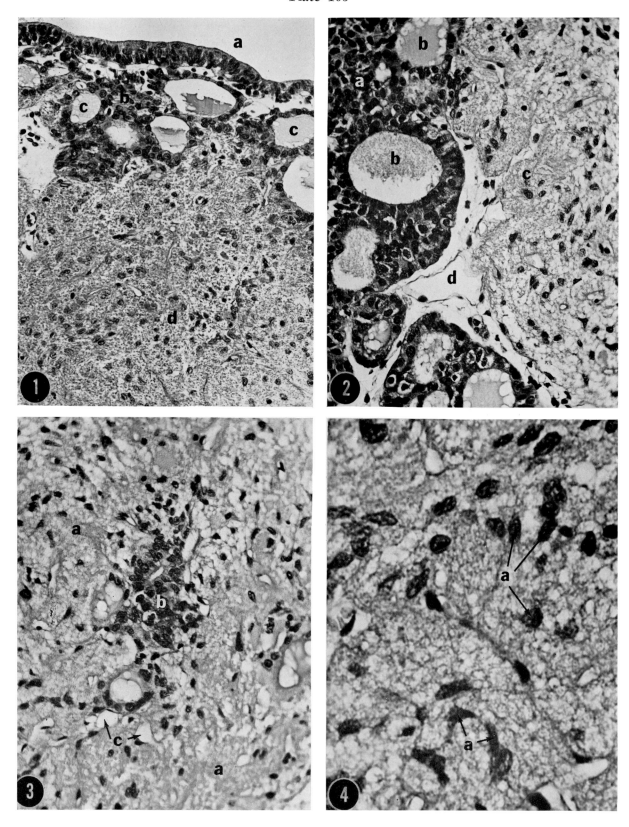

Plate 110

FIGURE 1. Thyroid gland. Cross section, Level 10. (H&E X56)
FIGURE 2. Thyroid gland. Cross section, Level 10. (H&E X420)
    a. Thyroid follicles
    b. Parenchymal cells
    c. Interstitium
FIGURE 3. Thyroid gland. Cross section, Level 10. (H&E X1100)
    a. Thyroid follicle
    b. Parenchymal cells
    c. Venule
    d. Interstitial plasma cells
    e. Arteriole
FIGURE 4. Thyroid gland. Cross section, Level 10. (H&E X1100)
    a. Interstitial fibroblasts
    b. Interstitial plasma cells
    c. Parenchymal cells

Plate 110

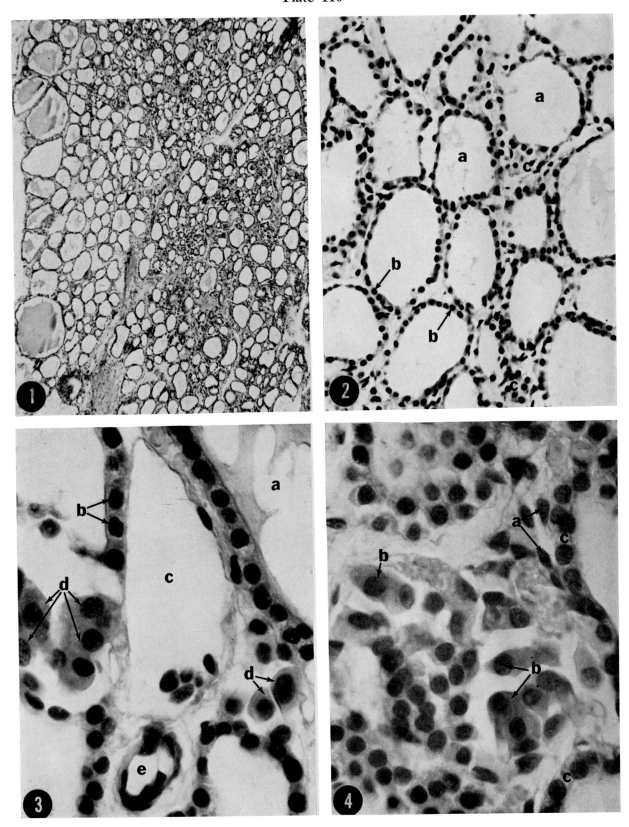

Plate 111

FIGURE 1. Parathyroid gland. Cross section, Level 9. (H&E X63)
    a. Parathyroid gland
    b. Capsule
    c. Thyroid follicles

FIGURE 2. Parathyroid gland. Cross section, Level 9. (H&E X160)
    a. Arteriole
    b. Venule
    c. Sinusoids
    d. Thyroid follicle

FIGURE 3. Parathyroid gland. Cross section, Level 9. (H&E X920)
    a. Parenchymal cells
    b. Sinusoids

FIGURE 4. Parathyroid gland. Cross section, Level 9. (H&E X1170)
    a. Sinusoids
    b. Parenchymal cells

Plate 111

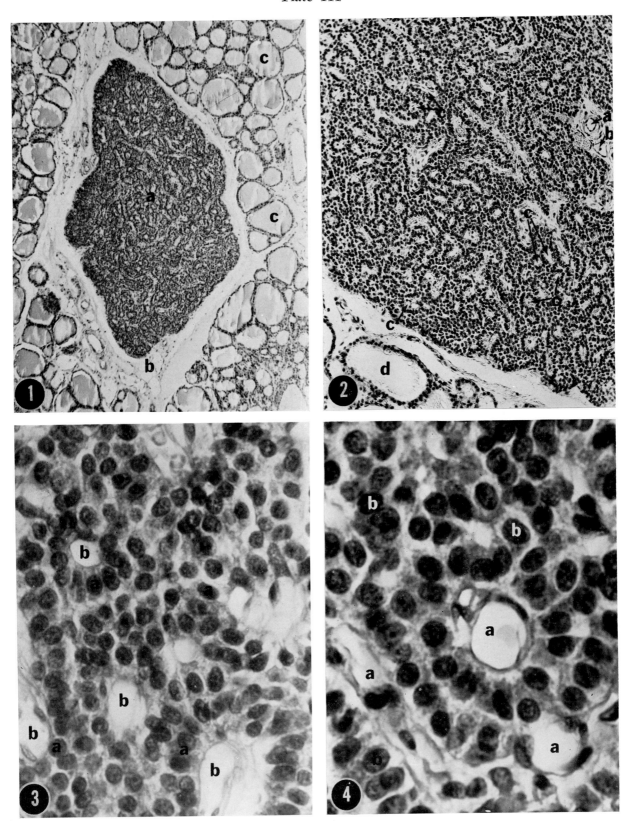

Chapter 10

Nervous System

The anatomy of the nervous system of the dog has been the subject of several texts. The emphasis, however, has been mainly on the gross anatomy, and cross sectional anatomy related to the study of the various tracts and nuclei. Basic and/or comparative histology has received little attention. Only three specific points of interest are presented here.

With the carotid sheath, the vagus nerve and the sympathetic chain form a single unit, the vagosympathetic trunk. The hippocampus (Ammon's horn) and more recently the gasserian ganglion are portions of the central nervous system of the dog which are most frequently examined for the diagnosis of rabies. In the same way, the presence of intranuclear inclusion bodies and demyelinization of the anterior medullary velum are pathologic changes which occur in canine distemper.

CENTRAL NERVOUS SYSTEM

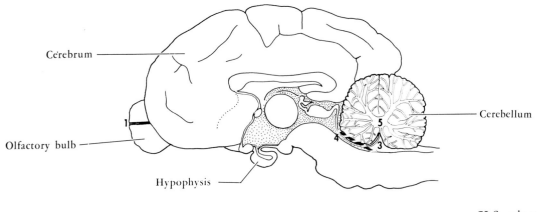

Cerebrum

Olfactory bulb

Hypophysis

Cerebellum

X-Section
Longitudinal

Midsagittal view

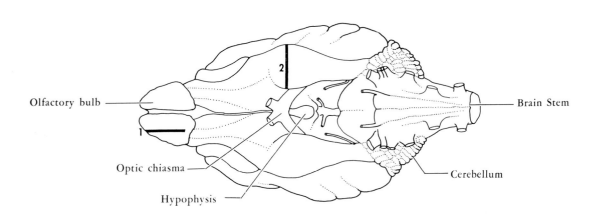

Olfactory bulb

Brain Stem

Optic chiasma

Hypophysis

Cerebellum

Ventral view

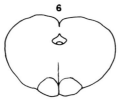

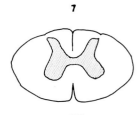

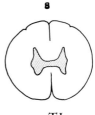

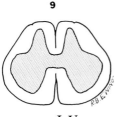

Brain stem

CI

TI

LV

Spinal cord
Plate 112

Plate 113

FIGURE 1. Vagosympathetic trunk and carotid artery. Cross section. (H&E X60)
  a. Carotid artery
  b. Carotid sheath
  c. Vagosympathetic trunk

FIGURE 2. Vagosympathetic trunk. Cross section. (H&E X210)
  a. Fasciculus
  b. Perineural septum
  c. Perineurium
  d. Arteriole
  e. Epineurium

FIGURE 3. Peripheral nerve. Longitudinal section. (H&E X150)
  a. Perineurium
  b. Endoneurium
  c. Blood vessel
  d. Myelinated nerve fibers

FIGURE 4. Peripheral nerve. Longitudinal section. (H&E X400)
  a. Schwann cell nucleus
  b. Neurolemma (sheath of Schwann)
  c. Myelinated nerve fiber
  d. Endoneurium
  e. Blood vessel

Plate 113

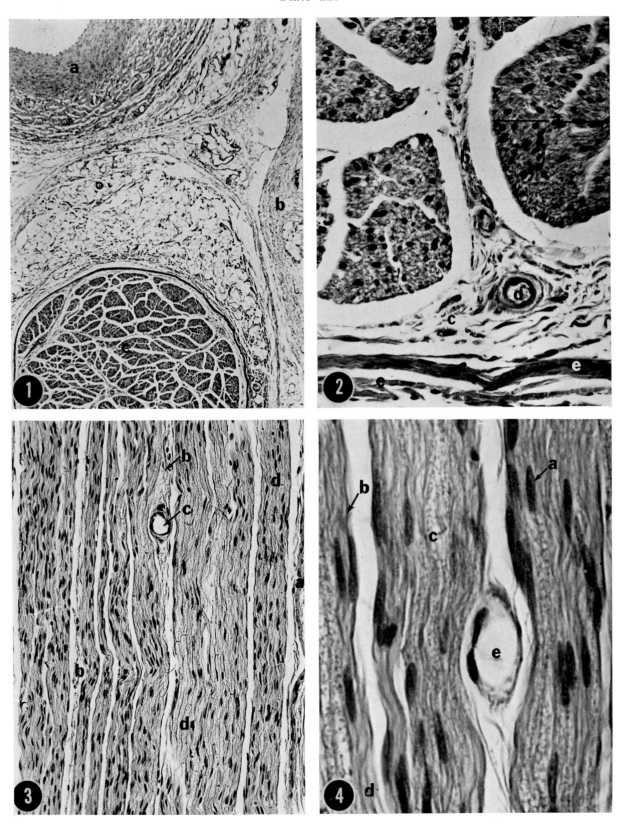

Plate 114

FIGURE 1. Autonomic ganglion. (Chromalum hematoxylin X150)
   a. Neuron cell bodies
   b. Venules
   c. Arteriole
   d. Capsule

FIGURE 2. Autonomic ganglion. (Chromalum hematoxylin X800)
   a. Nucleus of the neuron
   b. Satellite cell
   c. Endothelial nucleus
   d. Capillary
   e. Fibroblast

FIGURE 3. Sensory ganglion. (Toluidine blue X150)
   a. Neurons
   b. Capsule
   c. Interstitial connective tissue

FIGURE 4. Sensory ganglion. (Toluidine blue X400)
   a. Neurons containing Nissl substance
   b. Satellite cells
   c. Interstitial connective tissue

Plate 114

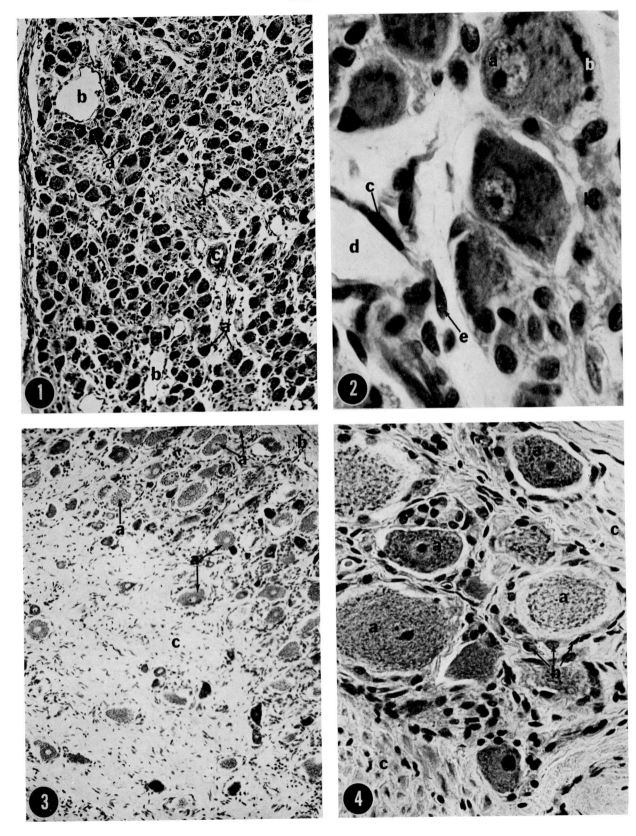

Plate 115

FIGURE 1. Brain stem at the level of sensory decussation. Cross section, Level 6. (Pal-Weigert X60)
    a. Nucleus of the spinal tract of the trigeminal nerve
    b. Medial lemniscus
    c. Pyramidal tract
    d. Hypoglossal nerve

FIGURE 2. Cervical spinal cord. Cross section, Level 7. (Pal-Weigert X70)
    See letter designations for Figure 4

FIGURE 3. Thoracic spinal cord. Cross section, Level 8. (Pal-Weigert X60)
    See letter designations for Figure 4

FIGURE 4. Lumbar spinal cord. Cross section, Level 9. (Pal-Weigert X60)
    a. Dorsal funiculus
    b. Lateral funiculus
    c. Ventral funiculus
    d. Dorsal column
    e. Intermediate column
    f. Intermediolateral column
    g. Ventral column
    h. Ventral medial fissure
    i. Dura mater
    j. Roots of spinal nerves
    k. Ventral spinal artery

Plate 115

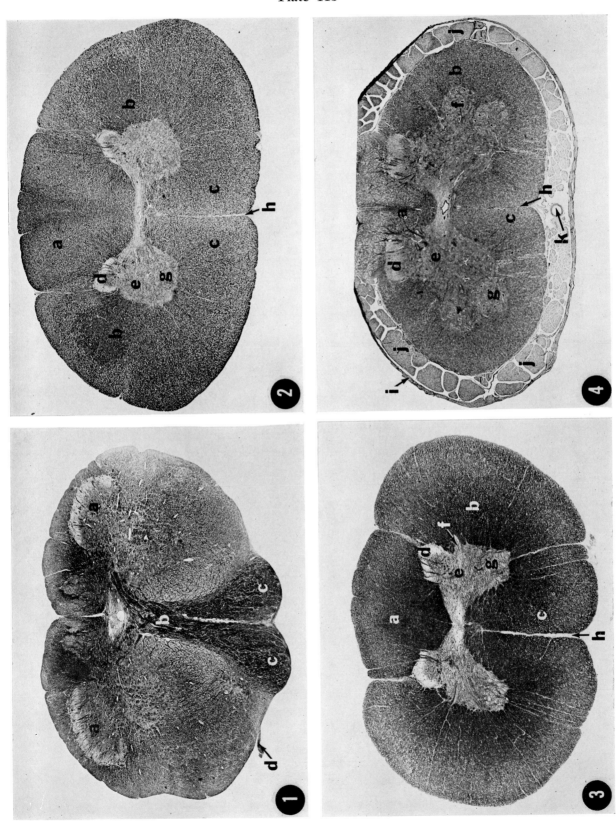

Plate 116

FIGURE 1. Ventral horn of the spinal cord. (Pal-Weigert X440)
  a. Nucleus
  b. Nucleolus
  c. Nissl substance
  d. Dendrite
  e. Glial cells
  f. Neuropil

FIGURE 2. Ventral horn of the spinal cord. (H&E X700)
  a. Soma of a multipolar neuron
  b. Blood vessels
  c. Glia cell nuclei

FIGURE 3. Central canal of spinal cord. (Pal-Weigert X260)
  a. Dorsal funiculus
  b. Dorsal commissure
  c. Ependymal cell lining of central canal. Notice cilia at arrows
  d. Ventral commissure
  e. Ventral funiculus

FIGURE 4. Spinal nerve fibers as seen in Plate 115, Figure 4. (Pal-Weigert X140)
  a. Ventrolateral funiculus
  b. Pia mater
  c. Space occupied by the myelin which has been dissolved away
  d. Axons
  e. Dura mater

Plate 116

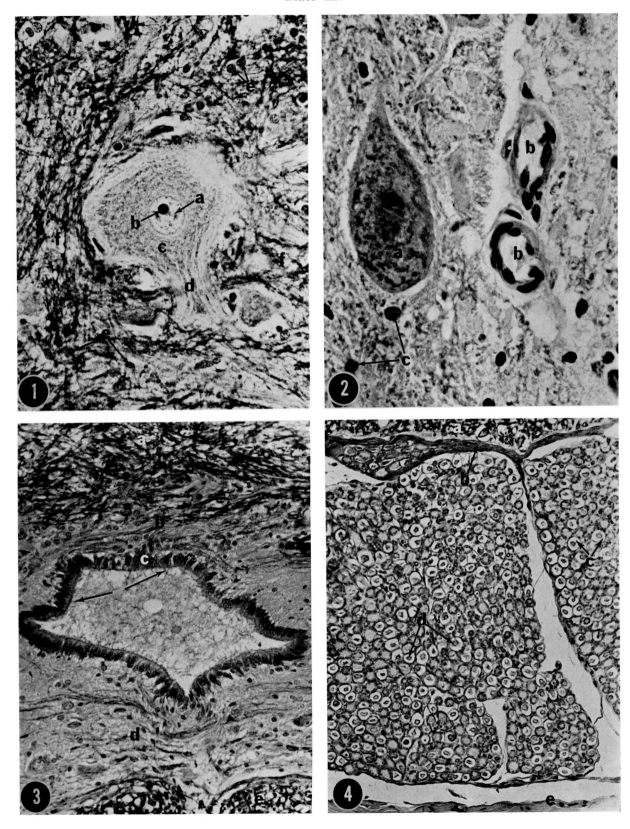

Plate 117

Figure 1. Hippocampus. Cross section, Level 2. (H&E X40)
  a. Tapetum
  b. Lateral ventricle
  c. Endoventricular alveus
  d. Fimbria
  e. Hippocampal fissure
  f. Thalamus
  g. Granular layer of the dentate gyrus
  h. Hippocampal gyrus

Figure 2. Hippocampus. Cross section, Level 2. (H&E X70)
  a. Margin of hippocampus
  b. Molecular layer
  c. Pyramidal cell layer
  d. Polymorphous cell layer
  e. Lacunar layer
  f. Endoventricular alveus
  g. Ventricular ependyma

Figure 3. Olfactory bulb. Longitudinal section, Level 1. (Pal-Weigert X90)
  a. Mitral cells in external molecular layer
  b. Lamina glomerulosa
  c. Internal molecular (plexiform) layer
  d. External molecular (plexiform) layer
  e. Olfactory tract

Figure 4. Olfactory glomerulus. Longitudinal section, Level 1. (Pal-Weigert X180)
  a. External granular layer
  b. Lamina glomerulosa
  c. Olfactory fila

Plate 117

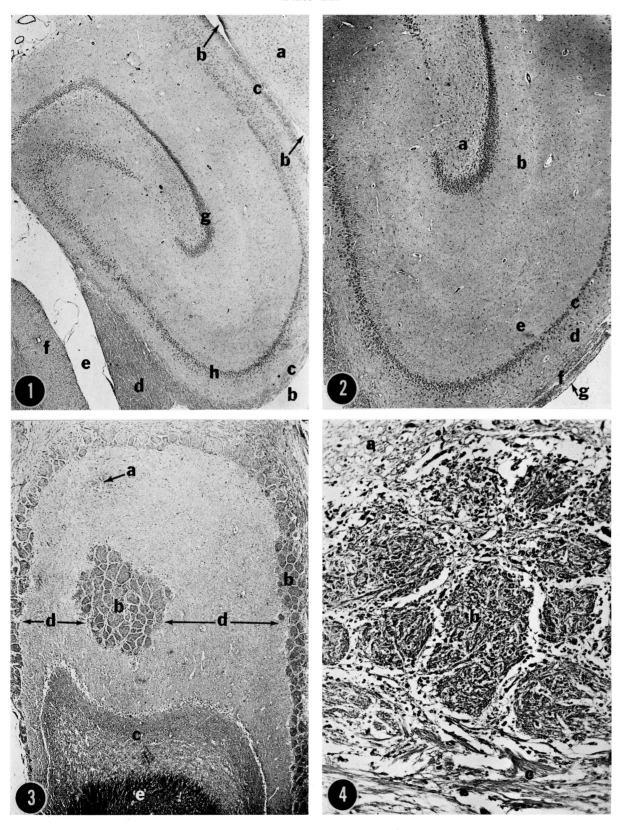

Plate 118

FIGURE 1. Choroid plexus of the fourth ventricle. Level 3. (Toluidine blue X165)
    a. Brain stem
    b. Cerebellum
    c. Tela choroidea
    d. Fourth ventricle
    e. Ependymal cells

FIGURE 2. Choroid plexus of the fourth ventricle. Level 3. (Toluidine blue X760)
    a. Ependymal cells
    b. Capillaries
    c. Fourth ventricle

FIGURE 3. Anterior medullary velum and the fourth (Trochlear) cranial nerve. Longitudinal section, Level 4. (H&E X210)
    a. Cerebellar cortex with Purkinje cells at arrows
    b. Anterior medullary velum containing the trochlear nerve
    c. Fourth ventricle
    d. Brain stem
    e. Artery
    f. Pia mater
    g. Ependymal cells

FIGURE 4. Anterior medullary velum. Level 4. (H&E X380)
    a. Trochlear nerve
    b. Fourth ventricle
    c. Ependymal cells

Plate 118

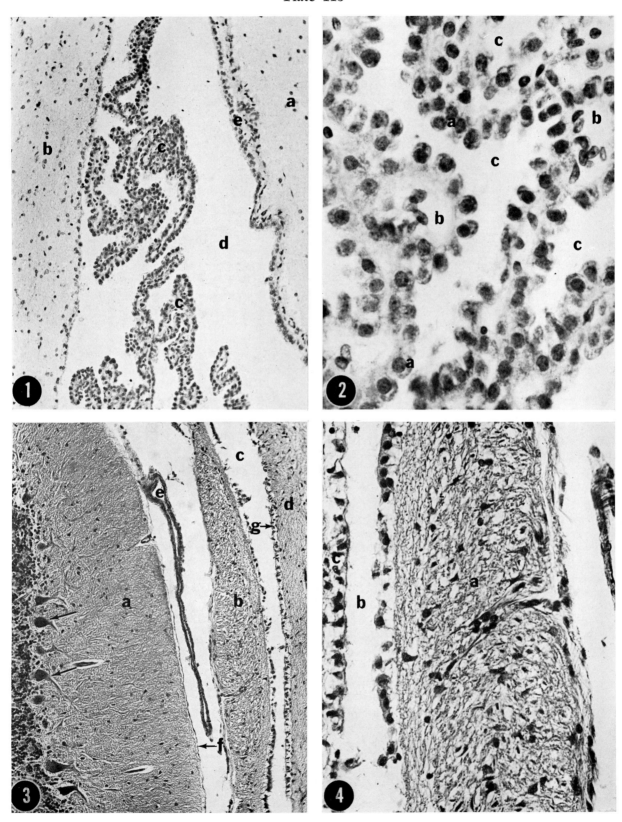

Plate 119

FIGURE 1. Folia of the cerebellum. Midsagittal section, Level 5. (Thionine X39)
   a. Cortex
   b. Core of white matter
   c. Interfolial sulcus
   d. Molecular layer
   e. Granular layer
   f. Pia mater
FIGURE 2. Portion of a cerebellar folium. Midsagittal section, Level 5. (Thionine X150)
   a. Molecular layer
   b. Intermediate layer of Purkinje cells
   c. Granular layer
   d. White matter
FIGURE 3. Cerebellar cortex. Midsagittal section, Level 5. (Thionine X375)
   a. Molecular layer
   b. Purkinje cell layer (Compare with plate 118, Figure 3)
   c. Granular layer

Plate 119

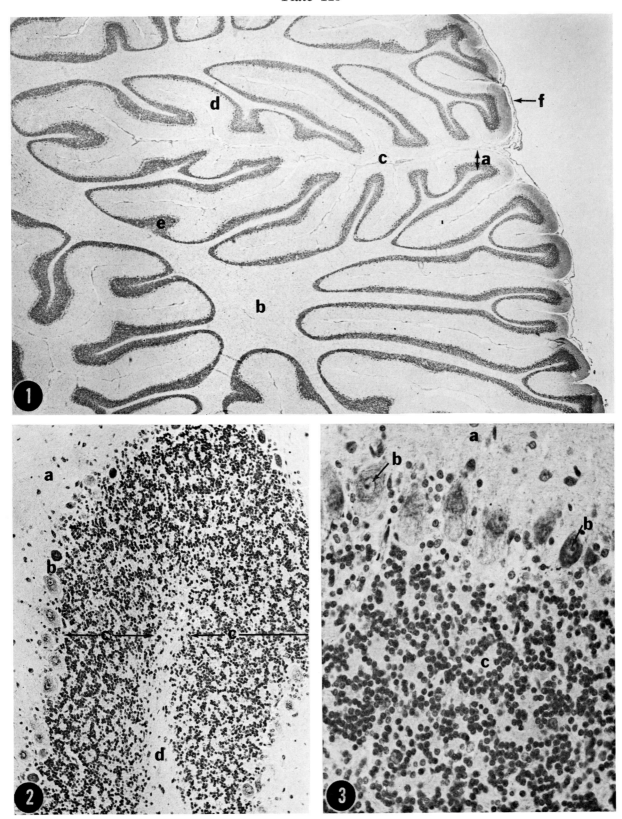

Bibliography

GENERAL REFERENCES

ANDREW, W.: *Textbook of Comparative Histology.* Oxford U. P., New York, 1959.

BRADLEY, O.C.: *Topographical Anatomy of the Dog.* Oliver and Boyd, Edinburgh, 1959.

CARLSON, W.D.: *Veterinary Radiology.* Lea & F., Philadelphia, 1967.

DOUGLAS, S.W., and WILLIAMSON, H.D.: *Principles of Veterinary Radiography.* Baillière, Tindall and Cox, London, 1963.

DUKES, H.H.: *The Physiology of Domestic Animals.* Comstock Publishing Associates, Ithaca, 1955.

ELLENBERGER, W.: *Handbuch der vergleichenden mikroskopischen Anatomie der Haustiere.* Paul Parey, Berlin, 1906-1911.

ELLENBERGER, W., and BAUM, H.: *Handbuch der vergleichenden Anatomie der Haustiere.* Revised by Otto Zietzschmann, Eberhard Ackerknecht and Hugo Grau. Springer-Verlag, Berlin, 1943.

FOX, M.W.: *Canine Pediatrics: Development, Neonatal and Congenital Diseases.* Thomas, Springfield, 1966.

GRAU, H., and WALTER, P.: *Grundriss der Histologie und vergleichende mikroskopische Anatomie der Haussäugetiere.* Paul Parey, Berlin, 1967.

KRAFT, H.: *Labor Methoden der Veterinärmedizin bei Haussäugetieren.* Parke Davis, München, 1964.

KRÖLLING, O., and GRAU, H.: *Lehrbuch der Histologie und vergleichenden mikroskopische Anatomie der Haustiere.* Paul Parey, Berlin, 1960.

LATIMER, H.B.: Variability in body and organ weights in the newborn dog and cat compared with that in the adult. *Anat Rec 157*:449-456, 1967.

MARTIN, P.: *Lehrbuch der Anatomie der Haustiere* I-IV, Schickhardt and Ebner, Stuttgart, 1912-1919.

MASON, M.M.: *Bibliography of the Dog.* Iowa State, Ames, 1959.

MILLER, M.E.: *Anatomy of the Dog.* Saunders, Philadelphia, 1964.

MÖLLENDORFF, W.v. and BARGMANN, W. (Eds.): *Handbuch de mikroskopischen Anatomie des Menschen.* Springer-Verlag, Berlin, 1929-1966, vols. 1-7. (Includes considerable comparative histology.)

MOORE, W., JR., and LAMBERT, P.D.: The chromosomes of the Beagle dog. *J Hered 54*:273-276, 1963.

NICKEL, R., SCHUMMER, A., and SEIFERLE, E.: *Lehrbuch der Anatomie der Haustiere.* Paul Parey, Berlin, 1961, vols. 1 and 2.

PRINCE, J.H.; DIESEM, C.D.; EGLITIS I., and RUSKELL, G.L.: *Anatomy and Histology of the Eye and Orbit in Domestic Animals.* Thomas, Springfield, 1960.

SCHWARZE, E.; *Kompendium der Veterinär-Anatomie.* Gustav Fischer, Jena, 1960-1966, vols. 1-5.

Note: As a general policy, titles which were listed in Mason's *Bibliography of the Dog* (1959) were omitted from our list of references. Mason compiled 303 pages of titles by author and in addition included an extensive subject index.

SISSON, S., and GROSSMAN, J.D.: *The Anatomy of the Domestic Animals.* Saunders, Philadelphia, 1953.

TEHVER, J.: Loomade Histoloogia. (Animal Histology—Estonian) Eesti Riiklik Kirjastus, Tallinn, 1962.

TRAUTMANN, A., and FIEBIGER, J.: *Fundamentals of the Histology of Domestic Animals.* Translated and revised by R.E. Habel and E.L. Biberstein. Comstock Publishing Associates, Ithaca. 1957.

WAMBERG, K.: *Radiological Atlas.* Normal and pathological pictures of dogs and cats. Medical Book Co., Copenhagen, 1966.

ZIETZSCHMANN, O.: *Lehrbuch der Entwicklungsgeschichte der Haustiere.* Richard Schoetz, Berlin, 1924.

INTEGUMENTARY SYSTEM

AOKI, T.: Stimulation of the sweat glands in the hairy skin of the dog by adrenalin, noradrenalin, acetylcholine, mecholyl and pilocarpine. *J Invest Derm,* 24:545-556, 1955.

AOKI, T., Cholinesterase activities associated with the sweat glands in the toe pads of the dog. *Nature,* Lond. 202:1124-1126, 1964.

BAKER, K.P.: Postnatal development of the dog's skin. *Brit Vet J,* 122:344-347, 1966.

BAKER, K.P.: Senile changes of dog skin. *J Small Anim Pract,* 8:49-54, 1967.

BAUM, H.: Die Lymphgefässe der Haut des Hundes. *Anat Anz,* 50:1-15, 1917.

BHARADWAJ, M.B., and CALHOUN, M.L.: Mode of formation of the preputial cavity in domestic animals. *Amer J Vet Res,* 22:764-769, 1961.

BODINGBAUER, J., and KLIMA, J.: Light and electron microscopic examination of the fine structure of dog hair (Doberman breed) with special reference to sex and environmental influences. *Mikroskopie,* 15:20-29, 1960.

BRUNSCH, A.: Vergleichende Untersuchungen am Haarkleid von Wildcaniden und Haushunden. *Z Tierzücht Zücht Biol,* 67:205-240, 1956.

CAUNA, N.L.: The mode of termination of sensory nerves and its significance. *J Comp Neurol,* 113:169-209, 1959.

CREED, R.F.S.: The histology of mammalian skin, with special reference to the dog and cat. *Vet Rec* 70:171-175, 1958.

CREED, R.F.S.: The histology of the reproductive system. The mammary glands. In Harrop, A.E. (Ed.): *Reproduction in the Dog.* Baillière, Tindall and Cox, London, 1960, pp. 57-60.

DANIEL, P.M., and PRICHARD, M.M.L.: Arterio-venous anastomoses in the external ear. *Quart J Exp Physiol,* 41:107-123, 1956.

EMERSON, J.L., and CROSS, R.F.: The distribution of mast cells in normal canine skin. *Amer J Vet Res,* 26:1379-1382, 1965.

EPLING, G.P.: The anatomy of the skin. In *Canine Medicine.* American Veterinary Publications, Evanston, 1959.

FERNANDO, S.D.A.: A histological and histochemical study of the glands of the external auditory canal of the dog. *Res Vet Sci,* 7:116-119, 1966.

GETTY, R.; BOWNE, J.G.; LOVELL, J.E.; and WHITEFORD, R.D.: Age changes in the common integument and sense organs of the dog. *J Geront,* 11:437, 1956.

GOGLIA, G.: Particolanita strutturali delle ghiandole sudoripare nei cuscinetti plantari di alcuni mammiferi. *Boll Soc Ital Biol Sper,* 28:432-433, 1952.

GOGLIA, G.: Sulla innervazione sensitiva dei cuscinetti plantari di alcuni mammiferi (cane e gatto). *Boll Soc Ital Biol Sper,* 28:433-435, 1952.

GOGLIA, G.: Ancora sulle ghiandole sudoripare dei cuscinetti plantari e digitali del cane. *Boll Soc Ital Biol Sper, 28*:1308-1309, 1952.

HANSEN, A.E.; SINCLAIR, J.G., and WIESE, H.F.: Sequence of histologic changes in skin of dogs in relation to dietary fat. *J. Nutr, 52*:541-554, 1954.

HEBRANT, G.: Sur les glandes anales du chien, anatomie, physiologie, pathologie. *Ann Méd Vét, 48*:633-641, 1899.

HILDEBRAND, M.: The integument in canidae. *J Mammal, 33*:419-428, 1952.

HUGHES, H.V., and DRANSFIELD, J.W.: The blood supply to the skin of the dog. *Brit Vet J, 115*:299-310, 1959.

HUGHES, H.V.: The Share Jones Memorial lecture. II. The skin of the dog. *Brit Vet J, 116*:4-13, 1960.

IRWIN, D.H.G.: Tension lines in the skin of the dog. *J Small Anim Pract, 7*:593-598, 1966.

IWABUCHI, T.: General sweating on the hairy skin of the dog and its mechanisms. *J Invest Derm, 49*:61-70, 1967.

KRAMER, R.P.: Histologische Untersuchungen über die senile Involution der Milchdrüsen von Hündinnen. Inaug. Diss., Hannover, 1963.

LINK, L.: Unusual skin papillae on the root of the tail of the dog. *Z Zellforsch, 56*:143-148, 1962.

LOVELL, J.E., and GETTY, R.: The hair follicle, epidermis, dermis, and skin glands of the dog. *Amer J Vet Res, 18*:873-885, 1957.

LOVELL, J.E., and GETTY, R.: The Integument. In Miller, M.E.; Christensen, G.C., and Evans, H.E.: *Anatomy of the Dog*. Saunders, Philadelphia, pp. 875-888, 1964.

MACHIDA, H.; GIACOMETTI, L., and PERKINS, E.: Histochemical and pharmacologic properties of the sweat glands of the dog. *Amer J Vet Res, 27*:566-573, 1966.

MANN, S.G.: The tylotrich (hair) follicle of the American oppossum. *Anat Rec, 160*:171-179, 1968.

MONTAGNA, W., and ELLIS, R.: Cholinergic innervation of the meibomian glands. *Anat Rec, 135*:121-127, 1959.

OHARA, K.: Die vergleichende-histologische Untersuchung der apokrinen Schweissdrüsen der weiblichen äussern Genitalien. I. Histologische Untersuchung. *Okajimas Folia Anat Jap, 31*:297-304, 1958.

OHKURA, Y.: Vergleichende-histologische Untersuchungen der Schweissdrüsen in der Haut der männlichen äusseren Genitalien beim Menschen und der Säugetieren. *Okajimas Folia Anat Jap, 31*:333-345, 1958.

OKAJIMA, K., and KANAIZUKA, Z.: Die Morphologie des Haarbalgmuskels bei den Säugetieren. *Okajimas Folia Anat Jap, 7*:445-456, 1929.

PARKS, H.F.: Morphological and cytochemical observations on the circumanal glands of dogs. Ph.D. thesis, Cornell University, Ithaca, 1950.

SCHAFFER, J.: Drüsen von einem bisher unbekannten (hepatoiden) Typus beim Hund. *Wien akad Anz*, No. 7-8, 1923.

SCHAFFER, J.: *Haut-drüsen-organe der Säugetiere*. Urban and Schwarzenberg, Berlin, 1940.

SCHWARTZMAN, R.M., and ORKIN, M.A.: A comparative study of canine and human dermatology. *Arch Derm 78*:630-636, 1958.

SCHWARTZMAN, R.M., and ORKIN, M.A.: *A Comparative Study of Skin Diseases of Dog and Man*. Thomas, Springfield, 1962.

SETOOKA, S.: Quantitative Untersuchung der Schweissdrüsen bei den Säugetieren. *Okajimas Folia Anat Jap, 31*:103-116, 1938.

SETOOKA, S.: Die Entwickelung der Schweissdrüsen in der behaarten Haut des Hundeembryos. *Okajimas Folia Anat Jap, 31*:117-125, 1958.

SILVER, I.A.: The anatomy of the mammary gland of the dog and cat. *J Small Anim Pract, 7*:689-696, 1966.

SKIBO, V.S.: Vascular system in normal skin of rabbits and dogs (Russ.) *Tr Tadzhikek Med Inst, 88*:71-74, 1967.

STIRLING, W.: Beiträge zur Anatomie der Kutis des Hundes. *Verh Kgl Sächs Ges Wiss* (Currently Akademie Wissenschaften) (Leipzig), *27*:221-233, 1875.

TAKAHARE, H., and KATO, Y.: Functional histology of the sweat gland of the dog. III. Cytological changes in the apocrine sweat gland and quantitative variation of PAS-positive materials in pharmacological stimuli. *Sci Bull Fac Agric Kyushu Univ, 22*:207-215, 1965-1966.

WAELEN, M.J.G.A.; SONNEVILLE, F., and BRAKKEE, A.J.M.: Skin and muscle circulation in dogs. In 63rd Meeting of the Netherlands Society of Dermatologists. *Dermatologica, 125*:334 (Abst.), 1962.

WALTER, P.: Die sensible Innervation des Lippen-Nasenbereiches von Rind, Schaf, Ziege, Schwein, Hund und Katze. Zur Frage der Zugehörigkeit von Empfindungsqualitaten zu bestimmten Rezeptoren des Tastsinnes. *Z Zellforsch, 53*:394-410, 1961.

WEBB, A.F., and CALHOUN, M.L.: The microscopic anatomy of the skin of mongrel dogs. *Amer J Vet Res, 15*:274-280, 1954.

WHEATLEY, V.R., and SHER, D.W.: Studies of the lipids of dog skin. I. The chemical composition of dog skin lipids. *J Invest Derm, 36*:169-170, 1961.

WIESE, H.F.; YAMANAKA, W.; COON, E., and BARBER, S.:Skin lipids of puppies as affected by kind and amount of dietary fat. *J Nutr, 89*:113-122, 1966.

WINKELMANN, R.K., and SCHMIT, R.W.: Cholinesterase in the skin of the rat, dog, cat, guinea pig and rabbit. *J Invest Derm, 33*:185-190, 1959,

ZIETZSCHMANN, O.: Vergleichend histologische Untersuchungen über den Bau der Augenlider der Haussäugetiere. *Graefes Arch Ophthal, 58*:61-122, 1904.

ZIMMERMAN, G.: The sweat glands in the dog. *Allatortvosi Lapok. 57*:16-17, 1934.

ZIMMERMANN, A.: Untersuchungen des Analtegumentes des Hundes. *Arch Wiss Prakt Tierheilk, 30*:472-515, 1904.

CARDIOVASCULAR SYSTEM

ABRAHAM, A.: *Die mikroscopische Innervation des Herzens und der Blutgefässe von Vertebraten.* Akademiai Kaido, Budapest, 1964.

ADAMS, W.E.: *The Comparative Morphology of the Carotid Body and Carotid Sinus.* Thomas, Springfield, 1958.

ASHLEY, L.: A determination of the diameters of ventricular myocardial fibers in man and other mammals. *Amer J Anat, 77*:325-363, 1945.

AYER, AA., and RAO, Y.G.: The coronary arterial patterns in some common laboratory animals: rabbit, dog and cat. *J Anat Soc India, 7*:5-8, 1958.

BAERG, R.D., and BASSETT, D.L.: Permanent gross demonstration of the conduction tissue in the dog heart with palladium iodide. *Anat Rec, 146*:313-318, 1963.

BAHR, G.F., and JENNINGS, R.B.: Ultrastructure of normal and asphyxic myocardium of the dog. *Lab Invest, 10*:548-571, 1961.

BAUM, H.: Das Lymphgefässsystem des Hundes. *Arch Wiss Prakt Tier-heilk, 44*: 521-650, 1918.

BERG, R.: Systematische Untersuchungen über das Verhalten der Äste der *Aorta abdominalis* bei Canis *familiaris. Mh Veterinaermed, 17*:307-315, 1962.

BERG, R., and SMOLLICH, A.: Systematische Untersuchungen über die Auf-
zweigung der Aa. *Subclaviae* bei *Canis familiaris. Anat Anz, 110*:410-416,
1962.

BERGSTRAND, I., and EKMAN, C.A.: Lieno-portal venography in the study of portal
circulation in the dog. *Acta Radiol*, Stockholm, *47*:257-268, 1957.

BERTHO, E.: Anatomie comparée normale des artères et des veines coronaries
du coeur de différéntes espèces animales (l'homme, le chien, le veau, le porc,
le mouton, le cheval, le chevreuil et l' original. *Arch Anat* (Strasb), *47*:283-
309, 1964.

BERTHO, E. and GAGNON, G.: Injection complète en trois dimensions, de la vascularisation coronarienne à l'aide d'une substance plastique en couleur.
Laval Med, 30:156-168, 1960.

BERTHO, E., and GAGNON, G.: A comparative study in three dimensions of the
blood supply of the normal interventricular septum in human, canine, bovine,
procine, ovine and equine heart. *Dis Chest, 46*:251-262, 1964.

BLAIR, E.: Anatomy of the ventricular coronary arteries in the dog. *Cir Res,
9*:333-341, 1961.

BLOOR, C.M., and LOWMAN, R.M.: Radiological anatomy of coronary arteries of
the dog. *Circ Res, 11*:36-46, 1962.

BÖHME, G.: Die Herzbeutel-Zwerchfell-Verbindung beim Hund. *Anat Anz,
115*:83-88, 1964.

BONGARTZ, G.: Über Struktur und Funktion der vena cava caudalis bie Rind,
Schaf, Pferd, Schwein und Hund. *Z Zellforsch, 48*:24-50, 1958.

BOUCEK, R.J.; TAKASHITA, R., and FOJACO, R.: Relation between microanatomy
and functional properties of the coronary arteries (Dog). *Anat Rec, 147*:199-
207, 1963.

BOUCEK, R.J.; FOJACO, R., and TAKASHITA, R.: Anatomic considerations for regional intimal changes in the coronary arteries. *Anat Rec, 148*:161-169, 1964.

BOUCEK, R.J.; TAKASHITA, R., and FOJACO, R.: Functional anatomy of the ascending aorta and the coronary ostia (Dog). *Amer J Anat, 114*:273-282, 1964.

BROWN, R.E.: The pattern of the microcirculatory bed in the ventricular myocardium of domestic mammals. *Amer J Anat, 116*:355-373, 1965.

CALLOW, A.D.: The vascular anatomy and collateral circulation of the hind-
quarters of the dog. *Exp Med Surg, 7*:99-117, 1949.

CARROW, R., and CALHOUN, M.L.: The extent of cardiac muscle in the great
veins of the dog. *Anat Rec, 150*:249-256, 1964.

CHAUDHRY, M.S.: Histochemical localization of sino-atrial node in the rat and
dog. *Anat Rec, 142*:222, 1962.

CHRISTENSEN, G.C., and CAMPETI, F.L.: Anatomic and functional studies of the
coronary circulation in the dog and pig. *Amer J Vet Res, 20*:18-26, 1959.

CHRISTENSEN, G. C.: The blood supply to the interventricular septum of the
heart—a comparative study. *Amer J Vet Res, 23*:869-874, 1962.

CHUNGCHAROEN, D.; DEBURGH DALY, M., and SCHWEITZER, A.: The blood supply
of the carotid body in cats, dogs and rabbits. *J Physiol, 117*:347-358, 1952.

COLERIDGE, J.C.G.; HEMINGWAY, A.; HOLMES, R.L., and LINDEN, R.J.: The location of atrial receptors in the dog: a physiological and histological study.
J Physiol, 136:174-197, 1957.

DAY, S.B.: A left coronary artery originating from a single coronary stem in a
dog. *Anat Rec, 134*:55-59, 1959.

DEKOCK, L.L.: The sinusoids of the carotid body tissue as part of the reticulo-
endothelial system. *Acta Anat, 42*:213-226, 1960.

DE LA TORRE, E.; MITCHELL, O.C.; and NETSKY, M.G.: Anatomic and angiographic study of the vertebral-basilar arterial system in the dog. *Amer J Anat, 110*: 187-197, 1962.

DIGULIELMO, L.; BALDRIGHI, V.; MONTEMARTINI, C., and SCHIFINO, A.: Roentgen investigation of the coronary veins in the dog. *Acta Radiol, 53*:191-200, 1960.

ELISKOVA, M., and ELISKA, O.: Subepicardiac veins of the dog's heart and their anastomoses. *Acta Univ Carol* (Med) (Praha), *12*:21-30, 1966.

EL ETREBY, M.F.: Zur Orthologie und Pathologie der Glomera digitalia, der sog. arterio-venösen Anastomosen in den Extremitätenenden des Hundes. Inaug. Diss., Munich, 1963.

FEDORVA, A.G.: The receptors of the main veins of the limbs in dogs and monkeys. *Biull Eksp Biol Med, 46*:857-861, 1958.

FERNANDES, F.A., and BORELLI, V.: Blood supply to the sinuatrial node in dogs. *Arq Inst Biol* (S. Paulo), *33*:119-124, 1966.

FISCHER, G.M., and LLAURADO, J.G.: Collagen and elastin content of canine arteries selected from functionally different vascular beds. *Circ Res, 19*: 394-399, 1966.

FLORENTIN, P., and NAGHAVI, M.: Particularities anatomiques du systeme porte du chien. *Rec Med Vet Ecole d'Alfort, 136*:85-94, 1960.

FORBES, M.: Peripheral Blood Leucocyte Karyotype Analysis of Ten Breeds of Dogs (*Canis familiaris*). M.S. thesis, Michigan State University, East Lansing, 1964.

FRANKLIN, K.J.: *A Monograph on Veins.* Thomas, Springfield, 1937.

FRATER, R.W.M., and ELLIS, JR., F.H.: The anatomy of the canine mitral valve. With notes on function and comparisons with other mammalian mitral valves. *J Surg Res, 1*:171-178, 1961.

FURUHATTA, K.: Studies on *sinus arteriae carotis interna* in dogs. *Vet Res Japan, 1*:176-178, 1954.

GRAU, H.: Ein Beitrag zur Histologie und Altersanatomie der Lymphgefässe des Hundes. Z. *Mikr Anat Forsch, 25*:207-237, 1931.

HAMLIN, R.L.: Radiographic anatomy of heart and great vessels in healthy living dogs. *J Amer Vet Med Ass, 136*:265-273, 1960.

HAMLIN, R.L.; SMITH, C.R., and SMETZER, D.L.: Ostium secundum type interatrial defects in the dog. *J Amer Vet Med Ass, 143*:149-157, 1963.

HARA, T.: Morphological and histochemical studies on the cardiac conduction system of the dog. *Arch Histol Jap, 28*:227-246, 1967.

HARKNESS, M.L.R.; HARKNESS, R.D., and McDONALD, D.A.: The collagen and elastin content of the arterial wall of the dog. *Proc Roy Soc* (*Biol*), *146*:541-551, 1957.

HEGEDUS, S.A., and SCHACKLEFORD, R.T.: A comparative-anatomical study of the cranio-cervical venous system in mammals, with special reference to the dog: relationship of anatomy to measurements of cerebral blood flow. *Amer J Anat, 116*:375-386, 1965.

HERMAN, L.; STUCKEY, J.H., and HOFFMAN, B.F.: Electron microscopy of Purkinje fibers and ventricular muscle of dog heart. *Circulation, 24*:954-955, 1961.

HIGGINBOTHAM, F.H.: Ventricular coronary arteries of beagles. *J Atheroscler Res, 6*:474-488, 1966.

HIGGINBOTHAM, F.H., and HIGGINBOTHAM, A.C.: Histochemical study of beagle aorta. *J Atheroscler Res, 7*:89-102, 1967.

HIGGINBOTHAM, F.H., and HIGGINBOTHAM, A.C.: Histochemical differentiation in beagle aorta. *J Atheroscler Res, 8*:37-43, 1968.

HIRSCH, E.F.; NIGH, C.A.; KAYE, M.P., and COOPER, T.: Terminal innervation of the heart. II. Studies of the perimysial innervation apparatus and of the sensory receptors in the rabbit and in the dog with the techniques of total extrinsic denervation, bilateral, cervical vagotomy, and bilateral thoracic sympathectomy. *Arch Path, 77*:172-187, 1964.

HÖGLUND, R.: An ultrastructural study of the carotid body of horse and dog. *Z Zellforsch, 76*:568-576, 1967.

HOLMES, R.L.: Structures in the atrial endocardium of the dog which stain with methylene blue, and the effects of unilateral vagotomy. *J Anat, 91*:259-266, 1957.

HOLMES, K.R., and BROWN, R.E.: Postnatal changes in the terminal vascular bed of the canine ventricular myocardium. M.S. thesis, Michigan State University. *Anat Rec, 157*:261 (Abst.), 1967.

HOLT, J.P.; RHODE, E.A.; PEOPLES, S.A., and KINES, H.: Left ventricular function in mammals of greatly different size (horse, ox, pig, dog). *Circ Res, 10*:798-806, 1962.

HOUSE, E.W., and EDERSTROM, H.E.: Anatomical changes with age in the heart and ductus arteriosus in the dog after birth. *Anat Rec, 160*:289-295, 1968.

INTONTI, F.; NYLANDER, G., and TJERNBERG, B.: Lymph vessels of the greater omentum. *Vasc Dis, 1*:203-205, 1964.

ITO, T.: Anatomical, histological and experimental studies on the nerves innervating the heart of the dog. *Fukushima J Med Sci, 17*:180-181, 1960.

JAIN, S.P., and HAZARY, S.: Coronary arterial patterns in man and some other mammals. *J Anat Soc India, 7*:1-4, 1958.

JAMES, T.N.: Anatomy of the sinus node of the dog. *Anat Rec, 143*:251-265, 1962.

JAMES, T.N.: Anatomy of the A-V node of the dog. *Anat Rec, 148*:15-28, 1964.

JAMES, T.N.; SHERF, L.; FINE, G., and MORALES, A.R.: Comparative ultrastructure of the sinus node in man and dog. *Circulation, 34*:139-163, 1966.

JAMES, T.N., and SHERF, L.: Ultrastructure of myocardial cells. *Amer J Cardiol, 22*:389-416, 1968.

JAMIESON, J.D., and PALADE, G.E.: Specific granules in atrial muscle cells. *J Cell Biol, 23*:151-172, 1964.

KAWAMURA, K.: Electron microscope studies on the cardiac conduction system of the dog. I. The Purkinje fiber. *Jap Circ J, 25*:594-616, 1961.

KERSHNER, D.; HOOTON, T.C., and SHEARER, E.M.: Production of experimental portal hypertension in the dog; anatomy of the hepatic veins in the dog. *Arch Surg, 53*:425-434, 1946.

KIM, M.L.; HAHN, R.S., and BECK, C.S.: La revascularisation du myocarde par arterialisation du systeme veineux coronaire. III. Histologie du coeur et des vaisseaux coronaires apres revascularisation chez le chien. *Rev Chir* (Par), *90*:151-166, 1952.

LATIMER, H. B.: Weights of the ventricular walls of the heart in the adult dog. *Univ Kans Sci Bull, 42*:3-11, 1961.

LATIMER, H.B.: The weight and thickness of the two ventricular walls in the newborn dog heart. *Anat Rec, 152*:225-229, 1965.

LEEDS, S.E.; UHLEY, H.N.; SAMPSON, J.J., and FRIEDMAN, M.: A new method for measurement of lymph flow from the right duct in the dog. *Amer J Surg, 98*:211-216, 1959.

LUMB, G.L.; SHACKLETT, R.S., and DAWKINS, W.A.: The cardiac conduction tissue and its blood supply in the dog. *Amer J Path, 35*:467-487, 1959.

McKibben, J.S., and Christensen, G.C.: The venous return from the interventricular system of the heart: A comparative study. *Amer J Vet Res, 25*:512-517, 1964.

Meek, W.J.; Keenan, M., and Theisen, H.J.: The auricular blood supply in the dog; general auricular supply with special reference to the sinoauricular node. *Amer Heart J, 4*:591-599, 1929.

Michel, G.: Zur mikroskopischen Anatomie der Purkinjefasern in Herzen des Schweines und des Hundes. *Mh Veterinaermed, 17*:848-850, 1962.

Michell, G., and Jefferson, K.: Angiography of the coronary circulation in living dogs using timed diastolic injections. *Brit Heart J, 24*:11-16, 1962.

Miller, A.J.; Pick, R., and Katz, L.N.: Lymphatics of the mitral valve of the dog. Demonstration and discussion of the possible significance. *Circ Res, 9*:1005-1009, 1961.

Mizeres, N.J.: The course of the left cardioinhibitory fibers in the dog. *Anat Rec, 127*:109-117, 1957.

Mizeres, N.J.: The origin and course of the cardioaccelerator fibers in the dog. *Anat Rec, 132*:261-279, 1958.

Moir, T.W., and Eckstein, R.W.: Venous drainage of the septal artery of the dog. *Circulation, 22*:790-791, 1960.

Moniz de Bettencourt, J.; Silvia Carvalho, J.; Pulido Valente, J.L., and Rato, J.A.: L'anatomie de l'artére hépatique du chien au point de vue physiologique. *CR Soc Biol (Paris), 155*:1613-1616, 1961.

Montgomery, R.L.; Reese, D.J.; Ellis, F.W., and Hooker, C.W.: Motor innervation of the superior vena cava of the dog. *Anat Rec, 157*:289-290 (Abst.), 1967.

Moore, D.H., and Ruska, H.: Electron microscope study of mammalian cardiac muscle cells. *J Biophys Biochem Cytol, 3*:261-268, 1957.

Morehead, R.P., and Little, J.M.: Changes in the blood vessels of apparently healthy mongrel dogs. *Amer J Path 21*:339-355, 1945.

Muratori, G.: Contributi allo studio della struttura microscopica del seno carotideo nell'uomo e in alcuni mammiferi. *Anat Anz 119*:466-479, 1966.

Nandy, K., and Bourne, G.H.: A study of the morphology of the conducting tissue in mammalian hearts. *Acta Anat, 53*:217-226, 1963.

Napolitano, L.M.; Willman, V.L.; Hanlon, C.R., and Cooper, T.: Intrinsic innervation of the heart. *Amer J Physiol, 208*:455-458, 1965.

Neill, S.A.; Gaisford, W.D., and Zuidema, G.D.: A comparative anatomic study of the hepatic veins in the dog, monkey and human. *Surg Gynec Obstet, 116*:451-456, 1963.

Nickel, R., and Wissdorf, H.: Vergleichende Betrachtung der Arterien an der Schultergliedmasse der Haussäugetiere. *Zbl Veterinaermed, 11A*:265-292, 1964.

Nonidez, J.F.: Arterio-venous anastomoses in the sympathetic chain ganglia of the dog. *Anat Rec, 82*:593-607, 1942.

Northup, D.W.; Van Liere, E.J., and Stickney, J.C.: The effect of age, sex and body size on the heart weight-body weight ratio in the dog. *Anat Rec, 128*:411-417, 1957.

Nylander, G., and Olerud, S.: The distribution of the vasa vasorum in abdominal aorta and the vena cava inferior in dogs. *Angiology, 11*:522-529, 1960.

Otsuka, N., Hara, T., and Okamoto, H.: Histotopochemische Untersuchungen am Reizleitungs system des Hundeherzens. *Histochemie, 10*:66-73, 1967.

Papez, J.W.: Heart musculature of the atria. *Amer J Anat, 27*:255-285, 1920.

PAULICK, H-J.: Venen der Vordergliedmasse des Hundes. Inaug. Diss., Hannover, 1967.

PHILLIPS, C.E., JR.; DEWEESE, J.A.; MANNING, J.A., and MAHONEY, E.B.: Maturation of small pulmonary arteries in puppies. *Circ Res,* 8:1268-1273, 1960.

PREUSS, F., and MULLER, W.: Die Ursprungsgefässe der Vasa digitalia des Hundes, ein Beitrag zur vergleichend-anatomischen Bezeichnung der Hand- und Fussgefässe. *Berlin Munchen Tierarztl Wschr,* 78:281-283, 1965.

PRICE, Z.; EIDE, B.; PRINTZMETAL, M., and CARPENTER, C.: Ultrastructure of the dog cardiac muscle cell. *Circ Res,* 7:858-865, 1959.

PRIER, J.E.; SCHAFFER, B., and SKELLEY, J.F.: Direct lymphangiography in the dog. *J Amer Vet Med Ass,* 140:943-947, 1962.

POBERAI, M.; GELLERT, A.; NAGY, I.; LIPPAI, J.; KOZMA, M., and NAGY, S.: Vergleichende histologische Untersuchungen über die Struktur der Wand der Lymphgefässe. III. Histologische Struktur der Wand der peripherisch Lymphgefässe. *Acta Morph Acad Sci Hung,* 11:229-238, 1962.

PTOKHOV, M.P.: The endothelium of the cardiac valves in cats, dogs and monkeys. *Arkh Anat,* 42:29-34, 1962.

RAKUSAN, K., and DU MESNIL DE ROCHEMONT, W.: Capillaries in heart and skeletal muscle of dog and rabbit. *Proc Soc Exp Biol Med,* 124:838-840, 1967.

REINHARD, K.R.; MILLER, M.E., and EVANS, H.E.: The craniovertebral veins and sinuses of the dog. *Amer J Anat,* 111:67-87, 1962.

RHODES, W.H.; PATTERSON, D.F., and DETWEILER, D.K.: Radiographic anatomy of the canine heart. *J Amer Vet Med Ass,* 137:283-389, 1960.

RODRIQUES, A.: Thoracic duct in dogs. *XII Congr Ont Zool Lesbonne,* 2:702-710 (Fr.), 1935.

RODRIQUEZ, F.L.; ROBBINS, S.L., and BANASIEWICZ, M.: The descending septal artery in human, porcine, equine, ovine bovine and canine hearts. A postmortem angiographic study. *Amer Heart J.* 62:247-259, 1961.

RÜMPLER, G.: Venen am Kopf des Hundes. Inaug. Diss., Hannover, 1967.

RYBACK, R.S., and MIZERES, N.J.: Histology of the nodal artery in the dog and man. *Anat Rec,* 148:398 (Abst.), 1964.

SAKUMA, S.: Electron microscopic studies on arterial blood vessels of the spleen, especially on their relationship to the reticuloendothelial system. *Tohoku J Exp Med,* 94:23-25, 1968.

SATO, H.: Innervation of heart in dog. *Tohoku J Exp Med,* 59:343-356, 1954.

SCHNEIDER, H.P.; TRUEX, R.C., and KNOWLES, J.O.: Comparative observations of the hearts of mongrel and greyhound dogs. *Anat Rec,* 149:173-179, 1964.

SCHULZE, W.: Elektronenmikroskopische Untersuchung des embryonalen Hunderherzmuskels. *Z Mikr Anat Forsch,* 68:271-284, 1961.

SCOTT, E.B.: Cardiac muscle: The ultrastructure (in man, dog, rat). *Minn Med* 48:1292-1295, 1965.

SEIDEL, W.; AKUTSU, T.; MIRKOVITCH, V., and KOLFF, W.J.: A mitral valve prosthesis and a study of the thrombosis on heart valves in dogs. *J Surg Res,* 2:168-175, 1962.

SERAFINI-FRACASSINI, A., and FRASSON, P.: Histochemical observations on the carotid body of the dog. *Acta Anat,* 63:240-248, 1966.

SERAFINI-FRACASSINI, A., and VOLPIN, D.: Some features of the vascularization of the carotid body in the dog. *Acta Anat,* 63:571-579, 1966.

SHERIDAN, J.P.: The canine heart. The results of 100 random autopsies. *J Small Anim Pract,* 8:373-381, 1967.

SHEVCHUK, M.G.: Experimental plasticity of the coronary arteries. Anastomoses between the coronary arteries occurring normally in the dog. *Arkh Anat,* 38:80-83, 1960; *Referat Zh Biol,* No. 1611223, 1961.

SKELLEY, J.F.; PRIER, J.E., and KOEHLER, R.: Applications of direct lymphangiography in the dog. *Amer J Vet Res,* 25:747-755, 1964.

SMIRNOV, A.D.: The structure of the wall of the common carotid and femoral arteries of dogs. *Dokl Akad Nauk SSSR,* 103:705-708, 1955.

SMOLLICH, A., and BERG, R.: Beobachtung über das Verhalten der Äste des Aortenbogens bei *Canis familiaris, Felis domestica* and *Sus scrofa domesticus. Anat Anz, 107*:309-316, 1959.

SOKOLOV, V.V.: Blood supply of cardiac valves in some predatory animals (Russ.), *Arkh Anat,* 52:93-96, 1967.

SOMMER, J.R., and JOHNSON, E.A.: Cardiac muscle. A comparative study of Purkinje fibers and ventricular fibers. *J Cell Biol,* 36:497-526, 1968.

STENGER, R.J., and SPIRO, D.: The ultrastructure of mammalian cardiac muscle. *J Biophys Biochem Cytol,* 9:325-351, 1961.

SXKANDERA, J.: Studies on the blood vessels supplying the wall of the thoracic aorta in experimental animals. *Folia Morphol* (Warsz), *26*:383-392, 1967.

TERNER, I.M.: Data on the comparative anatomy of the lymphatic system in the anterior extremities of mammals. *Proceedings of the Sixth All-Union meeting of anatomists, histologists and embryologists,* 1958. *Khar'kov. 1*:491-493, 1960; *Referat Zh Biol,* No. 221196, 1962.

THOMAS, C.E.: The muscular architecture of the ventricles of hog and dog hearts. *Amer J Anat, 101*:17-57, 1957.

THOMAS, C.E.: The muscular architecture of the atria of hog and dog hearts. *Amer J Anat, 104*:207-236, 1959.

TRUEX, R.C., and WARSHAW, L.J.: The incidence and size of the moderator band. *Anat Rec, 82*:361-372, 1942.

TRUEX, R. C., and ANGULO, A.W.: Comparative study of the arterial and venous systems of the ventricular myocardium with special reference to the coronary sinus. *Anat Rec, 113*:467-492, 1952.

TSAREV, N.I.: The sources of innervation of facial veins (Russ.). *Arkh Anat,* 52:67-72, 1967.

TUCKER, J.L., JR., and KREMENTZ, E.T.: Anatomical corrosion specimens. I. Heart-lung models prepared from dogs. *Anat Rec, 127*:655-665, 1957.

TUSKUMA, K.: Study on the innervation of large arteries. *Osaka City Med J,* 9:4295-4304, 1960.

UHLEY, H.N., and RIVKIN, L.: Peripheral distribution of the canine A-V conduction system. Observations on gross morphology. *Amer J Cardiol,* 5:688-691, 1960.

UHLEY, H.N.; REICH, S.B., and RIVKIN, L.: Radioautography of the conduction system of the dog's heart with I[131]. *Amer J Physiol,* 198:859-860, 1960.

VANBREENEN, V.L.: Intercalated discs of heart muscle studied by the electron microscope. *Anat Rec, 117*:49-63, 1953.

VITUMS, A.: Portal veins in the dog. *Zbl Veterinaermed,* 6:723-741, 1959.

VITUMS, A.: Anomalous origin of the right subclavian and common carotid arteries in the dog. *Cornell Vet,* 52:5-15, 1962.

VITUMS, A.: Die Anastomosen zwischen der Pfortader und dem Hohlvenensystem unter Berücksichtigung ihrer funktionellen Bedeutung bei den Haustieren, insbesondere beim Hund. *Berlin Muncher Tierarztl Wschr,* 76: 335-339, 1963.

WALKER, W.F.; MacDONALD, J.S., and PICKARD, C.: Hepatic vein sphincter mechanism in the dog. *Brit J Surg, 48*:218-220, 1960.

WALTER, P.: Die Röntgenstereoskopie nach der Methode von Prof. Dr. A. Hasselwander in der Veterinäranatomie mit Untersuchungen an Herz und Zwerchfell des Hundes. *Anat Anz, 103*:38-56, 1956.

WIEBOLDT, A.: Venen der Körperwand des Hundes und der Katze. Inaug. Diss., Hannover, 1966.

WOOLLARD, H.H.: The innervation of the heart. *J Anat, 60*:345-373, 1926.

WOODRUFF, C.E.: Studies on the vasa vasorum. *Amer J Path, 2*:567-569, 1926.

WOODWARD, K.T.; BERMAN, A.R.; MICHAELSON, S.M.; and ODLAND, L.T.: Plasma, erythrocyte and whole blood volume in the normal beagle. *Amer J Vet Res, 29*:1935-1944, 1968.

YAMAGISHI, T.: Fine structure of lymph vessels in the abdominal wall of the diaphragm of dogs, and their attitude following absorption of China ink. *Nagoya Med J, 7*:1-6, 1961.

YOKOYAMA, H.O.; JENNINGS, R.B., and WARTMAN, W.B.: Intercalated disks of dog myocardium. *Exp Cell Res, 23*:29-44, 1961.

YOSHIKAWA, T., and SUZUKI, T.: On the anatomical study of the intercostal artery in the dog. *Jap J Vet Sci, 22*:541, 1960.

LYMPHATIC ORGANS

BERENDES, M.: The proportion of reticulocytes in the erythrocytes of the spleen as compared with those of circulating blood, with special references to hemolytic states. *Blood, 14*:558-563, 1959.

CHRETIEN, P.B.; BEHAR, R.J; KOHN, Z.; MOLDOVANU, G.; MILLER, D.G., and LAWRENCE, W. JR.: The canine lymphoid system: A study of the effect of surgical excision. *Anat Rec, 159*:5-15, 1967.

CHRISCENTI, G.: Rapporti tra ghiandole a secrezione interna e anello lingatico di Waldeyer. II. Ancora sugli aspetti morfologici della tonsilla palatina di cane in sequito a somministrazione di cortisone. *Otorinolaryng Ital, 22*:67-80, 1954.

FINSTAD, J.; PAPERMASTER, B.W., and GOOD, R.A.: Evolution of the immune response. II. Morphologic studies on the origin of the thymus and organized lymphoid tissue. *Lab Invest, 13*:490-512, 1964.

GALINDO, B., and FREEMAN, J.A.: Fine structure of splenic pulp. *Anat Rec, 147*:25-41, 1963.

GODWIN, M.C.: The mammalian thymus. IV. The development in the dog. *Amer J Anat, 64*:165-201, 1939.

HAYES, T.G.: The embryonic development of ellipsoids in the spleen. *Amer J Vet Res, 29*:1245-1250, 1968.

JACOBSEN, G.D.: Studies on the structure and function of ellipsoid sheaths of dog and cat spleens. *Diss Abstr, 26*:5642, 1966.

KRIVSKY, I.L.: Age structural characteristics of regional lymphatic nodes in dog (Russ.). *Arkh Anat 53*:25-34, 1967.

KARBE, E.: The development of the cranial lymph nodes in the dog. *Anat Anz, 116*:155-164, 1965.

KELLY, W.D.: The thymus and lymphoid morphogenesis in the dog. *Fed Proc, 22*:600, 1963.

LATIMER, H.B.: The prenatal growth of the dog spleen. *Growth, 16*:47-54, 1952.

LAUDE, M., and LIBERSA, C.: Lesveins anastomotiques du hile de la rate du chien. Anatomie descriptive. *C.R. Assoc Anat,* (Paris) *132*:630-639, 1966.

LENTZ, W.J., and LEE, D.G.: The tonsillar tissue of the dog. *Vet Extens Q*, *105*:23-26, 1947.

LEWIS, O.J.: The blood vessels of the adult mammalian spleen. *J. Anat*, *91*:245-250, 1957.

LORBER, M.: The splenic hemogram of the unanesthetized dog. *Proc Soc Exp Biol Med*, *113*:173-176, 1963.

MALL, F.P.: The branchial clefts of the dog with special reference to the origin of the thymus gland. *Johns Hopkins Univ Biol Lab*, *4*:193-216, 1888.

MALL, F.P.: On the circulation through the pulp of the dog's spleen. *Amer J Anat*, *2*:315-332, 1903.

MEDUEDEUA, M.P.: Age features and accidental changes in the thymus gland of the dog. *SB Nauch Tr Vitebskogo Med Inst*, *11*:29-35, 1964.

MEYER, A.W.: The occurrence of supernumerary spleens in dogs and cats, with observations on *corpora libera abdominalis*. IV. Studies on hemal nodes. *Anat Rec*, *8*:147-172, 1914.

MILLS, E.S.: The vascular arrangements of the mammalian spleen. *Quart J Exp Physiol*, *16*:301-319, 1926.

PINES, L., and MAJMAN, R.: The innervation of the thymus. *J Nerv Ment Dis*, *69*:361-384, 1929.

SHIER, K.J.: The morphology of the epithelial thymus: Observation on the lymphocyte depleted and fetal thymus. *Lab Invest*, *12*:316-326, 1963.

SMITH, C.: Studies on the thymus of the mammal. VIII. Intrathymic lymphatic vessels. *Anat Rec*, *122*:173-179, 1955.

SOLNITSKY, O.: The Schweigger-Seidel sheath (ellipsoid) of the spleen. *Anat Rec*, *69*:55-75, 1937.

THOMAS, C.E.: An electron- and light-microscope study of sinus structure in perfused rabbit and dog spleens. *Amer J Anat*, *120*:527-551, 1967.

VAN R. DREYER, B.J.: The segmental nature of the spleen. *Blood*, *18*:468-476, 1961.

VINCENT, S., and HARRISON, H.S.: On the hemolymph glands of some vertebrates. *J Anat Physiol*, *31*:176-197, 1897.

WEISS, L.: Observations on the red pulp of the spleen of rabbits and dogs by electron and light microscopy. *Anat Rec*, *139*:286 (Abst.), 1961.

WENZELL, N.: Comparative studies of the wall structure of the thoracic duct of sheep and dogs. Inaug. Diss., Munich, 1965.

ZAPPALA, A.: Segmental blood supply of the spleen. *Anat Rec*, *142*:294, (Abst.), 1962.

ZWILLENBERG, L.O., and ZWILLENBERG, H.H.: Elektronmikroskopische Beobachtungen an den Hülzenarteriolen in der Milz des Hundes. *Experientia*, *18*: 136-137, 1962.

RESPIRATORY SYSTEM

ACKERKNECHT, E.B.: Die Atmungsorgane der Fleischfresser. Ellenberger, W., and Baum, H.: *Handbuch der vergleichenden Anatomie der Haustiere*. Springer-Verlag, Berlin, 1943, pp. 505-507.

BARONE, R.: Arbre bronchique et vaisseaux pulmonaires chez le chien. CR *Assoc Anat (Paris)*, *44*:132-144, 1958.

BARONE, R.; LOMBARD, M., and MORAND, M.: The vomero-nasal organ, vomero-nasal nerve and terminal nerve in the dog. *Bull Soc Sci Vet Lyon*, *68*:257-270 1966.

BAST, T.H.: The maxillary sinus of the dog, with special reference to certain new structures, probably sensory in nature. *Amer J Anat, 33:* 449-483, 1924.

BERRY, J.L.; BRAILSFORD, J.F., and DE BURG DALY, I.: The bronchial vascular system in the dog. *Proc Roy Soc (Biol), 109:*214-228, 1931.

BOATMAN, E.S., and MARTIN, H.B.: Electron microscopy of the alveolar pores of Kohn. *Amer Rev Resp Dis, 88:*779-784, 1963.

BOYDEN, E.A., and TOMPSETT, D.H.: The postnatal growth of the lung in the dog. *Acta Anat, 47:*185-215, 1961.

CHAUDHRY, M.S.: A study of the bronchopulmonary vasculature in postnatal growth of the dog. *Diss Abst, 25:*2163, 1964.

CHRISTENSEN, G.C., and TOUSSAINT, S.: Vasculature of external nares and related areas in the dog. *J Amer Vet Med Ass, 131:*504-509, 1957.

CORRELL, N.O., JR., and LANSTON, H.T.: Pulmonary lymphatic drainage in the dog. *Surg Gynec Obstet, 107:*284-286, 1958.

DUNNILL, M.S.: Effect of lung inflation on alveolar surface area in the dog. *Nature (London), 214:*1013-1014, 1967.

ENGEL, S.: The respiratory tissue of the dog. *Acta Anat. 35:*301-310, 1958.

FILLENZ, M.: Nerve fibres to blood vessels in the dog's lung. *J Physiol, 169:*80P, 1963.

FRANZMANN, A.F.: *Beiträge zur vergleichende Anatomie und Histologie des Kehlkopfes der Säugetiere mit besonderer Berücksichtigung der Haussäugetiere.* C. Georgi, Bonn, 1907.

GOCO, R.V.; KRESS, M.B., and BRANTIGAN, O.C.: Comparison of mucus glands in the tracheobronchial tree of man and animals. *Ann NY Acad Sci, 106:*555-571, 1963.

GRAEGER, K.: Die Nasenhöhle und die Nasennebenhöhlen beim Hund unter besonderer Beruchsichtigung der Siebbeinmuscheln. *Deutsch Tieräerztl Wschr, 65:*425-429, 468-472, 1958.

GREENBERG, S.D., and WILLMS, R.K.: Regeneration of respiratory epithelium. An experimental study in dogs. *Arch Path, 73:*53-58, 1962.

HARTROFT, W.S.: Comparative pulmonic alveolar size in man, cat, rabbit, monkey, guinea pig, goat, dog, baboon, rat and mouse. *Anat Rec, 97:*417, 1947.

HEGNER, D.: Das Blutgefässystem der Nasenhöhle und ihrer Organe von *Canis familiaris* gleichzeitig ein Versuch der funktionellent Deutung der Venen plexus. Inaug. Diss., Giessen, 1962.

ILIESCO, G.F.: Recherches anatomiques sur les cavités nasales chez le chien. *Arch Anat (Strasb), 6:*229-262, 1926.

KADOWAKI, S.: The nerve supply of the nasopalatine duct and Jacobson's organ in the late foetal stage in dogs. *Arch Histol Jap, 17:*437-458, 1959.

KARPF, A.: Das innere Lymphgefäss-system der Lunge. *Anat Anz, 116:*442-451, 1965.

KARTAWIRIA, K.: A contribution to the microscopic anatomy of the postnatal epiglottis of the domestic animals. M.S. thesis, Michigan State University, East Lansing, 1964; Abst. in *Anat Rec, 151:*445-446, 1965.

KAWATA, S., and OKANO, M.: Sensory innervation of the septum nasi of the dog and horse. *Bull Coll Agricl Vet Med Nihon Univ, 11:*126, 1959.

KAWATA, S., and OKANO, M.: Histological analysis of sensory nerve of the ethmoid bone of the dog. *Arch Histol Jap, 17:*609-615, 1959.

KIRSCH, R.: Über das Vorkommen von Mastzellen in der Lunge bei Rind und Hund. Inaug. Diss., Hannover, 1959.

KNOWLTON, C.D., and McGREGOR, G.W.: How and when the mucous membrane of the maxillary sinus regenerates; an experimental study in the dog. *Arch Otolaryng,* 8:647-656, 1928.

KOISHI, K.: On the caryometry of the epithelia of the terminal and respiratory bronchioles, alveolar ducts and alveoli in carnivores. *Hirosaki Med J,* 11:68-77, 1960.

KOIZUMI, H.: On sensory innervation of larynx in dog. On innervation of taste-buds in larynx in dog. *Tohoku J Exp Med,* 58:199-210, 1953.

LASHKOV, V.F.: Innervation of the mucosa of the respiratory zone of the nose. (Russ.). *Arkh Anat,* 41:78-84, 1961.

LOOSLI, C.G.; ADAMS, W.E., and THORNTON, T.M.: The histology of the dog's lung following experimental collapse with special reference to the nature of the alveolar lining. *Anat Rec,* 105:697-721, 1949.

LUKYANOVA, V.P.: The natural shape of lungs and their lobes in the pleural cavity of dogs. *Tr Odessk S Kh Inst,* pp. 103-114, 1955.

LYAZINA, U.K.: Topography of the bronchial veins. *Tr Khar'kovsk. Med Inst,* 65:285-290, 1965.

McLAUGHLIN, R.F., JR., TYLER, W.S., and CANADA, R.O.: The comparative anatomy of the pulmonary vascular tree. *Med Thorac,* 19:523-527, 1962.

NEGUS, V.E.: *The Comparative Anatomy and Physiology of the Larynx.* W. Hineman, London, 1949.

NEGUS, V.E.: *The Comparative Anatomy and Physiology of the Nose and Para-nasal Sinuses.* Livingston, Edinburgh, 1958.

NIEWENHUIS, R.: Comparative histology of the trachea of the dog and cat. M.S. thesis, Michigan State University, 1961; Abst. in *Anat Rec,* 154:454, 1966.

PARKER, B.M.; ANDRESEN, D.C., and SMITH, J.R.: Observations on arteriovenous communications in lungs of dogs. *Proc Soc Exp Biol Med,* 98:306-308, 1958.

PHILLIPS, C.E., JR.; DeWEESE, J.A.; MANNING, J.A., and MAHONEY, E.B.: Maturation of small pulmonary arteries in puppies. *Circulat Res,* 8:1268-1273, 1960.

PIERARD, J.: Comparative anatomy of the carnivore larynx, with special reference to the cartilages and muscles of the larynx in the dog. M.S. thesis, Cornell Univ., Ithaca, 1963.

PIERARD, J.: Anatomie comparée du larynx du chien et d'autres carnivores. *Canad Vet J,* 6:11-15, 1965.

POPOVIĆ, S.: Eine Darstellung der morphologischen Eigentümlichkeiten des knor-peligen Nasengerüstes bei Haussäugetiere. *Anat Anz,* 114:379-388, 1964.

READ, E.A.: A contribution to the knowledge of the olfactory apparatus in dog, cat and man. *Amer J Anat* 8:17-48, 1908.

REEVES, J.T.: Microradiography of intrapulmonary bronchial veins of the dog. *Anat Rec,* 159:255-261, 1967.

RENZONI, A.: Sul componente elastico della parete bronchiole in alcune specie animali. *Arch Vet Ital,* 8:389-398, 1957.

SKLYADNEVA, V.M.: Innervation of the cartilaginous plates of the bronchi in the dog. *Dokl Akad Nauk SSSR* (Biol. Sci. Sect. Transl.), *128*:831-833, 1959-1960.

STAHL, U.: Breed differences in nasal cartilages of dogs. *Wiss Z Humboldt Univ,* 11:83-98, 1962.

TUCKER, J.L., JR., and KREMENTZ, E.T.: Anatomical corrosion specimens. II. Bronchopulmonary anatomy in the dog. *Anat Rec,* 127:667-676, 1957.

VOGEL, P.H.: The innervation of the larynx of man and the dog. *Amer J Anat,* 90:427-440, 1952.

WATSON, J.H., and VALENTINE, V.: Observations on ultrathin sections of dog lung by methods of electron microscopy. *Henry Ford Hosp Med Bull,* 7:161-173, 1959.

YANAI, S.: On the myelinated nerve fibers supplied to the trachea, the bronchus and the lung in dogs. *Fukushima J Med Sci,* 8:151 (Abst.) 1961.

ZIEMIANSKI, A.; OBREBOWSKI, A., and KOMPF, A.: Innervation of the sites of division of the bronchi by the vagi nerves in the dog. *Folia Morphol* (Warsz), 26:471-478, 1967.

DIGESTIVE SYSTEM

ALLISON, J.E.; HOFFMAN, H.H.; FAULKNER, K.K., and PAGE, C.H.: Enteric plexus fibers in the mesentery of cats, dogs and rabbits. *J Comp Neurol,* 117:383-385, 1961.

ANDO, S.: A study of the vascular supply of the pancreas. *Fukoka Acta Med,* 50:4247-4274, 1959.

ANDREWS, W.H.: Micro-anatomy of hepatic circulation. *Nature Lond.* 164:1011-1012, 1949.

ARNALL, L.: Some aspects of dental development in the dog: I. Calcification of crown and root of the deciduous dentitions. II. Eruption and extrusion. *J Small Anim Pract,* 1:169-173,259-267, 1961.

BACANER, M., and POLLYCOVE, M.: Regional circulation in the intact dog colon. *Fed Proc,* 20:98, 1961.

BAKEYEVA, N.A.: Innervation of the ileocaecal area of the intestine in man and dog. *Tr Stalinabadsk Med Inst,* 25:87-135, 1957.

BARNETT, C.H.: Spiral structure within the hepatic portal vein of mammals. *Proc Zool Soc* (London), 123:747-752, 1954.

BAUER, W.H.: Effect of estrone on tooth buds and bones in growing dogs. *J Amer Coll Dent,* 12:192-201, 1945.

BENNETT, G.A.: The lyssa of the dog. *Anat Rec,* 88:422 (Abst.), 1944.

BERRY, H.L.: Collagenous fiber patterns in the submucosa of the small intestine of the dog. *Anat Rec,* 143:107-116, 1962.

BOSMA, J.F.: Myology of the pharynx of cat, dog and monkey with interpretation of the mechanism of swallowing. *Ann Otol,* 65:981-992, 1956.

BOWNE, J.G.: Macroscopic and microscopic structure and age changes in the lingual papillae of the dog. M.S. thesis, Iowa State University, Ames, 1956.

BOYDEN, E.A., and SCHWEGLER, R.A., JR.: The sphincter of Oddi in the dog. *Amer J Physiol,* 116:14, 1936.

BOYNE, P.J., and MILLER, C.W.: A study of tooth development by tetracycline induced fluorescence. *J Dent Res* 40:1079, 1961.

BROWN, M.E.: The occurrence of arterio-venous anastomoses in the tongue of the dog. *Anat Rec,* 69:287-297, 1937.

CALVARI, A.R.: Osservazioni sulla colangiocolecistografia con Bilivistan (SH 847) nel cane. *Veterinaria* (Milano), 16:116-121, 1967.

CANOSA, C.A., and REHM, W.S.: Microscopic dimensions of the pit region of the dog's gastric mucosa. *Gastroenterology,* 35:292-297, 1958.

CHEPRASOVA, A.F.: On the question of duodenal innervation in the dog. (Experimental-morphologic study) *Tr Stalinabadsk Med Inst,* 25:191-197, 1957.

CHIU, S.L.: The superficial hepatic branches of the vagi and their distribution to the extrahepatic biliary tract in certain mammals. *Anat Rec,* 86:149-155, 1943.

CORDES, D.O., and MOSHER, A.H.: Brown pigmentation (lipofuscinosis) of canine intestinal muscularis. *J Path Bact,* 92:197-206, 1966.

Cuq, P.: La segmentation héatique des carnivores. *Recl Méd Vet, 141*:233-268, 1965.

Cuq, P., Blin, P.C., and Bérenger, A.: Topographie de la veine porte intra-hepatique du chien. *Recl. Méd Vet, 141*:5-15, 1965.

Cuq, P.; Blin, P.C., and Bérenger, A.: Topographie artérielle du foie du chien. *Recl Méd Vet, 141*:123-135, 1965.

Daigo, M.: Stereoroentgenographical studies on the arteries of the tongue and vicinity. I. Arteries of the tongue of the dog. *Jap J Vet Sci, 22*:552, 1960.

Demina, M.A.: Histochemical study of cholinesterase activity in taste buds of some laboratory animals (Russ.). *Arhk Anat, 53*:111-114, 1967.

D'Errico, A.A.: Contribution to the study of extra-hepatic pathways of bile in the dog. *Folia Clin Biol, 28*:90-95, 1959.

Dyce, K.M.: The muscles of the pharynx and palate of the dog. *Anat Rec, 127*: 497-508, 1957.

Eglitis, J.A., and Hayes, E.R.: Free surface of the gall bladder epithelium with the light microscope. *Anat Rec, 140*:61-70, 1961.

Elbert, M.E.: On the problem of the cyto-architecture of Auerbach's plexus of the small intestines in the cat and dog. *Tr Mosk Vet Akad, 18*:35-38, 1956.

Elias, H.: Comparative histology of domestic animals. I. The digestive system. 2. The stomach of domestic mammals. *Middlesex Vet, 4*: 66-69, 1944.

Elias, H.: Comparison of duodenal glands in domestic animals. *Amer J Vet Res, 8*:311-313, 1947.

Elias, H., and Sokol, A.: Dependence of the lobular architecture of the liver on the porto-hepatic blood pressure gradient. *Anat Rec, 115*:71-85, 1953.

Elsen, J., and Arey, L.B.: On spirality in the intestinal wall. *Amer J Anat, 118*:11-20, 1966.

Emmelin, N., and Holmberg, J.: The presence of beta-receptors in the sub-maxillary gland of the dog. *Brit J Pharmacol, 30*:371-378, 1967.

Godlowski, Z.Z., and Calandra, J.C.: Salivary glands as endocrine organs. *J Appl Physiol, 15*:101-105, 1960.

Godlowski, Z.Z., and Calandra, J.C.: Argentaffine cells in the submaxillary glands of dogs. *Anat Rec, 140*:45-47, 1961.

Goetsch, E.: The structure of the mammalian esophagus. *Amer J Anat, 10*:1-40, 1910.

Hammond, J.B., and LaDeur, L.: Fibrillovesicular cells in the fundic glands of the canine stomach: evidence for a new cell type. *Anat Rec, 161*:393-412, 1968.

Harvey, B.C.H.: A study of the structure of the gastric glands of the dog and of the changes which they undergo after gastroenterostomy and occlusion of the pylorus. *Amer J Anat, 6*:207-243, 1906.

Hashimoto, Y.; Tsuiki, S.; Quinterelli, G., and Pigman, W.: A comparison of submaxillary glands of humans, cattle, dogs, and rats. *Biochim Biophys Acta, 48*:404-406, 1961.

Hebel, R.: Untersuchungen über das Vorkommen von lymphatischen Darm-krypten in der Tunica submucosa des Darmes von Schwein, Rind, Schaf, Hund und Katze. *Anat Anz, 109*:7-27, 1960.

Hellman, B.; Wallgren, A., and Hellerstrom, C.: Two types of islet alpha cells in different parts of the pancreas of the dog. *Nature (London), 194*:1201-1202, 1962.

Hendrickx, A.G.: The pharyngeal pouches of the dog. *Anat Rec, 149*:475-483, 1964.

HILTON, W.A.: The morphology and development of intestinal folds and villi in vertebrates. *Amer J Anat, 1*:459-505, 1902.

HINRICHSEN, J.: Über das Vorkommen von Mastzellen im Darmtraktus des Hundes. Inaug. Dass., Hannover, 1956.

HJERTQUIST, S.: Biophysical and histochemical studies on tooth germs from normal and rachitic dogs. *Acta Path Microbiol Scand, 50*:163-176, 1960.

HUNT, T.E.: Differential counts of the islet cells of the dog pancreas. *Anat Rec, 67*:27 (Abst.), 1936.

IENAGA, S.: The fine structure of the surface epithelial cells of the proximal digestive tract of the dog as revealed with the electron microscope. *Fukuoka Acta Med, 52*:408-417, 1961.

INTONTI, F.; NYLANDER, G., and TJERNBERG, B.: Lymph vessels of the greater omentum. A preliminary investigation (dog). *Vasc Dis, 1*:203-205, 1964.

IRWIN, D.A.: The anatomy of Auerbach's plexus. *Amer J Anat, 49*:141-166, 1931.

JAMIOKOWSKA, K.: The lymphatic vessels of the small intestine (calf, dog, rabbit, man.) Russ.—Eng. summ. *Folia Morph* (Warsz.), *14*:123-144, 1963.

JANKOVIĆ, Z.: The hepatic venous system of the dog. *Acta Vet Belg, 4*:69-81, 1954.

JANKOVIĆ, Z., and ANDRIC, R.: Beitrag zur Kenntnis des arteriellen Leberkreislaufes beim Hunde. *Acta Anat, 61*:460 (Abst.), 1965.

JOHNSON, F.R.; McMINN, R.M.H., and BIRCHENOUGH, R.F.: The ultrastructure of the gall-bladder epithelium of the dog. *J Anat, 96*:477-487, 1962.

JOHNSON, F.R., and YOUNG, B.A.: Undifferentiated cells in gastric mucosa. *J Anat, 102*:541-551, 1968.

JOHNSON, L.E., and MANN, F.C.: Lymphatic system of the liver. *Amer J Physiol, 163*:723-724 (Abst.), 1950.

KAMAN, J.: Postnatal development of lobe formation of dog liver. *Česk Morfol, 9*:1-16, 1961.

KARIMOV, E.K.: Lymphovasal structure of the normal esophagus of the dog. *Tr Tadzhiksk Med Inst, 88*:25-28, 1967.

KARUPU, V.YA.: Preparation for the study of the peripheral nervous system of the liver of several animals and man. *Arkh Anat, 41*:83-90, 1961.

KELLEY, M.L., JR., DEWEESE, J.A., and GORDON, E.A.: Studies of the ileocolonic junctional zone of dogs. *Gastroenterology, 46*:746 (Abst.), 1964.

KOVACIC, S.U.: Contribucion al estudio histologico comparativo de la porcion anterior del tubo digestivo encarnivoros. *Zooiatria* (Santiago), *9*:60-66, 1959.

KOZMA, M.; POBERAI, M.; VARGA, L.; GELLÉRT, A., and FÖLDI, M.: The lymphatics of the tongue. *Acta Anat, 49*:252-259, 1962.

KRAPVIKIN, A.A.: Materials on macroscopy and microscopy of rectal glands in man and some animals. *Tr Kharkovsk Med Inst, 45*:41-49, 1957; *Referat Zh Biol,* No. 7181, 1960.

KRATOCHVIL, M.; PAYER, J., and REIDEL, J.: Das System der Leberarterie und ihr Verhältnis zum Pfortadersystem in der Leber des Hundes. *Acta Anat, 31*:246-260, 1957.

KRAWITT, E.L.; ZIMMERMAN, G.R., and CLIFTON, J.A.: Location of secretin in dog duodenal mucosa. *Amer J Physiol, 211*:935-938, 1966.

KUIDA, H., NAKANISHI, S., and ARAYA, S.: Growth of dog tooth germs and change in contents of P, Ca, and Mg. *Bull Tokyo Med Dent Univ, 7*:167-178, 1960.

LACY, P.E.: Electron microscopic identification of different cell types in the islets of Langerhans of the guinea pig, rat, rabbit and dog. *Anat Rec, 128*:255-268, 1957.

LAWSON, D.D.; NIXON, G.S.; NOBLE, H.W., and WEIPERS, W.L.: Dental anatomy and histology of the dog. *Res Vet Sci, 1*:201-204, 1960.

MANN, C.V., and SHORTER, R.G.: Structure of the canine esophagus and its sphincters. *J Surg Res, 4*:160-163, 1964.

MANN, F.C.: Accessory pancreas in the dog. *Anat Rec, 19*:263-268, 1920.

MARKS, I.N.; KOMAROV, S.A., and SHAY, H.: Acid secretory responses to histamine and the parietal cell mass in the dog. *Amer J Physiol, 195*:528-534, 1958.

MARKS, I.N.; KOMAROV, S.A., and SHAY, H.: Maximal acid secretory response to histamine and its relation to parietal cell mass in the dog. *Amer J Physiol, 199*:579-588, 1960.

MARTIN, B.F.: The goblet cell pattern in the large intestine. *Anat Rec, 140*:1-15, 1961.

McMINN, R.H.M., and KUGLER, J.H.: The glands of the bile and pancreatic ducts: Autoradiographic and histochemical studies. *J Anat, 95*:1-11, 1961.

MEISS, J.H.; GRINDLAY, J.H., and ELLIS, F.J., JR.: The gastroesophageal sphincter mechanism. II. Further experimental studies in the dog. *J Thorac Surg, 36*: 156-165, 1958.

MELEKHIN, G.P.: Parasympathetic innervation of the parotid gland in dogs. *Arkh Anat, 30*:53-56, 1953.

MICHAIL, S., and KARAMANLIDIS, A.: Morphologie du plexus myentérique d'Auerbach de l'intestine grêle du chien. *Acta Anat, 67*:424-436, 1967.

MONIZ DE BETTENCOURT, J., CARVALHO; J. SILVA; PULIDO VALENTE, J.L., and RATO, J.A.: Anatomy of the hepatic artery in the dog, from a physiological point of view. *C R Soc Biol (Paris), 155*:1613-1616, 1961.

MOOSER, M.: Zahnärztlich-vergleichende Untersuchungen an 425 Hundeschädeln. *Schweiz Arch Tierheilk, 100*:208-223, 1958.

MUNGER, B.L., CARAMIA, F., and LACY, P.E.: The ultrastructure basis for the identification of cell types in the pancreatic islets. II. Rabbit, dog and opossum. *Z Zellforsch, 67*:776-798, 1965.

MURTI, G.S., and BORGMANN, R.: Intracytoplasmic periodic acid-Schiff-positive nonglycogenic globules in canine liver: their histochemical characterization. *Amer J Vet Res, 26*:63-67, 1965.

NAZAROVA-ANDREEVA, T.A.: The problem of the sensory innervation of the dog's tongue. *Dokl Akad Nauk SSSR, 141*:212-214, 1961; (Biol. Sci. Sect. Transl., 141 (1/6): 1020-1021, 1962.)

NIKONOV, A.P.: The sensory innervation of intramural nerve ganglia of dog esophagus. *Arkh Anat, 36*:96-98, 1959; *Referat Zh Biol*, No. 91255, 1961.

NOER, R.J.: The blood vessels of the jejunum and ileum: A comparative study of man and certain laboratory animals. *Amer J Anat, 73*:293-334, 1943.

OGAWA, T.; JEFFERSON, N.C., and NECHELES, H.: Comparative study of bile drainage in dog and man. *Amer J Surg, 99*:57-62, 1960.

PANCIERA, R.J.: A study of morphological changes in the digestive system of aged dogs. *Diss Absts, 21*:3427-3428, 1961.

PEREZ CASAS, A.: Contribution a l'etude du sphincter d'Oddi chez *Canis familiaris*. *Acta Anat, 34*:130-153, 1958.

RAGINS, H.; DITTBRENNER, M., and DIAZ, J.: Comparative histochemistry of the gastric mucosa: A survey of the common laboratory animals and man. *Anat Rec, 150*:179-193, 1964.

RAKHAWY, M.T.: Histochemistry of human and dog tongues with special reference to the gustatory epithelia. *Diss. Absts, 23*:21-22, 1962.

REVELL, D.G.: The pancreatic ducts in the dog. *Amer J Anat, 1*:443-457, 1902.

RICHTER, W.R.; BISCHOFF, M.B., and CHURCHILL, R.A.: An observation of fine tubules within the endoplasmic reticulum in a dog liver. *Z Zellforsch, 70*:180-184, 1966.

RITCHIE, H.D.; GRINDLAY, J.H., and BOLLMAN, J.L.: Flow of lymph from the canine liver. *Amer J Physiol 196*:105-109, 1959.

RITCHIE, W.P., JR.; BARZILIA, A., and DELANEY, J.D.: Mucosal cellular populations and distribution in the normal canine stomach. *Anat Rec, 155*:111-115, 1966.

ROUILLER, C.: *The Liver: Morphology, Biochemistry, Physiology.* Academic, New York, 1963-1964.

SACK, O.W.: The early development of the embryonic pharynx of the dog. *Anat Anz, 115*:59-80, 1964.

SCHOFIELD, R.H.A.: Observations on taste goblets in the epiglottis of the dog and cat. *J Anat Physiol, 10*:475-477, 1876.

SEDAR, A.W., and FRIEDMAN, M.H.F.: Correlation of the fine structure of the gastric parietal cell (dog) with functional activity of the stomach. *J Biophys Biochem Cytol, 11*:349-363, 1961.

SHACKLEFORD, J.M., and KLAPPER, C.E.: Structure and carbohydrate histochemistry of mammalian salivary glands. *Amer J Anat, 111*:25-47, 1962.

SICULAR, A.; COHEN, B.R.; ZIMMERMAN, A.; WOLF, B.S.; and KARK, A.E.: The significance of the canine intra-abdominal esophagus as an antiefflux mechanism. *Amer J Gastroent, 41*:599-610, 1964.

SMALL, E.; OLSEN, R., and FRITZ, T.: The canine pancreas. *Vet Med Small Anim Clin, 59*:627-642, 1964.

SOHN, W.T., and AREY, L.B.: The persistence of argentaffin cells in the excised intestine of the dog and rabbit. *Anat Rec, 109*:408, 1951.

SONNTAG, C.F.: The comparative anatomy of the tongues of mammalia. VIII. Carnivora. *Proc Zool Soc Lond*, pp. 129-153, 1923.

STEIN, R.J.; RICHTER, W.R.; MOIZE, S.M., and RDZOK, E.J.: Comparative hepatic ultrastructure of the street dog and registered beagles. *Fed Proc, 23*:578, 1964.

STEIN, R.J.; RICHTER, W.R., and BRYNGOLFSSON, G.: Ultrastructural pharmacopathology. I. Comparative morphology of the livers of the normal street dog and the purebred beagle. A base-line study. *Exp Molec Path, 5*:195-223, 1966.

STEINER, J.W., and CARRUTHERS, J.S.: Studies on the fine structure of the terminal branches of the biliary tree. I. The morphology of normal bile canaliculi, bile pre-ductules (Duct of Hering) and bile ductules. *Amer J Path, 38*:639-661, 1961.

STOVICHEK, G.F.: Data on the cerebrospinal afferent innervation of the esophagus in dogs. *Arkh Anat, 40*:22-26, 1961.

SULZMANN, R.: Beiträge zur Histologie der Zahnpulpa. III. Mitteilung: Die mikroskopische Morphologie der Arterien und Venen in den permanenten monoradikulären Zähnen von Mensch und Hund. *Anat Anz, 121*:497-503, 1967.

TAKASHIMA, T.: Stereological studies on several ducts and vessels by injection method of acrylic resin. XIX. Arterial distribution of the submandibular gland in some mammals. *Okajimas Folia Anat Jap, 43*:363-383, 1967.

TEHVER, J.: Stäbchensaum der Oberflächen-und Foveolarepithelzellen im Magen der Haussäugetiere. *Anat Anz, 68*:255-259, 1929.

TEIXEIRA, E.D.; CARDOSA, A.D., and BERGAN, J.J.: Studies of canine pancreatic ductal and arterial anatomy. *Anat Rec, 157*:390-391, 1967.

TITKEMEYER, C.W., and CALHOUN, M.L.: A comparative study of the structure of the small intestine of domestic animals. *Amer J. Vet Res, 16*:152-157, 1955.

TITKEMEYER, C.W.: Applied anatomy of the perineal region of the dog. *MSU Vet,* *18*:162-164, 1958.

TOMBOL, T., and VAJDA, J.: Über die Lymphzirkulation des Pancreas. *Anat Anz,* *110*:400-409, 1962.

TUCKER, C.C., and HELLWIG, C.A.: Histopathology of the anal crypts. *Trans Amer* *Proct Soc,* (34th Annual Session) *47*:52, 1933.

VEILLEUX, R.: Le reseau canaliculaire pancreatique chez le chien. Sa signification en expérimentation. *Presse Med, 66*:1697-1698, 1958.

WEBER, A.F.; HASA, O., and SAUTTER, J.H.: Some observations concerning the presence of spirilla in the fundic glands of dogs and cats. *Amer J Vet Res,* *19*:677-680, 1958.

URINARY SYSTEM

AMON, H., and SANCAK, B.: Vergleichende morphologische Untersuchungen über die subepithelialen Bindegewebslagen der Harnblase. *Anat Anz, 121*: 349-358, 1967.

AL-RADHAWY, M.A.: Development of the urogenital system of the dog. M.S. thesis, Kansas State University, Manhattan, Kansas, 1958.

ARNAUTOVIĆ, A.: Contribution à l'étude de la vascularisation du rein chez le chien. *Acta Anat, 42*:261 (Abst.), 1960.

ARNAUTOVIC, I.: The distribution of the renal artery in the kidney of the dog. *Brit Vet J, 115*:446-448, 1959.

BELKIN, V.Sh.: Vascular structure of the normal urinary bladder in dogs and rabbits. *Tr Tadzhiksk Med Inst, 88*:15-21, 1967.

BHARADWAJ, M.B., and CALHOUN, M.L.: Histology of the urethral epithelium of domestic animals. *Amer J Vet Res, 20*:841-851, 1959.

BHARADWAJ, M.B.: Histology of the urethra and accessory sex glands of the domestic animals and observations on the surgical insertion of the urinary bladder-neck into the descending colon in the dog. Ph.D. thesis, Michigan State University, 1960, pp. 285; *Diss Abstr, 21*:3222, 1961.

BOHNE, A.W.; OSBORNE, R.W., and HETTLE, P.J.: Regeneration of the urinary bladder in the dog, following total cystectomy. *Surg Gynec Obstet, 100*:259-264, 1955.

BONTING, S.L.; POLLACK, V.E.; MUEHRCKE, R.C., and KARK, R.M.: Quantitative histochemistry of the nephron. *Science, 127*:1342-1343, 1958.

CALHOUN, M.L.: Comparative histology of the ureters of domestic animals. *Anat Rec, 133*:365-366 (Abst.), 1959.

CHRISTENSEN, G.C.: Circulation of blood through the canine kidney. *Amer J Vet Res, 13*:236-245, 1952.

CRABO, B.: On the glycogen contents in the renal epithelium of some domestic and laboratory animals. *Acta Morph Neerl Scand, 4*:71-78, 1961.

DOLEZEL, S.: The structure of kidney connective tissue in the dog and its relationship to the kidney vessels and nerve fibers. (Czech. w/Russ. Ger. summ.) *Česk Morfol, 5*:16-20, 1957.

EGEN, H.: Über das Vorkommen von Mastzellen in Harntraktus vom Hund. Inaug. Diss., Hannover, 1956.

FITZGERALD, T.C.: The renal circulation of domestic animals. *Amer J Vet Res,* *1*:89-95, 1940.

FOOTE, J.J., and GRAFFLIN, A.L.: Cell contours in the two segments of the proximal tubule in the cat and dog nephron. *Amer J Anat, 70*:1-20, 1942.

GRAHAME, T.: The pelvis and calyces of the kidneys of some mammals. *Brit Vet J, 109*:51-55, 1953.

HAMMERSEN, F.: The capillary bed of the renal fibrous capsule. A contribution to the problems in blood vessel analysis in the terminal vascular bed. *Angiology, 12*:511-516, 1961.

HARTROFT, P.M., and NEWMARK, L.N.: Electron microscopy of renal juxta-glomerular cells. *Anat Rec, 139*:185-199, 1961.

HUBER, G.C.: The arteriolae rectae of the mammalian kidney. *Amer J Anat, 6*:391-406, 1907.

HUHN, D.; STEINER, J.W., and MOVAT, H.Z.: The fine structure of the mesangium in the kidney glomerulus of the dog and mouse. *Z Zellforsch, 56*:213-230, 1962.

KAMENSKAIA, N.L.: Some characteristics of the structure of the walls of the kidney arteries and of the veins. *Dokl Akad Nauk SSSR, 100*:1001-1004, 1955; *Referat Zh Obshchei Biol* No. 32082.

KINOSHITA, Y., and FUJISAKI, S.: Electron microscopic studies of the glomerulus. *Acta Med Biol* (Niigata), *11*:15-40, 1963.

KÜGELGEN, A. VON: *Die Gefässarchiterktur der Niere; Untersuchungen an der Hundeniere.* George Thieme Verlag, Stuttgart, 1959.

KÜGELGEN, A. VON: Extraglomulärer Kreislauf über die Gafässe des Nierenbeckens in der Hundeniere. *Anat Anz, 108*:351-352, 1960.

KUNKEL, P.A., JR.: The number and size of the glomeruli in the kidney of several mammals. *Bull Johns Hopkins Hosp, 47*:285-291, 1930.

LATIMER, H.B.: The growth of the kidneys and the bladder in the fetal dog. *Anat Rec, 109*:1-12, 1951.

MARSCHNER, H.: Art-und Altersmerkmale der Nieren der Haussäugetiere. *Z Anat Entwicklungsgesch, 107*:353-377, 1937.

MAYER, E., and OTTOLENGHI, L.A.: Protrusion of tubular epithelium into the space of Bowman's capsule in kidneys of dogs and cats. *Anat Rec, 99*:477-509, 1947.

MOFFAT, D.B., and FOURMAN, J.: Ectopic glomeruli in the human and animal kidney. *Anat Rec, 149*:1-11, 1964.

MONTALDO, G.: Modalita di svilup o della parete del capillare nel glomo del rene fetale nell'uomo e in animali superiori (pecora, cane). *Boll Soc Ital Biol Sper, 31*:164-165, 1955.

MOORE, R.D.: The histology of the bladder and proximal urethra of the domestic animals. Ph.D. Thesis, Michigan State University, East Lansing, 1956. Abst. in *Anat Rec, 127*:338, 1957.

MOVAT, H.Z. and STEINER, J.W.: Studies of nephrotoxic nephritis. I. The fine structure of the glomerulus of the dog. *Amer J Clin Path, 36*:289-305, 1961.

MUNKACSI, I.; NAGY, Z.; TAKACS, L.; LALLAY, K.; and GOMORI, P.: Vascular shunts in the renal cortex of the dog. *Rev canad Biol, 22*:353-363, 1963.

NAKAMURA, S.: Beobachtungen über die Fette in den Harnkanälchen von Katze und Hund. *Okajimas Folia Anat Jap, 13*:45-54, 1935.

PEIRCE, E.C., II: Renal lymphatics. *Anat Rec, 90*:315-335, 1944.

PFEIFFER, E.W.: Comparative anatomical observations of mammalian renal pelvis and medulla. *J. Anat, 102*:321-331, 1968.

PIRRO, A.: Indagine istologica sulla tunica muscolare della vesica del cane. *Boll Soc Ital Biol Sper, 27*:251-253, 1951.

RYTAND, D.A.: The number and size of mammalian glomeruli as related to kidney and to body weight, with methods for their enumeration and measurement. *Amer J Anat, 62*:507-520, 1938.

Scott, J.E., and DeLuca, F.G.: Further studies on the ureterovesical junction of the dog. *Brit J Urol, 32*:320-323, 1960.

Simić, V. and Popović, S.: Morphologische Grundmerkmale und Verschiedenheiten der Nieren bei den kleinen Wiederkäuern und Fleischfressern. (*Ovis aries, Canis familiaris* et *Felis domestica*). *Anat Anz, 113*:224-231, 1963.

Smith, C.: A study of the lipid content of the kidney tubule. *Amer J Anat, 27*:69-97, 1920.

Speers, F.G.: A histologic study of the urinary system of the newborn beagle dog. M.S. thesis, Michigan State University, East Lansing, Michigan, 1967.

Sperber, I.: Studies on the mammalian kidney. *Zool Bidrag Uppsala, 22*:249-431, 1944.

Swann, H.G., and Railey, M.J.: Weights of right and left kidney in dogs. *Texas Rep Biol Med, 17*:256-258, 1959.

Thompson, S.W., II; Cooke, J.E., and Hoey, H.: Histochemical studies of acidophilic, crystalline intranuclear inclusions in the liver and kidney of dogs. *Amer J Path, 35*:607-623, 1959.

Vimtrup, B.J.: On the number, shape, structure and surface area of the glomeruli in the kidneys of man and mammals. *Amer J Anat, 41*:123-151, 1928.

Walker, B.E.: A comparative study of transitional epithelium with the electron microscope. *Anat Rec, 130*:385 (Abst.), 1958.

Woodburne, R.T.: The sphincter mechanism of the urinary bladder and the urethra. *Anat Rec, 141*:11-20, 1961.

Yadava, R.P., and Calhoun, M.L.: Comparative histology of the kidney of domestic animals. *Amer J Vet Res, 19*:958-968, 1958.

FEMALE GENITAL SYSTEM

Ancel, P., and Bouin, P.: Rut et corps jaune chez la chienne. *C R Soc Biol (Paris), 65*:365-367, 1908.

Arenas, N., and Sammartino, R.: Le cycle sexuel de la chienne. Etude histologique. *Bull Histol Appliq Physiol Path, 16*:229-259, 1939.

Barone, R., and Pavaux, C.: Blood vessels of the female genital tract in domestic animals. *Bull Soc Sci Vét Lyon, 64*:33-51, 1962.

Bouin, P., and Ancel, P.: Sur le follicule de Graaf mur et la formation du corps jaune chez la chienne. *C R Soc Biol (Paris), 65*:314-316, 1908.

Creed, R.F.S.: The histology of the reproductive system. In *Harrop*, A. E. (Ed.): *Reproduction in the Dog*. Baillière, Tindall and Cox, London. 1960, pp. 38-60.

Courrier, R., and Gerlinger, H.: Le cycle glandulaire de l'épithélium de l'oviducte chez la chienne. *C R Soc Biol* (Paris), *87*:1363-1365, 1922.

Evans, H.M., and Cole, H.H.: The oestrous cycle in the dog. I. The vaginal smear. II. Coincident changes in the genital organs. *Anat Rec, 35*:10, 11 (Absts.) 1927.

Fitch, K.L.: A study of uterine glycogen during the estrous cycle of the dog. *J Morph 113*:331-343, 1963.

Forsberg, J. G.: Origin of vaginal epithelium. *Obstet Gynec, 25*:787-791, 1965.

Gerlinger, H.: Le cycle oestrien de l'utérus chez la chienne et ses rapports chronologiques avec le cycle oestrien de l'ovaire. *C R Soc Biol* (Paris), *89*: 193-195, 1923.

Gier, H.T., and Marion, G.B.: Formation of the corpus luteum of the cow and the dog. *Anat Rec, 142*:235, 1962.

Griffiths, W.F.B., and Amoroso, E. C.: Proestrus, oestrum, ovulation and mating in the greyhound bitch. *Vet Rec, 51*:1279-1284, 1939.

GURAYA, S.S., and GREENWALD, G.S.: A comparative histochemical study of interstitial tissue and follicular atresia in the mammalian ovary. *Anat Rec, 149*:411-434, 1964.

HELM, F.C.: Zu den zyklischen Veränderungen der Uterusschleimhaut der Hünden. *Zbl Veterinaermed, 12A*:45-56, 1965.

HOOPER, B.E.; HALL, A., III, and DALE, H.E.: Characteristics of the vaginal smear in the bitch. *Small Anim Clin, 1*:355-359, 1961.

KABRA, S.G.: On the intracellular localization of alkaline phosphatase in the ovary of dog. *Current Sci, 34*:639-640, 1965.

KABRA, S.G.; CHATURVEDI, R.P., and UJWAL, Z.S.: A study of alkaline phosphatase and mitochondria in the dog ovary. *Indian J Med Res, 55*:279-283, 1967.

KAMPMEIER, O.F.: On the problem of "parthenogenesis" in the mammalian ovary. *Amer J Anat, 43*:45-76, 1929.

KARAMYSHEVA, V.J.:The structure of the intramural ganglia of the ovary. *Byul Nauchn Tr Ryazansk Otd Vses Nauchn Obshch Anatomov Gistol i Embriol, 4*: 18-19, 1958.

KARAMYSHEVA, V.J.: The structure of the nerve end apparatus in the ovary. *Dokl Akad Nauk SSSR, 121*:730-733, 1958.

KELLER, K.: Ueber den Bau des Endometriums beim Hunde mit besonderer Berücksichtigung der cyklischen Veränderungen an der Uterindrüsen. *Anat Hefte* (Wiesbaden), *39*:307-391, 1909.

KOCH, FR.: Vergleichend-anatomische und histologische Untersuchungen über den Bau der Vulva und Klitoris der Haustiere. Inaug. Diss., Bonn, 1909.

KUNTZ, A.: The innervation of the gonads in the dog. *Anat Rec, 17*:203-219, 1919.

LEE, F.C.: The tubo-uterine junction in various animals. *Vet J, 85*:16-34, 1929.

LESBOUYRIES, G.: *Reproduction des Mammifères Domestiques*. Vigot Frères, Éditeurs, Paris, 1949.

MARSHALL, F.H.A., and HALNAN, E.T.: On the post oestrous changes occurring in the generative organs and mammary glands of the dog. *Proc Roy Soc London* (B), *89*:546-559, 1917.

MARSHALL, F.H.A., and JOLLY, W.A.: Contributions to the physiology of mammalian reproduction. Part I. The oestrous cycle in the dog. *Philos Trans Roy Soc London* (B), *198*:99-122, 1906.

MULLIGAN, R.M.: Histological studies on the canine female genital tract. *J Morph, 71*:431-448, 1942.

MUNSTER, W.: Über das Vorkommen von Mastzellen im weiblichen Genitaltraktus beim Hund. Inaug. Diss., Hannover, 1960, pp. 66.

O'SHEA, J.D.: Histochemical observations on mucin secretion by subsurface epithelial structures in the canine ovary. *J Morph, 120*:347-358, 1966.

PATZELT, V.: Über das Ovarium der Karnivoren und seine Zwischenzellen. *Z Mikr Anat Forsch, 61*:309-359, 1955.

SCHOTTERER, A.: Beitrag zur Feststellung der Eianzahl in verschiedenen Altersperioden bei der Hündin. *Anat Anz, 65*:177-192, 1928.

SCHUTTE, A.P.: Canine vaginal cytology. I. Technique and cytological morphology. II. Cyclic changes. III. Compilation and evaluation of cellular indices. *J Small Anim Pract, 8*:301-306, 307-311, 316-317, 1967.

STRAHL, H.: Der puerperale Uterus der Hündin. *Anat Hefte,* Erste Abt, *5*:335-399, 1895.

SZABO, P.L.: Ultrastructure of the developing dog oocyte. *Anat Rec, 157*:330 (Abst.), 1967.

TAKEMURA, R.; MATSUDA, T.; KOYA, T.; WATANABE, Y., and YAMAGUCHI, S.: On the caryometry of the epithelia of the vagina and *portio vaginalis uteri* in dogs. (*Canis familiaris*). (Jap. with Eng. summ.) *Hirosaki Med J 10*:536-542, 1959; *Biol Abst, 35*, Part 3, No. 27072, 1960.

TANAKA, K.: Morphological study on the canine ovary. *Jap J Vet Res, 10*:80-81, 1962.

TEHVER, G.: Morphological investigation on the ovarian follicles in domestic animals. *Acta et comment.* (Univ Tartuensis) 3:1-124, 1946.

VAN DER STRICT, O.: La structure de l'oeuf chienne et la genese du corps jaune. *C R Assoc Anat, 10*:1-9, 1908.

WILKERSON, W.V.: The rete ovarii as a normal structure of the adult mammalian ovary. *Anat Rec, 26*:75-77, 1923.

MALE REPRODUCTIVE SYSTEM

ARCADI, J.A.: Some polysaccharide components of the prostate gland of the dog. *Anat Rec, 112*:593-607, 1952.

BARTLETT, D.J.: Studies on dog semen. I. Morphological characteristics. *J Reprod Fert, 3*:173-188, 1962.

BASCOM, K.F., and OSTERUD, H.L.: Quantitative studies on the testicle. II. Pattern and total tubule length in the testicles of certain common mammals. *Anat Rec, 31*:159-169, 1925.

BERG, O.A.: The normal prostate gland of the dog. *Acta Endocr, 27*:129-139, 1958.

BHARADWAJ, M.B., and CALHOUN, M.L: Mode of formation of the preputial cavity in domestic animals. *Amer J Vet Res, 22*:764-769, 1961.

BRANDES, D.: The fine structure and histochemistry of prostatic glands in relation to sex hormones. *Int Rev Cytol, 20*:207-276, 1966.

BULLÓN, A., and LÓPEZ, F.L.: Über die Innervation der menschlichen Samenblase und des homologen Organes beim Hunde. *Z mikr Anat Forsch, 65*:133-152, 1959.

CHRISTENSEN, G. C.: Angioarchitecture of the canine penis and the process of erection. *Amer J Anat, 95*:227-261, 1954.

CORONA, G.L.: Osservazioni sulla innervazione delle vie spermatiche e della prostata nel cane. *Classe di Science, 86*:505-512, 1953.

CREED, R.F.S.: The histology of the reproductive system. In Harrop, A.E. (Ed.): *Reproduction in the Dog.* Baillière, Tindall and Cox, London, 1960, pp. 23-38.

CURTIS, G.M.: The morphology of the mammalian seminiferous tubule. *Amer J Anat, 24*: 339-394, 1918.

DEYSACH, L.J.: The comparative morphology of the erectile tissue of the penis with especial emphasis on the probable mechanism of erection. *Amer J Anat, 64*:111-131, 1939.

GARCIA, T.P.: Aportaciones a los métodos de recogida y contrastación del esperma de perro. *Revta Patron Biol Anim, 3*:97-150, 1957.

GERBER, H.: Zur funktionellen Anatomie der Prostata des Hundes unter Berücksichtigung verschiedener Altersstufen. *Schweiz Arch Tierheilk, 103*: 537-561, 1961.

GORDON, N.: The position of the canine prostate gland. *Amer J Vet Res, 22*:142-146, 1961.

GRASSO, R.: Sobre las celulas argentafines de la uretra y de la glandula prostatica. *Arch Histol* (B Air), 5:227-270, 1954.

HART, B.L., and KITCHELL, R.L.: External morphology of the erect glans penis of the dog. *Anat Rec, 152*:193-198, 1965.

HESS, K. J.: Der Truncus corporis penis des Hundes. *Anat Anz, 114*:62-78, 1964.

HOOKER, C.W.; PFEIFFER, C.A., and DeVITA, J.: The significance of the character of the interstitial cells of the testis in the aged dog. *Anat Rec, 94*:471-472 (Abst.), 1946.

KUNTZ, A.: The innervation of the gonads in the dog. *Anat Rec, 17*:203-219, 1919.

LATIMER, H.B.: The growth in weight of the testis, ovaries and uterus in the fetal dog. *Anat Rec, 124*:419 (Abst.), 1956.

LESBOUYRIES, G.: *Reproduction des Mammifères Domestique.* Vigot Frères, Éditeurs, Paris, 1949.

MALONE, J.Y.: Spermatogenesis in the dog. *Trans Amer Micr Soc, 37*:97-108, 1918.

MELCHIOR, I.: Über den Ductus Deferens des Hundes unter besonderer Berücksichtigung der Pars ampullari. *Acta Anat, 23*:330-336, 1955.

NICANDER, L.: Fine structure and cytochemistry of nuclear inclusions in the dog epididymis. *Exp Cell Res, 34*:533-541, 1964.

NISHIKI, T.: Electron microscopy of spermatogenesis in the carnivora. (In Jap. with Eng. Summ.) *J Nara Med Ass, 11*:9-24, 1960.

OKI, S.: Histology and innervation, especially, sensory innervation of *pars praeprostatica, pars prostatica and pars membranacea urethrae* and *prostata* in dog. *Arch Histol Jap, 14*:441-461, 1958.

O'SHEA, J.D.: Studies on the canine prostate gland. I. Factors influencing its size and weight. *J Comp Path Ther, 72*:321-331, 1962.

SCHLOTTHAUER, C.F., and BOLLMAN, J.L.: The prostate gland of the dog. *Cornell Vet, 26*:342-349, 1936.

SEAMAN, A.R.: The lipids in the prostate gland of the dog. *J. Urol, 75*:324-333, 1956.

SEAMAN, A.R., and KAUFMAN, L.: The intrinsic blood supply of the prostate gland of the dog as demonstrated by the azo-dye technique. *Acta Anat, 40*:178-185, 1960.

SEAMAN, A.R., and STUDEN, S.: A comparative histochemical study of the bound lipids of the prostate gland of the dog, and the ventral prostate gland of the rat. *Acta Histochem, 9*:304-319, 1960.

SEAMAN, A. R., and WINELL, M.: A histochemical study of the esterases of the prostate gland of the dog. *Acta Histochem, 8*:381-392, 1959.

SEAMAN, A. R., and WINELL, M.: The ultrafine structure of the normal prostate gland of the dog. *Acta Anat, 41*:1-28, 1962.

SMITH, L.W.: Senile changes of the testis and prostate gland in dogs. *J Med Res, 40*:31-51, 1919.

SOLIS, J.A.: Some anatomical features of the penile bone of the dog heretofore undescribed. *Phil J. Anim Indust, 9*:103-109, 1947.

STACH, W., and SCHULTZ, E.: Über osmium-zinkjodid-affine Dendritenzellen im Nebenhodenepithel des Hundes. *Anat Anz, 120*:276-280, 1967.

STACH, W., and SCHULTZ, E.: Beitrang zur Innervation des Nebenhodens. *Anat Anz, 120*:259-274, 1967.

TAKAHATA, K.; KUDO, M.; FURUHATA, K.; SIGIMURA, M., and TAMURA, T.: Fine angioarchitecture in the penis of the dog. *Jap J Vet Res, 10*:203-214, 1962.

VAERST, L.: Über die Blutversorgung des Hundepenis. *Gegenbaurs Morph Jahrb, 81*:307-352, 1938.

WALKER, G.: The blood vessels of the prostate gland. *Amer J Anat, 5*:73-78, 1905.

WALTON, K.N.; SCHIRMER, H.K.A., and SCOTT, W.W.: Cholinesterase activity in the dog prostate gland. *Invest Urol, 1*:307-311, 1964.

WENZEL, J., and KELLERMANN, P.: Vergleichende Untersuchungen über das Lymphgefäss-system des Nebenhodens und Hodens von Mensch, Hund und Kaninchen. *Z Mikr Anat Forsch, 75*:368-387, 1967.

ZARZYCKI, J., and CZECHOWICZ, K.: Histogenesis of os priapi in dog. *Folia Morph, (Warsz), 12*:19-25, 1961.

ENDOCRINE SYSTEM

AKULININ, A.A.: Innervation of the adrenal glands in pig and dog. *Uch Zap Vietbsk Vet Inst 14*:164-168, 169-173, 1956.

BACHMANN, R.: *Möllendorff's Handbuch der mikroskopischen Anatomie der Menschen.* Vol. VI, Part 5—Vergleichende Anatomie der Nebenniere. Springer-Verlag, Berlin, 1954, pp. 15-117.

BAKER, D.D.: Comparison of the weights of suprarenals of dogs in oestrus, pregnancy and lactation. *J Morph, 62*:3-15, 1938.

BANN, R. C.; STORINO, H.E., and SCHMIT, R.W.: The mass of the zona glomerulosa following complete anterior and posterior hypophysectomy and subtotal removal of the pars tuberalis in the dog. *Endocrinology, 66*:403-408, 1960.

BASIR, M.A.: The vascular supply of the pituitary body in the dog. *J Anat, 66*: 387-399, 1932.

BLOODWORTH, J.M.B., JR., and POWERS, K.L.: The ultrastructure of the normal dog adrenal. *J Anat, 102*:457-476, 1968.

BOTAR, J.: Physiologisch-morphologische Untersuchungen über die Innervation des Nebennieremarks beim Hund. *Acta Anat, 35* (Suppl. 33): 1-88, 1958.

BRONDI, C., and CASTORINA, S.: Il circolo arterioso del surrene nel cane. *Minerva Chir, 8*:380-383, 1953.

CARLON, N: Cytologie du lobe anterieur de l'hypophyse du chien. *Z Zellforsch, 78*:76-91, 1967.

CARLON, N., and STAHL, A.: Étude experimentale de la cytologie du lobe antérieur de hypophyse chez le chien. *C R Soc Biol,* (Paris) *160*:578-581, 1966.

CELESTINO DA COSTA, A.: Les signes histologiques de la fonction de la médullaire surrénale. *C R Assoc Anat, 42*:382-389, 1956.

COLE, J.W.; LEUCHTENBERGER, C., and MCKALEN, A.: Cellular changes during surgical stress. III. Cytochemical alterations in the adrenal of dogs. *Surg Gynec Obstet, 107*:690-692, 1958.

COULOUMA, P.: L'innervation des glandes surrénales du chien. *C R Assoc Anat, 28*:208-234, 1933.

DIEPEN, R.; ENGELHERDT, F., and SMITH-AGREDA, V.: Über Ort und Art der Entstehung des Neurosekretes im supraoptico-hypophysären System bei Hund und Katze. *Verh Anat Ges, 52*:276-288, 1954.

DOUGLAS, W.W.; POISNER, A.M., and TRIFARO, J.M.: Lysolecithin and other phospholipids in the adrenal medulla of various species. *Life Sciences, 5*:809-815, 1966.

ELIAS, H.: Comparative histology of domestic animals. III. Endocrine glands. 1. The adrenal gland. *Middlesex Vet,* Spring-Summer, 1945.

FINERTY, J.C., and KELLER, A.D.: Regional localization of adrenocorticotrophic cells in the anterior hypophysis of the dog. *Anat Rec, 139*:228-229, 1961.

FLINT, J.M.: The frame work of the glandula parathyroides. *Amer J Anat, 4*:77-81, 1904.

FRENCH, C.: The thyroid gland and thyroid glandules of the dog. *J Comp Med Vet Arch*, *22*:1-15, 1901.

FRITZ, T.E.; NORRIS, W.P., and FLYNN; R.J.: Thyroiditis in a closed colony of Beagles. (Abst.) *18th Annual Meeting American Association for Laboratory Animal Science*, 1967.

GABE, M.: Donnees histochimiques sur les cellules parafolliculaires de la glande thyroide du chien. *Acta Anat*, *38*:332-344, 1959.

GILMORE, J. W.; VENZKE, W.G., and FOUST, H.L.; Growth changes in body organs. II. Growth changes in the thyroid of the normal dog. *Amer J Vet Res*, *1*:66-72, 1940.

GODWIN, M.C.: Complex IV in the dog with special emphasis on the relation of the ultimobranchial body to interfollicular cells in the postnatal thyroid gland. *Amer J Anat*, *60*:299-339, 1937.

GODWIN, M.C.: The development of the parathyroids in the dog with emphasis on the origin of accessory glands. *Anat Rec*, *68*:305-318, 1937.

GORTON, B.: The anatomy of the parathyroids of the dog. *Vet J*, *81*:130-133, 1925.

GRAU, H., and DELLMANN, H.D.: Über tierartliche Unterschiede der Epithelkorperchen unserer Haussäugetiere. *Z Mikr Anat Forsch*. *64*:192-214, 1958.

GRUENWALD, P., and KONIKOV, W.M.: Cell replacement and its relation to the zona glomerulosa in the adrenal cortex of mammals. *Anat Rec*, *89*:1-21, 1944.

HUGHSON, W.: Meningeal relations of the hypophysis cerebri. (Dog). *Bull Johns Hopkins Hosp*, *35*:232-234, 1924.

HULSEMANN, M.: Vergleichende histologische Untersuchungen über das Vorkommen von Gliafasern in der Epiphysis cerebri von Säugetieren. *Acta Anat*, *66*:249-278, 1967.

ITO, T.: Comparative observations of the transitional area between the zona glomerulosa and the zona fasciculata in the adrenal cortices of several mammalian species. (Jap.) *Arch Histol Jap*. *18*:79-105, 1959.

KAGAMI, A.; MORITA, S., and DAIGO, M.: On the variation of the arteries distributed in the adrenals of the dogs. *Nippon Vet Zootechn Coll*, *11*:47-51, 1962.

KINGSBURY, B.F.: The pharyngeal hypophysis of the dog. *Anat Rec*, *82*:39-57, 1942.

KÖHLER, H.: Altersveränderungen der Schilddrüse (Glandula thyreoidea) und der Epithelkörperchen (Glandulae parathyreoideae) des Hundes. 2. Beitrag zur Altersanatomie des Hundes. Inaug. Diss., Hannover, 1942.

KROOK, L.: Spontaneous hyperparathyroidism in the dog. *Acta Path Microbiol Scand*, *41* (Suppl. 122):5-88, 1957.

LAQUEUR, G.L.: Neurosecretory pathways between the hypothalamic paraventricular nucleus and the neurohypophysis. *J Comp Neurol*, *101*:543-563, 1954.

LASOWSKY, J.M.: Zur Morphologie der Drüsenzellen der Schilddrüse. *Virchow Arch Pat Anat*, *259*:68-78, 1926.

LINDT, S.: Morphological study of dog adrenals in various diseases. *Arch Exp Veterinaermed*, *16*:143-203, 1962.

MAJOR, R.H.: Studies on the vascular system of the thyroid gland. *Amer J. Anat*, *9*:475-492, 1909.

MIKAMI, S., and ONO, K.: Cytological studies on the dog anterior pituitary with special reference to its staining properties. *J Fac Agr Iwate Univ*, *2*:440-448, 1956; Abst. *Acta Anat Jap*, *2*:1-2, 1957.

MIKAMI, S., and ONO, K.: Cytological observations on the zona tuberalis of the anterior pituitary of the dog. *J Fac Agr Iwate Univ.,* 3:194-201, 1957.

MODELL, W.: Observations on the structure of the blood vessels within the thyroid gland of the dog. *Anat Rec,* 55:251-269, 1933.

NICANDER, L.: Histological and histochemical studies on the adrenal cortex of domestic and laboratory animals. *Acta Anat,* 14 (Suppl. 16):1-88, 1952.

NICANDER, L.: A histochemical study of adrenal glycogen. *Acta Anat,* 31:388-397, 1957

NONIDEZ, J.F.: The origin of the "parafollicular" cell, a second epithelial component of the thyroid gland of the dog. *Amer J Anat,* 49:479-505, 1932.

OKANA, H.; OHTA, Y.; SAWA, H., and FUJIWARA, I.: Cubical anatomy of several ducts, and vessels by injection method of acrylin resin. IX. On the vascular system of the suprarenal gland in the dog and cat. *Okajimas Folia Anat Jap,* 34:553-570, 1960.

PLANEL, H., and GUILHEM, A.: Localisation variable du glycogène dans la glande surrénale des mammifères. *C R Assoc Anat,* (Paris) 45:615-628, 1960.

RANDOLPH, K.H.: Growth changes in the adrenal gland of the dog from birth to two years of age. M.S. thesis, Iowa State University, Ames, 1950.

SCHWARTZ, H.G.: The meningeal relations of the hypophysis cerebri. *Anat Rec,* 67:35-51, 1936.

SHANKLIN, W.M.: On the presence of nerve cells in the neurohypophysis of the dog. *J Anat,* 77:241-242, 1943.

SMITH, E.M.; CALHOUN, M.L., and REINEKE, E.P.: The histology of the anterior pituitary, thyroid and adrenal of thyroid-stimulated purebred English bull-dogs. *Anat Rec,* 117:221-240, 1953.

TREVES, G.: l'ipofisi senile del cane. *Arch De Vecchi Anat Pat,* 30:771-794, 1959.

VICARI, E.M.: Thyroid and parathyroid size in various purebred dogs and their hybrids, with histological findings. *Anat Rec,* 52 (Suppl.):40 (Abst.), 1932.

VICARI, E.M.: Observations on the nature of the parafollicular cells in the thyroid gland of the dog. *Anat Rec,* 68:281-285, 1937.

VICARI, E.: Variations in structure of the parathyroid glands of dogs. *Anat Rec,* 70:80 (Abst.), 1938.

WISLOCKI, G.B., and CROWE, S.J.: Experimental observations on the adrenals and the chromaffin system. *Bull Johns Hopkins Hosp,* 35:187-193, 1924.

WOLFE, J.M., and CLEVELAND, R.: Cell types found in the anterior hypophysis of the dog. *Anat Rec,* 52:43-44, 1932.

WURSTER, D.H., and BENIRSCHKE, K.: Development of the hypothalamohypophysial neurosecretory system in the fetal armadillo (Dasypus novemcinctus), with notes on rabbits, cat and dog. *Gen Comp Endocr,* 4:433-441, 1964.

NERVOUS SYSTEM

ADRIANOV, O.S., and MERING, T.A.: Anatomico physiological features of the cerebral cortex in the dog. *Zh Vysshei Nerv Deist Pavlov,* 9:471-478, 1959.

ADRIANOV, O.S., and MERING, T.A.: *Atlas of the Canine Brain,* Edwards, Ann Arbor, 1964.

ALKSNE, J.: An electron microscope study of the arachnoid villi of the dog. *J Cell Biol,* 19:3A-4A (Abst), 1963.

ANDRES, K.H.: Structure of the subfornical organ in dogs. *Z Zellforsch.* 68:445-473, 1965.

ANDRES, K.H.: Über die Feinstruktur der Arachnoidea und Dura mater von Mammalia. *Z Zellforsch,* 79:272-295, 1967.

ANGEL, J.L.: Cranial changes in hybrid dogs. *Amer J Phys Anthrop,* 5:229 (Abst.), 1947.

BARGMANN, W., and SCHEIBLER, T.H.: Histologische und cytochemische Unter-suchungen am Subcommissuralorgan von Säugern. *Z Zellforsch,* 37:583-596, 1952.

BEDFORD, T.H.B.: The movement of cerebrospinal fluid over the cerebral hemi-spheres of the dog. *J Physiol,* 128:51P-52P, 1955.

BOTAR, J.; AFRA, D.; MORITZ, P.; SCHIFFMAN, H.; and SCHULZ, M.: Die Neuren-zellen und Ganglien des *N. vagus. Acta Anat,* 10:284-314, 1950.

BOWNE, J.G.: Neuroanatomy of the brachial plexus of the dog. *Diss. Abstr,* 20:844, 1959.

BRAITENBERG, V., and ATWOOD, R.P.: Morphological observations on the cere-bellar cortex. *J Comp Neurol,* 109:1-33, 1958.

BREAZILE, J., and THOMPSON, W.D.: Motor cortex of the dog. *Amer J Vet Res,* 28:1483-1486, 1967.

BRIDGE, C.J.: Innervation of spinal meninges and epidural structures. *Anat Rec,* 133:553-564, 1959.

BROWN, J.O.: Pigmentation of certain mesencephalic tegmental nuclei in the dog and cat. *J Comp Neurol,* 81:249-257, 1944.

BUXTON, D.F.: Function and anatomy of the corticospinal tracts of the dog and raccoon. *Anat Rec,* 157:222-223 (Abst.), 1967.

CAMMERMEYER, J.: The distribution of oligodendrocytes in cerebral gray and white matter of several mammals. *Amer J Anat,* 107:107-127, 1960.

CORDER, R.L., and LATIMER, H.B.: The prenatal growth of the brain and of its parts and of the spinal cord in the dog. *J Comp Neurol,* 90:193-212, 1949.

CROCK, H.V.: The arterial supply and venous drainage of the vertebral column of the dog. *J Anat,* 94:88-99, 1960.

DIEPEN, R.; ENGELHARDT, F., and SMITH-AGREDA, V.: Über Ort und Art der Entstehung des Neurosekretes im supraoptico-hypophysären System bei Hund und Katze. *Verh Anat Ges,* 29:276-288, 1954.

DUBEY, P.N.; KULKARNI, L.S., and GOSAIR, V.S.: Compartive study of nucleus cervicalis in cat and dog—a quantitative study. *J Anat Soc India,* 14:7-11, 1965.

FANKHAUSER, R.: Veränderungen im Bereich der Wirbelsäule beim alternden Hund. *Schweiz Med Wschr,* 85:845-846, 1955.

FANKHAUSER, R.: Untersuchungen über die arachnoidalen Zotten und Granula-tionen bei Tieren. *Schweiz Arch Tierheilk,* 104:13-34, 1962.

FEW, A.B.: The occurrence of lipofuscin pigment as related to aging in the lumbar spinal cord, dorsal root ganglia and paravertebral ganglia of the dog and pig. *Diss Abstr,* 27B:2964, 1967.

FLETCHER, T.F., and KITCHELL, R.L.: Anatomical studies on the spinal cord seg-ments of the dog. *Amer J Vet Res,* 27:1759-1767, 1966.

FOX, M.W.: The postnatal growth of the canine brain and correlated anatomical and behavioral changes during neuro-ontogenesis. *Growth,* 28:135-141, 1964.

FOX, M.W.; INMAN, O.R., and HIMWICH, W.A.: The postnatal development of neocortical neurons in the dog. *J Comp Neurol,* 127:199-206, 1966.

FOX, M.W.; INMAN, O.R., and HIMWICH, W.A.: The postnatal development of the spinal cord of the dog. *J Comp Neurol,* 130:233-240, 1967.

GASTINGER, W., and HENSCHEL, E.: Vorläufige Mitteilung über die röntgen-ologische Gefäss-darstellung der Kopfarterien beim lebenden Tier, insbeson-dere beim Hunde. *Zbl Veterinaermed,* 7:984-990, 1960.

GOLDANI, J.: About the glio-vascular architectures of the cerebrospinal nuclei and aging changes (in dogs). *Anat Rec, 157*:359 (Abst.), 1967.

GOLUB, D.M.: Some materials on sympathetic nervous system structure in embryogenesis of mammalia (Dog). *Arkh Anat, 44*:34-42, 1964.

GREENBERG, S.R.: A fiber analysis of the vagus cardiac rami and the cervical sympathetic nerves in the dog. *J Comp Neurol, 104*:33-48, 1956.

GROFOVA, I., and PETROVICKY, P.: The cytoarchitecture of the reticular formation of the isthmus region and midbrain in the dog. *Česk Morfol, 11*:349-357, 1963.

HAGEN, E.: Morphologische Beobachtungen im Hypothalamus und in der Neurohypophyse des Hundes nach Teilläsion des Infundibulum. *Acta Anat, 31*:193-219, 1957.

HAINES, D.E., and JENKINS, T.W.: Studies on the epithalamus. I. Morphology of post-mortem degeneration: the habenular nucleus in dog. *J Comp Neurol, 132*:405-418, 1968.

HAYMAKER, W.; ANDERSON, E., and NAUTA, W.J.H. (Eds.): *The Hypothalamus.* Thomas, Springfield, 1968.

HOERLEIN, B.F., and PETTY, M.F.: Contrast encephalography and ventriculography in the dog-preliminary studies. *Amer J Vet Res, 22*:1041-1056, 1961.

HOERLEIN, B.F.: *Canine Neurology.* Saunders, Philadelphia, 1965.

HORODYSKA, M., and KREINER, J.: The brain ventricles in the dog. *Acta Biol Exp, 22*:243-250, 1962.

HUBER, C.G.: Studies on the neuroglia. *Amer J Anat, 1*:45-61, 1901.

JANKLEWICZ, E.: Habenular complex in the dog's brain. *Acta Biol Exp* (Warsz.), *27*:367-387, 1967.

KASHIHARA, S.: An anatomical study on the vagus nerve in the cat and dog. *Igaku Kenkyu, 28*:4744-4758, 1958.

KETZ, H.A.: Die Altersveränderungen im Zentralnervensystem der Haustiere. *Z Alternsforsch, 13*:103-111, 1959.

KNOCHE, H.: Über das Vorkommen eigenartiger Nervenfasern (Nodulus-Fasern) in Hypophyse und Zwischenhirn von Hund und Mensch. *Acta Anat, 18*:208-233, 1953.

KREINER, J.: The quantitative myelinization of brains and spinal cords in dogs of various size. *Acta Anat, 33*:50-64, 1958.

KREINER, J.: The myeloarchitectonics of the frontal cortex of the dog. *J Comp Neurol, 116*:117-133, 1961.

KULLANDA, K.M.: Representation of some internal organs in the cerebral and cerebellar cortex in cats and dogs. *Akad Med Nauk SSSR,* Moscow, 1958; *Referat Zh Biol,* No. 59692D, 1959.

KULLANDA, K.M.: On representation of internal organs in the cortex of the cerebrum and cerebellum of cats and dogs. III. Representation of the *n. pudendi* in the cerebral cortex of cats. IV. Representation of the *nn. pelvici* and *pundendi* in the cerebral cortex of dogs. *Buill Eksp Biol Med, 49*:8-12, 16-22, 1960.

KULLANDA, K.M.: Representation of the internal organs in the cerebral and cerebellar cortices of cats and dogs. V. Individual differences in the specific cortical projection areas. *Buill Eksp Biol Med* (Transl.), *49*:425-427, 1960.

KULLANDA, K.M.: Comparative characteristics of the representation zones for the pelvic and pudendal nerves in the cerebral cortex of cats and dogs. *Fiziol Zh SSSR* (Transl.) *46*:1567-1578, 1960.

LAQUEUR, G.L.: Neurosecretory pathways between the hypothalamic paraventricular nucleus and the neurohypophysis. *J Comp Neurol 101*:543-554, 1954.

LASSEK, A.M., and RASMUSSEN, G.L.: A comparative fiber and numerical analysis of the pyramidal tract. *J Comp Neurol, 72*:417-428, 1940.

LATIMER, H.B.: The relative weights of the major divisions of the brain and the cord in several species of animals. *Univ Kansas Sci Bull, 31*:211-221, 1946.

LIM, R.K.S.; LIU C-N, and MOFFITT, R.L.: *A Stereotaxic Atlas of the Dog's Brain.* Thomas, Springfield, 1960.

MACCOTTER, R.E.: The nervus terminalis in the adult dog and cat. *J Comp Neurol, 23*:145-152, 1915.

MARCARIAN, H.Q., and JENKINS, T.W.: Vascular patterns in the canine sympathetic chain. *Amer Heart J, 73*:491-499, 1967.

MIZERES, N.J.: The anatomy of the autonomic nervous system in the dog. *Amer J. Anat, 96*: 285-318, 1955.

MURAKAMI, R., and YO, T.: On the atypical forms of spinal ganglion nerve cells in dog, cat and rabbit. (Jap. with Eng. summ.) *Hirosaki Med J, 14*:467-473, 1963.

NARKIEWICZ, O., and BRUTKOWSKI, S.: The organization of projections from the thalamic mediodorsal nucleus to the prefrontal cortex of the dog. *J Comp Neurol, 129*:361-374, 1967.

NEWBERNE, J.W.; ROBINSON, V.B.; ESTILL, L., and BRINKMAN, D.C.: Granular structures in brains of apparently normal dogs. *Amer J Vet Res, 21*:782-786, 1960.

NISHIKAWA, S.; YŌ, T.; IWAI, S., and SHIRATORI, S.: Bipolar and multipolar spinal ganglion nerve cells of dog (*Canis familiaris*). *Hirosaki Med J 8*:611-622, 1957.

OWENS, G.: Arterial perfusion of the isolated canine brain. *Amer J Physiol, 197*: 475-477, 1959.

PAIVA, O.M.: Anatomia do plexus coeliacus e dos nervi splanchnici no cão. *Folia Clin Biol, 28*:184-206, 1958-1959.

PETROVA-MURAFA, V.G.: The vascular fields of the cerebral hemispheres. *Sb Nauchm Rabot Kazansk Med Inst, 4*:174-188, 1957.

PETROVICKY, P., and GROFOVA, I.: The cytoarchitecture of the *formatio reticularis pontis* (brain) of the dog. *Česk Morfol, 11*:341-348, 1963.

POGORZELSKI, J.K.: Studies of the vascular system of choroid plexuses of the lateral ventricles of the brain and of the pia mater in some laboratory animals. *Folia Morph* (Warsz), *13*:21-42, 1962.

POGORZELSKI, J.K.: Studies on the structure of arteriovenous anastomoses in the choroid plexuses of the lateral ventricles of the brain. *Folia Morph*, (Warsz) (Eng. transl.), *14*:(22)1-6, 1963.

POGORZELSKI, J.K.: Intima cushions in the arteries of the choroid plexuses of the lateral cerebral ventricles. *Folia Morph.* (Warsz), *15*(23):386-388, 1964.

POLLAY, M., and WELCH, K.: The function and structure of canine arachnoid villi. *J Surg Res, 2*:307-311, 1962.

SANBE, S.: Studies on the incoming and outgoing myelinated nerve fibers of the sympathetic superior cervical ganglion. *Fukushima J Med Sci, 8*:109-129, 1961.

SANO, Y.; SAITO, O., and ISHIDA, Y.: A study of the comparative histology of the hypothalamo-hypophysial system. (Jap. with Eng. summ.) *Arch Histol Japon, 18*:457-462, 1959.

SATO, T.: Anatomical, histological and experimental studies of the roots and branches of the ciliary ganglion in dogs. *Fukushima Med J, 11*:363-384, 1961.

SCHLAPP, M.G.: The microscopic structure of cortical areas in man and some mammals. *Amer J Anat*, 2:259-281, 1903.

SCHWILL, A.: Untersuchungen über den Feinbau einiger Stammganglien des Grosshirns beim Hund. Inaug. Diss., Hannover, 1951.

SCHWILL, C.: Untersuchungen über den Feinbau der Grosshirnrinde beim Hund. Inaug. Diss., Hannover, 1951.

SEIFERLE, E., Zur Topographie des Gehirns bei lang-und kurzköpfigen Hunderassen. *Acta Anat*, 63:346-362, 1966.

SHELEPA, D.D.: The nerves of the pia mater of the brain of man, cat and dog. *Tr Krymsk Med Inst*, 18:14-20, 1957.

SHRYOCK, E.H. and CASE, N.M.: Light and electron microscopy of the choroid plexus in dogs. *Anat Rec*, 124:361 (Abst.), 1956.

SINGER, M.: *Brain of the Dog in Section*. W.B. Saunders, Philadelphia, 1962.

SINHA, B.P.: Cytoarchitectonics of the temporal lobe of puppy less than a month old. *J Anat Soc India*, 16:18-25, 1967.

SPOONER, R.L.: Cerebral angiography in the dog. *J Small Anim Pract*, 2:243-252, 1961.

SULKIN, N.M.: Histochemical studies on microproteins in nerve cells of the dog. *J Biophys Biochem Cytol*, 1:459-468, 1955.

SULZMANN, R.: Zur Morphologie des Ependyms im Zentralkanal des Hundes. *Anat Anz*, 109:351-357, 1961.

SWIECIMSKA, Z.: The corpus callosum of the dog. *Acta Biol Exp*, 27:389-411, 1967.

SYCH, L.: The external capsule in the dog's brain (myeloarchitectonics and topography). *Acta Biol Exp*, 20:91-101, 1960.

SYCHOWA, B.: The morphology and topography of the thalamic nuclei of the dog. *Acta Biol Exp*, 21:101-120, 1961.

SYCHOWA, B.: Medial geniculate body of the dog. *J Comp Neurol*, 118:355-371, 1962.

TALANTI, S.: Investigations on the Purkinje cells in the cerebellum of some domestic animals. *Acta Vet Scand*, 1:41-51, 1960.

TATEISHI, K.; UEDA, F.; YAMAGATA, T.; HAYASHIMOTO, I., and TAMIGUCHI, H.: On the postnatal development of the inferior olivary nucleus of the dog. *Kobe J Med Sci*, 5:74, 1959.

TENEROWICZ, M.: The morphology and topography of the claustrum in the brain of the dog. *Acta Biol Cracoviensia Ser Zool*, 3:105-113, 1960.

TORS'KA, I.V.: Phenomena of amitotic division of nerve cells of the central nervous system in adult dogs. *Fiziol Zh Akad Nauk Ukrain RSK*, 9:32-41, 1963.

VOLKNER, D.: Cytoarchitektonische Studien an Hirnen verschieden grosser Hunde (Konigspudel und Zwergpudel). *Z Mikr Anat Forsch*, 62:267-315, 1956.

WOOLSEY, C.N.: Comparative studies on dual somatic afferent areas in cerebral cortex of rabbit, cat, dog, pig, sheep and monkey. *Fed Proc*, 5:116, 1946.

WOZNIAK, W., and SKOWRONSKA, W.: Comparative anatomy of pelvic plexus in cat, dog, rabbit, macaque and man. *Anat Anz*, 120:457-473, 1967.

ZAMBRANO, D., and DE ROBERTIS, E.: Ultrastructure of the hypothalamic neurosecretory system of the dog. *Z Zellforsch*, 81:264-282, 1967.

ZHUKOVA, G.P.: Structural features of the projections in the spinal cord and medulla oblongata. (Eng. summ.) *Arkh Anat*, 41:58-64, 1961.

ZHUKOVA, G.P., and LEONTOVICH, T.A.: Specificity of neuronal structure and topography of the reticular formation in the brain and spinal chord of Carnivora. *Zh Vysshei Nerv Deiat*, 14:122-147, 1964.

BLOOD AND BONE MARROW

ADULADZE, A.V.: On the question of myelograms of dogs. (Russ., Eng. summ.) *Arkh Anat, 38*:51-55, 1960; *Referat. Zhur., Biol.* No. 8162, 1961.

ALBRITTON, E.C. (Ed.): *Standard Values in Blood.* W.B. Saunders, Philadelphia, 1952.

ALEXANDRAV, A. F.: Die Morphologie des Sternumpunktates von Hunden. *Folia Haemat, 41*:428-434, 1930.

ARCHER, R.K.: *Haematological Techniques for Use on Animals.* F.A. Davis, Philadelphia, 1965.

ATWAL, O.S., and MCFARLAND, L.Z.: Histochemical study of the distribution of alkaline phosphatase in leukocytes of the horse, cow, sheep, dog and cat. *Amer J Vet Res, 28*:971-974, 1967.

BLOOMENTHAL, E.D.; OLSON, W.H., and NECHELES H.: Studies on the bone marrow cavity of the dog: fat embolism and marrow pressure. *Surg Gynec Obstet 94*:215-222, 1952.

BRUNK, R.: Hämatologische Standardwerte. *Munch Tierarztl Wschr, 78*:415-417, 1965; *79*:167-168, 1966.

CARR, M.H., and SCHLOERB, P.R.: Blood components in the dog: normal values. *J Lab Clin Med, 53*:646-652, 1959.

COLBY, E.M.B., and CALHOUN, M.L.: Accessory nuclear lobule on the polymorphonuclear neutrophil leukocyte of domestic animals. *Acta Cytol, 7*:346-350, 1963.

DIAGO, M.; MORITA, S.; KAWAHARA, G., and KAGAMI, A.: Stereoroentgenographical and topographical studies on the anatomy of peripheral blood vessels in domestic animals and domestic fowls. 12. Individual deviation of peripheral terminal branch running beneath the nail and the courses of running of the *arteriae digitales propriae* of the anterior and posterior extremity in the dog. 13. Dorsal and plantar arteries of hind limbs in the dog. *Bull Nippon Vet Zootech Coll, 14*:64-82, 83-103, 1965.

DOXEY, D.L.: The eosinophils of the greyhound. *Vet Rec, 75*:1063, 1963.

DOXEY, D.L.: The extent of variations in the blood picture of normal dogs and the deviations encountered in some canine diseases. Ph.D. Thesis, Department of Veterinary Medicine, University of Edinburgh, Scotland, 1964.

DRINKER, C.K.; DRINKER, K.R., and LUND, C.C.: The circulation in the mammalian bone-marrow, with especial reference to the factors concerned in the movement of red-blood cells from the bone-marrow into the circulating blood as disclosed by perfusion of the tibia of the dog and by injections of the bone-marrow in the rabbit and cat. *Amer J Physiol, 62*:1-92, 1922.

DUDOK DEWIT, C.; COENEGRACHT, N.A.C.J.; POLL, P.H.A., and LINDE, J.D.v.d.: The practical importance of blood groups in dogs. *J Sm Anim Pract, 8*:285-289, 1967.

EBERL, W.: Das Zellbild von Knochenmark-ausstrichen des Hundes. *Diss Wien,* 1943.

EDERSTROM, H.E.: Comparison of RBC counts in central and peripheral blood in various laboratory animals. *Proc Soc Exp Biol Med, 70*:172-173, 1949.

FAIRMAN, E., and WHIPPLE, G.H.: Bone marrow volume in adult dogs. *Amer J Physiol, 104*:352-357, 1933.

FOA, P.: L'azione erito e leucocateretica del midollo ossea adiposo del cane. *Haematologica, 16*:673-688, 1935.

FORBES, M.: Peripheral Blood Leucocyte Karyotype Analysis of Ten Breeds of

Dogs (*Canis familiaris*). M.S. Thesis, Michigan State University, East Lansing, 1964.

GREENBERG, M.I.; ATKINS, H.L., and SCHIFFER, L.M.: Erythropoietic and reticulo-endothelial functions in bone marrow in dogs. *Science, 152*:526-528, 1966.

HAMILTON, L.H., and HORVATH, S.M.: Comparison of blood cell counts from major vessels in the dog. *Proc Soc Exp Biol Med, 86*:360-363, 1954.

IVANIAN, A.K.: On the effect of age and sex on the morphological state of the peripheral blood and bone marrow of healthy dogs. (Russ.). *Pat Fiziol Eksp Ter, 5*:32-38, 1961.

JASPER, D.E., and JAIN, N.C.: The influence of adrenocorticotropic hormone and prednisolone upon marrow and circulating leukocytes in the dog. *Amer J Vet Res, 26*:844-850, 1965.

JONES, R.P., and PARIS, R.: The greyhound eosinophil. *J Sm Anim Pract* (Suppl.), *4*:29-33, 1963.

KAUFMAN, D.M.: A study of the shape and specificity of megakaryocyte nuclei. *Anat Rec, 42*:365-391, 1929.

LALA, P.K.; PATT, H.M., and MALONEY, M.A.: An evaluation of erythropoiesis in canine marrow. *Acta Haemat, 35*:311-318, 1966.

LOCATELLI, A., and QUARENGHI, F.: Sulla presenza di "Drumstik" secondo David-son et Smith, nel nucleo dei polimorfonucleati neutrofili di *Canis familiaris. Haematologica, 43*:423-427, 1958.

LORBER, M.: Peripheral blood and bone marrow in dogs subsequent to the routing of splenic blood into the systemic circulation. *Acta Haemat, 21*:232-241, 1959.

MASTRANGELO, P.: Contributo allo studio del valore globulare negli animali domestici. Nota 4: Ricerche nei cani. *Acta Med Vet (Napoli), 12*:501-508, 1966.

MICHAELSON, S.M.; SCHEER, K., and GILT, S.: The blood of the normal beagle. *J. Amer Vet Med Ass, 148*:532-534, 1966.

NOYAN, A.: A cytological study of the normal bone marrow in dog, with special reference to biopsy methods. M.S. Thesis, Ohio State, Columbus, 1947.

PAULSSON, S., and ABERG, B.: Clinical chemical and haematological normal values. *Svensk Veterinärtidning, 17*:462-464, 473-476, 1965.

PORTER, K.A.: A sex difference in morphology of dog. *Nature (London), 179*: 784-785, 1957.

POVETKINA, Z.G.: The normal values of hematologic indices in the dog. *Fiziol Zh SSSR Sechenov, 49*:366-369, 1963.

RAKHMATOVA, M.R.: The influence of the nervous system on bone marrow hemopoiesis. (Russ.). *Biull Eksp Biol Med, 52*:788-791, 1961.

REBER, E.F.; KREIER, J.P.; NORTON, H.W., and MALHPTRA, O.P.: Standard blood values in the beagle dog. *Illinois State Acad Sci, 54*:79-82, 1961.

REIHART, O.F., and REIHART, H.W.: Diseases of Blood and Blood-forming Organs. In *Canine Medicine.* Catcott, E.J. (Ed.): Am. Vet. Publications, Santa Barbara, California, 1968, pp 339-386.

RYAZHKIN, G.A.P.: Normal values for composition of peripheral blood and of bone marrow of dogs. (Russ.). *Biull Eksp Biol Med, 41*:387-389, 1956.

SCHALM, O.W.: *Veterinary Hematology.* Lea and F., Philadelphia, 1965, pp. 192-211.

SCHERMER, S.: *Die Blutmorphologie der Laboratoriumstiere,* F.A. Davis, Philadelphia, 1967, pp. 85-99.

SOAVE, O.A., and BOYLE, C.C.: A comparison of the hemograms of conditioned and non-conditioned laboratory dogs. *Lab Anim Care, 15*:359-362, 1965.

SPRANGER, J.P.C., and HIME, J.M.: Bone marrow biopsy from the femur of the dog. *Vet Rec 73*:1080-1081, 1961.

STASNEY, J., and HIGGINS, G.M.: A quantitative cytologic study of the bone marrow of the adult dog. *Amer J Med Sci, 193*:462-470, 1937.

STEIN, A.H., JR.; MORGAN, H. C., and REYNOLDS, F.C.: Variations in normal bone-marrow pressures. *J Bone Joint Surg, 39*:1129-1134, 1957.

THOMAS, R.E., and KITTRELL, J.E.: Effect of altitude and season on the canine hemogram. *J Amer Vet Med Ass, 148*:1163-1167, 1966.

USACHEVA, I.N.: Peripheral blood and bone marrow indices in normal dogs. (Russ.). *Biull Eksp Biol Med, 44*:105-109, 1957.

USACHEVA, I.N.: Comparative data on the morphological constitution of bone marrow punctures and smears from the sternum and femur of healthy dogs. (Russ.). *Biull Eksp Biol Med, 56*:112-113, 1963.

WELS, A., and HORN, V.: Beitrag Erythrozytometrie bei Hund und Katze. *Kleintier-Praxis. 12*:93-120, 1967.

WIRTH, D.: *Grundlagen einer klinischen Hämatologie der Haustiere.* Urban and Schwarzen, Wien/Innsbruck, 1950.

WOODWARD, K.T.; BERMAN, A.R.; MICHAELSON, S.M., and ODLAND, L.T.: Plasma, erythrocyte and whole blood volume in the normal beagle. *Amer J. Vet Res, 29*:1935-1944, 1968.

YOUNG, L.E.; O'BRIEN, W.A.; SWISHER, S.N.; MILLER, G., and YUILE, C.L.: Blood groups in dogs—their significance to the veterinarian. *Amer J Vet Res, 13*: 207-213, 1952.

Index

Chief cells
  parathyroid, 219
  stomach, 132, 134
Choroid plexus, 248
Circumanal glands, 3, 14, 104
Circumflex coronary artery, 32
Circumvallate papilla see vallate
Claw, 22
Clitoris, 196, 198
Colon, 144, 146, 148
Conical papillae, 102, 112
Coronary artery and vein, 32, 36
Corpus cavernosum penis, 159, 202, 216
Corpus cavernosum urethrae, 176, 202, 216
Crypts of Lieberkuhn, 103, 136, 138, 140,
  146, 148
Cumulus oophorous, 182
Cystic duct, 156

D

Dartos muscle, 20
Dermis, 10, 12, 28, 88
  arrector pili muscle, 8, 10, 12, 26, 28
  papillary layer of, 8, 20
  reticular layer of, 8, 20
Digital pad, 3, 22
Digestive system, 102-157
Duct
  common bile, 136
  cystic, 156
  interlobular hepatic, 152
  nasopalatine, 85
  thoracic, 56
Ductus deferens, 202, 212
  ampulla of, 202, 212
Duodenum, 103, 136

E

Endocardium, 34
Endocrine system, 219-235
  adrenal, 219, 222, 224, 226
  hypophysis, 219
  parathyroid, 219, 234
  thyroid, 219, 232, 234
Endometrium, 178, 190
Ependyma, 244, 248
Epicardium, 34
Epidermal peg, 3
Epidermis, 3, 8, 88
  stratum corneum, 3, 8
  stratum germinativum, 8
  stratum granulosum, 8
  stratum lucidum, 3, 8
  stratum papillare, 20
  stratum reticulare, 20
Epididymis, 204, 210
  efferent ductules of, 204, 210
Epiglottis, 85, 94
Esophagus, 102, 126, 128
Eustachian tube, 92
External iliac artery and vein, 52
Eyelid, 20
  eyelash, 20

glands of Moll, 20
tarsal gland, 20
tarsal plate, 20
Zeis gland, 20

F

Female reproductive system, 178-201
Femoral artery and vein, 52
Fibrocartilage, heart, 32
Follicles
  hair, 8, 10, 12, 16, 20, 28
    connective tissue sheath of, 16
    dermal sheath of, 18
    external root sheath of, 10, 16, 18, 28
    follicular folds of internal root sheath, 16
    Henley's layer of, 16
    Huxley's layer of, 16
    internal root sheath of, 16
    tylotrich follicle, 8
    vitreous membrane of, 16
  hair follicle groups, 8, 26
  ovarian, 178, 180-184
    atretic, 184
    polyoocyte, 184
    primary, 182
    secondary, 182
  thyroid, 232, 234
Filiform papillae, 102, 108, 110
Foliate papillae, 102, 110, 112
Foot pad, 22
Fungiform papillae, 102, 108, 110, 112

G

Gall bladder, 156
Ganglion
  autonomic, 240
  myenteric (Auerbach's), 128, 134, 140
  sensory, 240
  submucosal (Meissner's), 138, 148
Gastric pits, stomach, 130
Glands
  adrenal, 219, 222-226
  anal, 14, 104, 148
  anal sac, 3, 14
  apocrine, 3
  Bowman's, 85
  bronchial, 86
  Brunner's, 136
  buccal, 106
  bulbourethral, 202
  cardiac, 126, 130, 132
  caudal (tail), 3, 12
  ceruminous, 24
  circumanal, 3, 14, 104
  duodenal, 103
  esophageal, 103, 126
  esophageal cardiac, 103
  fundic, 103, 134
  intestinal, 103
  labial, 12
  laryngosaccular, 94
  Lieberkühn, 103, 136, 138, 140
  merocrine, 3